UNITED STATES DEPARTMENT OF COMMERCE
Maurice H. Stans, *Secretary*
NATIONAL BUREAU OF STANDARDS ● Lewis M. Branscomb, *Director*

Ion-Selective Electrodes

Proceedings of a Symposium held at the
National Bureau of Standards
Gaithersburg, Maryland
January 30–31, 1969

Richard A. Durst, Editor

Institute for Materials Research
National Bureau of Standards
Washington, D.C. 20234

National Bureau of Standards Special Publication 314

Nat. Bur. Stand. (U.S.), Spec. Publ. 314, 474 pages (November 1969)
CODEN: XNBSA

Issued November 1969

ION-SELECTIVE ELECTRODES

Richard A. Durst

Institute for Materials Research
Analytical Chemistry Division
National Bureau of Standards
Washington, D. C. 20234

ABSTRACT

This volume contains a review of ion-selective electrodes, emphasizing the non-glass types, and provides a thorough and critical evaluation of the subject. It consists of eleven invited review papers and selected discussions from the Symposium on Ion-Selective Electrodes held at NBS on January 30-31, 1969. This publication provides a comprehensive survey of the field and should prove very valuable in advancing the state of the art. The chapters include discussions on the theory, characteristics, and methodology of all types of ion-selective electrodes; their use in thermodynamic, kinetic, and complex-ion studies; standards; pure and applied research in various biomedical areas of interest; industrial analysis and control systems; and applications to diverse analytical problems. Both the present status and future potential of these sensors are discussed in a wide range of scientific disciplines, from the physical sciences to biomedicine. Extensive bibliographies provide an excellent survey of the literature for anyone using or anticipating the use of these electrodes.

Key words: Ion-selective electrodes; specific-ion electrodes; review of ion-selective electrodes; symposium proceedings.

Library of Congress Catalog Card Number: 79-601302

FOREWORD

The Analytical Chemistry Division of the NBS Institute for Materials Research provides a major national focal point for analytical chemistry through its continuing efforts to encourage meaningful analytical measurements, to exercise leadership in attacking analytical problems of the nation, and to fill in gaps in critical measurement competences. This Division consists at present of about 120 technical personnel encompassing some 57 different analytical competences from activation analysis and atomic absorption to vacuum fusion and x-ray spectroscopy. These competences are charged with the responsibility for research at the forefront of analysis, as well as for an awareness of the practical sample be it Standard Reference Material or service analysis.

One important mechanism by which the Division exercises leadership in the "state of the art" of a competence is that of sponsoring special conferences and symposia. Experts from around the world are invited to these conferences to summarize the present status of the many facets of a particular competence. In addition, contributed papers as well as comments of rapporteurs or summaries of panel discussions are often used to help better define this status.

The first such conference sponsored by the Division was a broad one on "Trace Characterization — Chemical and Physical" held October 3-7, 1966 at the new NBS Laboratories at Gaithersburg, Maryland. On June 12-13, 1967 a seminar on a more restricted topic, "Quantitative Electron Probe Microanalysis," was held in these same facilities and on October 7-11, 1968 the Division hosted the 1968 International Conference on "Modern Trends in Activation Analysis." The hard-cover proceedings of each of these meetings are available from the Government Printing Office as NBS Monograph 100, NBS Special Publication 298 and NBS Special Publication 312 respectively.

As a continuation of these definitive "state of the art" conferences, the Analytical Chemistry Division and the NBS Institute for Materials Research were very pleased to host the Symposium on Ion-Selective Electrodes. The interest shown in this Symposium clearly demonstrated the breadth and vitality of this subject. Over 450 scientists representing a broad spectrum of industrial, governmental, and educational institutions attended. The format of the symposium provided an excellent opportunity for dialogue between specialists of varying backgrounds and interests.

This volume contains the invited papers presented at the Symposium, together with summaries of selected segments of the discussion sessions. Those interested in recent innovations in the area of quantitative electroanalytical chemistry will find this book on the non-glass ion-selective electrodes to be a very comprehensive source of information.

Particular thanks are due Richard A. Durst for his vision in perceiving the need for this symposium, and for his tireless efforts as Chairman and Editor in carrying this vision through to reality.

W. Wayne Meinke, *Chief*
Analytical Chemistry Division

PREFACE

This book is the formal report of the proceedings of the Symposium on Ion-Selective Electrodes sponsored by the Analytical Chemistry Division of the NBS Institute for Materials Research. The purpose of this meeting was to survey and evaluate the recent advances in the theory, development, and application of the non-glass types of ion-selective electrodes, and to provide the specialist and novice alike with a comprehensive review of the "state of the art" of these new electrochemical sensors.

This volume consists of the texts of the invited lectures, including additional material not presented at the symposium, and selected segments of the extensive (more than 2 1/2 hours) discussion sessions. The authors have discussed various aspects of the present and future capabilities of these electrodes, with emphasis placed on the applications and methodology in a wide variety of scientific disciplines. It is felt that the topics presented provide as broad a coverage of the interdisciplinary aspects of these electrodes as is feasible at this stage of their development.

Editorial changes have been made to achieve some measure of consistency of nomenclature both internally and with regard to the presently accepted international system of units (SI). However, I have endeavored to keep editorial changes to a minimum, especially with regard to content, in order to conserve the originality of the contributions. Consequently, certain fundamental discussions appear in more than one chapter, but in view of the diversity of approaches to this type of material, this duplication was intentionally preserved.

Typical of any new discipline, a multiplicity of terms has spontaneously appeared relating to the novel features of this technique. Normally, a slow and informal process of selection results in the acceptance of the "best" nomenclature. In order to accelerate this process with respect to two important terms, I should like to take advantage of an editor's prerogative to recommend the use of *ion-selective* and *selectivity ratio* for future adoption by scientists, manufacturers, and all other pertinent organizations. The term *ion-selective* does not imply sensitivity to one particular ion to the exclusion of all others as I feel the term *ion-specific* connotes. Although this fact of non-specificity is generally recognized by most scientists in the field, the term *ion-specific* may be misleading and serves no useful purpose. The term *selectivity ratio* (or *parameter)* is strongly recommended over the misnomer *selectivity constant,* since these values are now known to be dependent on the concentration and composition of the system. However, since I make these recommendations "unilaterally," I have not taken the liberty in this volume of editorially changing the terms preferred by the individual authors, although I strongly suggest the acceptance and use of the recommended terms.

In order to specify the procedures adequately, it has been necessary to identify commercial materials and equipment in this book. In no case does such identification imply recommendation or endorsement by the National Bureau of Standards, nor does it imply that the material or equipment is necessarily the best available for the purpose.

An undertaking of the magnitude of the symposium and this book would not have been possible without the cooperation and assistance of a large group of people within the Analytical Chemistry Division and the National Bureau of Standards. Many of these individuals served on numerous committees and assisted during the symposium in various capacities. Particular thanks are given to Dr. W. Wayne Meinke, Dr. Roger G. Bates, and Dr. John K. Taylor who guided me through the complicated initial stages of organizing the symposium and for their subsequent support in preparing this book. The NBS Office of Technical Information and Publications under the direction of W. R. Tilley, with special help from Robert T. Cook, Rubin Wagner, and Mrs. Rebecca Morehouse, gave invaluable assistance in many phases of the effort, varying from the initial publicity brochures and program to this final computer-assisted printing and publication of the proceedings. Within the Analytical Chemistry Division, special thanks are given to Mrs. Carolyn Smith and Mrs. Jean Gossard for their continuous effort in typing the coded manuscripts and other material, to Mrs. Joy Shoemaker and Robert Boreni for preparing the many tables and figures, and to my wife, Susan, for her help in the tedious task of indexing. Particular appreciation is expressed to Mrs. Rosemary Maddock who provided coordination and editorial assistance in the many phases of preparing this book.

April 15, 1969   Richard A. Durst

CONTENTS

Chapter 1. THEORY OF MEMBRANE ELECTRODE POTEN-TIALS: AN EXAMINATION OF THE PARAMETERS DETERMINING THE SELECTIVITY OF SOLID AND LIQUID ION EXCHANGERS AND OF NEUTRAL ION-SEQUESTERING MOLECULES

by George Eisenman

Chapter 2. SOLID-STATE AND LIQUID MEMBRANE ION-SELECTIVE ELECTRODES

by James W. Ross, Jr.

Chapter 3. HETEROGENEOUS MEMBRANE ELECTRODES

by Arthur K. Covington

Chapter 4. REFERENCE ELECTRODES

by Arthur K. Covington

Chapter 5. THERMODYNAMIC STUDIES

by James N. Butler

Chapter 6. ACTIVITY STANDARDS FOR ION-SELECTIVE ELECTRODES

by Roger G. Bates and Marinus Alfenaar

Chapter 7. STUDIES WITH ION-EXCHANGE CALCIUM ELECTRODES IN BIOLOGICAL FLUIDS: SOME APPLICATIONS IN BIOMEDICAL RESEARCH AND CLINICAL MEDICINE

by Edward W. Moore

Chapter 8.   ION-SELECTIVE ELECTRODES IN BIOMEDICAL RESEARCH

by Raja N. Khuri

Chapter 9.   ANALYTICAL   STUDIES   ON   ION-SELECTIVE MEMBRANE ELECTRODES

by Garry A. Rechnitz

Chapter 10.   INDUSTRIAL ANALYSIS AND CONTROL WITH ION-SELECTIVE ELECTRODES

by Truman S. Light

Chapter 11.   ANALYTICAL TECHNIQUES AND APPLICATIONS OF ION-SELECTIVE ELECTRODES

by Richard A. Durst

AUTHORS

George Eisenman attended Harvard College and Harvard Medical School graduating from the former *summa cum laude* in 1949 with an A.B. in Biology and graduating from the latter *magna cum laude* in 1953 with an M.D. He was elected to *Phi Beta Kappa* (Senior Sixteen) in 1948 and to *Alpha Omega Alpha* in 1952. He was a National Scholar at Harvard Medical School from 1949-53 and received the Maimonides Award of Harvard Medical School in 1953. He was elected to the American Physiological Society in 1954 and nominated for the Council of the Biophysical Society in 1966.

He was a Research Fellow of Harvard University in 1950, 1953-55; and a Research Associate from 1955-56. In 1956, he was appointed as Permanent Senior Staff Scientist in the Department of Basic Research of Eastern Pennsylvania Psychiatric Institute where he remained until 1962, leaving to become Associate Professor of Physiology at the University of Utah College of Medicine. In 1965, he joined the faculty of the University of Chicago as Professor of Physiology where he was also appointed Professor of Biophysics in 1967. In 1969, he became Professor in the Physiology Department at the University of California, Los Angeles. Dr. Eisenman has been visiting Professor at the Institute of Physics of the University of Genoa, Italy, during the summers of 1963 and 1964. He is a Consultant for the Corning Glass Works and for E. I. du Pont de Nemours Co.

His special research interest is in the mechanism by which ions and other solutes cross biological membranes. By working with simple cations and reducing biologic phenomena to a physical substrate, he has been developing theories of ion permeation through non-living membranes of sufficient structural complexity to approach the complexity conceivable in biological systems. He hopes that his research will contribute suffi-

ciently to the understanding of ion permeation to help eventually in
deducing the as yet unidentified mechanism (or mechanisms) by which
ions cross biological membranes.

James W. Ross was born in Ft. Lewis, Washington in 1928. In 1951, he
received an A.B. degree in Chemistry from the University of California at
Berkeley, followed by a three-year period during which he worked as a
chemist for the Tidewater Associated Oil Company. In 1957, he received
a Ph.D degree in chemistry from the University of Wisconsin. He joined
the chemistry faculty of the Massachusetts Institute of Technology as instructor in 1957, becoming Assistant Professor in 1959. In 1962, he left
M.I.T. to become one of the founders of Orion Research Incorporated
where he is presently serving as Vice President and Director of Research.

Dr. Ross is the author and co-author of numerous papers and patents
in the areas of analytical chemistry and electrochemistry.

For the past several years, Dr. Ross and his research group have been
working to develop specific sensing electrodes for use in chemical analysis and process control.

Arthur K. Covington graduated with First Class Honors from the University of Reading, England in 1953. He remained in Professor E. A. Guggenheim's department at Reading to work with Dr. J. E. Prue on the use of the glass electrode for precise thermodynamic measurements, receiving his Ph.D. in 1956. After a period in industry, he was in 1958 appointed Lecturer in the Chemistry Department, King's College, University of Durham, which later became the University of Newcastle upon Tyne. He was promoted to Senior Lecturer in 1967. While continuing his interest in glass electrodes, he has under Professor Lord Wynne-Jones' encouragement, broadened his interests to include investigation of reference electrode systems and of the properties of electrolyte solutions by thermodynamic and spectroscopic techniques. In 1965-66, he spent five months, while on sabbatical leave, in the Electrochemical Analysis Section of the NBS.

Dr. Covington is a Fellow of the Royal Institute of Chemistry and of the Chemical Society (London), and a member of the Faraday Society. He represents the Chemical Society on the British Standards Institution Committees on Glass Electrodes and pH Meters.

James N. Butler received a B.Sc. in Chemistry from Rensselaer Polytechnic Institute (1955) and a Ph.D. in Chemical Physics from Harvard University (1959). While at Harvard he was awarded research fellowships from the National Science Foundation and the General Electric Company for his doctoral studies in gas-phase reaction kinetics. These were conducted under the direction of Prof. G. B. Kistiakowsky.

He was on the faculty of the University of British Columbia from 1959 until 1963 when he joined Tyco Laboratories, Inc., as a Senior Scientist in Chemical Physics. In 1966, he was appointed Head of the Physical Chemistry Department.

Dr. Butler's general research interests are in chemical kinetics and thermodynamics; he is presently concentrating on studies of electrode kinetics and the thermodynamics of electrolyte solutions.

He is a member of the A.A.A.S., The New York Academy of Sciences, the American Chemical Society, the Faraday Society, and the Electrochemical Society. In 1967, he was appointed to the executive committee of the Boston Section, Electrochemical Society. Dr. Butler is the author of five books and more than fifty scientific papers.

Roger G. Bates is chief of the Electrochemical Analysis Section of the NBS. He was graduated from the University of Massachusetts and received his Ph.D. degree from Duke University in 1937. Following graduate study, he was awarded the Sterling Fellowship at Yale University and spent two years in research under the supervision of Professor H. S. Harned. He has been a member of the staff of the NBS since 1939 with the exception of two periods of study abroad. He spent the academic year 1953-54 in the laboratory of Professor G. Schwarzenbach in Zurich and studied for shorter periods in Paris and Oxford in 1962.

Dr. Bates has published about 160 technical articles. He is the author of the book "Determination of pH, Theory and Practice" and has contributed to many encyclopedias and monographs. He has also lectured widely in this country on the subject of acidity measurement and in 1959 was a Swiss-American Foundation lecturer in Basel and Zurich. His studies of electrolytic solutions and the standardization of pH brought him the Hillebrand Prize for 1955 of the Washington Section ACS and the gold medal for exceptional service of the Department of Commerce in 1957.

Since 1951, Dr. Bates has been active in both the Analytical Chemistry Division and the Physical Chemistry Division of the International Union of Pure and Applied Chemistry. He served a six-year term as president of the IUPAC Commission on Electrochemical Data and is a titular member of the Commission on Electrochemistry and the Commission on Symbols, Terminology, and Units at the present time, as well as of the U. S. National Committee for IUPAC.

Dr. Bates is a member of the editorial advisory boards of *Analytical Chemistry* and *Analytica Chimica Acta*. He is a member of the ACS council, representing the Division of Analytical Chemistry, and was the editor of the *Capital Chemist* in its first year of publication. He is also a member of the Washington Academy of Sciences, *Phi Beta Kappa*,

Sigma Xi, Phi Kappa Phi, and the Cosmos Club and is a fellow of the American Institute of Chemists. His selection to receive the 1969 ACS Award in Analytical Chemistry was recently announced.

Edward W. Moore was born in Madisonville, Kentucky on July 6, 1930, received his B.A. in Chemistry from Vanderbilt University in 1952 and his M.D. from Vanderbilt University Medical School in 1955. From 1955 to 1956, he interned in the Harvard Medical Services, Boston City Hospital, then received a year of residency training in internal medicine at the Lemuel Shattuck Hospital, during which time he worked on insulin metabolism in diabetes. From 1957 to 1959, he was a Clinical Associate at the National Cancer Institute in Bethesda, Md., working on several problems in cancer and leukemia, including studies of the central nervous system in acute leukemia and studies of the physiology and pharmacology of the blood-CSF barrier. Returning to Boston in 1959, another year was spent in the Harvard Medical Services at Boston City Hospital. In 1960, Dr. Moore began full-time research at the Lemuel Shattuck Hospital where he has remained up to the present time. He has been a U.S. Public Health Service Research Fellow, Fellow of The Medical Foundation of Boston and Research Career Development Awardee of The National Institute of General Medical Sciences.

His major interests are electrolyte metabolism and gastrointestinal physiology, with particular emphasis in physical chemistry and mathematical models. Over 60 works have been published in these and related areas.

Dr. Moore is a member of numerous organizations devoted to scientific excellence and is a member of *Phi Beta Kappa* and *Alpha Omega Alpha* honorary societies. At the present time, he is Associate Professor of Medicine and Instructor in Physiology, Tufts University Medical School;

Assistant in Medicine, Harvard University Medical School; Chief of
Gastroenterology and Director of the Metabolic and Gastrointestinal
Research Laboratories at the Lemuel Shattuck Hospital.

Raja N. Khuri was born in Beirut, Lebanon and received both his B.Sc.
degree (1955) and M.D. (1959) from the American University of Beirut.
The following year he was a Junior Assistant Resident in Medicine at the
American University Hospital (Beirut) and, from 1960 to January 1964,
was a Postdoctoral Research Fellow at the Harvard Medical School. He
returned to the American University of Beirut as Assistant Professor in
Physiology and Internal Medicine (1964-68) and became Associate
Professor and Chairman of the Department of Physiology in 1968. Dur-
ing 1968-69, Dr. Khuri has been Visiting Associate Professor of
Physiology at the Yale University School of Medicine.

His research interests are concerned with ion-selective microelectrodes
and their applications to biological systems, in general, and to studies in
renal physiology, in particular.

Garry A. Rechnitz received his undergraduate and graduate education at the Universities of Michigan and Illinois, respectively, spent five years on the faculty of the University of Pennsylvania, and is now Professor of Chemistry and Associate Provost for Natural Sciences and Mathematics at the State University of New York at Buffalo. His research interests include the properties and applications of ion-selective membrane electrodes, controlled-potential coulometry, the kinetics and mechanisms of analytical reactions, and other aspects of modern analytical chemistry. He is the author of more than sixty publications (including two books) in these areas.

Dr. Rechnitz is a member of the editorial advisory boards for *Talanta* and *Analytical Letters* as well as of a number of technical and honorary societies. Since 1966, he has been a fellow of the Alfred P. Sloan Foundation.

Truman S. Light was born in Hartford, Connecticut, received a Bachelor's degree in Chemistry and Physics from Harvard College, a Master's degree in Analytical Chemistry from the University of Minnesota and a Doctorate in Inorganic Chemistry from the University of Rome. From 1949 to 1959, Dr. Light was an Instructor and Assistant Professor at Boston College teaching Analytical Chemistry with emphasis on Physical Chemical Methods of Analysis. From 1959 to 1964, he was employed by the Avco Corporation, Research and Advanced Development Division in Wilmington, Mass., as a staff Scientist working on high temperature materials for the space industry and their related analytical problems. Since 1964, Dr. Light has been with The Foxboro Company. His research interests and publications are in the fields of analytical chemistry and application of instrumental methods of analysis to process control. His current research is concerned with studies of ion-selective electrodes.

Dr. Light is a member of *Sigma Xi*, the American Chemical Society, the Instrument Society of America, the Society of Applied Spectroscopy and the New England Association of Chemistry Teachers.

Richard A. Durst is a research chemist and project leader in electroanalytical measurements in the Microchemical Analysis Section of the NBS Division of Analytical Chemistry. He was graduated with Highest Honors from the University of Rhode Island (B.S. — 1960) and received his Ph.D. in analytical chemistry from the Massachusetts Institute of Technology (1963). While at M.I.T., he was a NSF Fellow and conducted polarographic research and electrolyte solution studies under the direction of Prof. D. N. Hume. Dr. Durst was a NRC-NBS Postdoctoral Research Associate with Dr. J. K. Taylor (1963-64), Visiting Assistant Professor at Pomona College (Calif.), Assistant Professor at Boston College (1965-66), and returned to NBS in 1966.

His general research interests include instrumental methods of analysis with emphasis on electroanalytical techniques. Presently, he is studying the analytical applications of ion-selective electrodes, especially for microanalysis.

Dr. Durst is a member of the American Chemical Society, the A.A.A.S., *Sigma Xi, Phi Kappa Phi,* the Polarographic Society (London), the Chemical Society of Washington, and a Fellow of the Washington Academy of Sciences.

CHAPTER 1

THEORY OF MEMBRANE ELECTRODE POTENTIALS: AN EXAMINATION OF THE PARAMETERS DETERMINING THE SELECTIVITY OF SOLID AND LIQUID ION EXCHANGERS AND OF NEUTRAL ION-SEQUESTERING MOLECULES

George Eisenman

Department of Physiology
University of California
Los Angeles, California

I. Introduction

Membrane electrodes specific to a wide variety of ions are coming of age, as evidenced by the contents of this volume. From the discovery by Cremer [1] and Haber and Klemensiewicz [2] at the beginning of the century of the H^+ selective glass electrode and the development in the late fifties by Eisenman and his colleagues [3-6] of specialized glass compositions specifically selective to ions such as Na^+, K^+, Ag^+, NH_4^+, Tl^+, Li^+, and Cs^+, we have recently progressed to the use of liquid ion exchangers for divalent cations [7] and a variety of anions [8]. Electrodes based on solid-state crystals have been developed by Frant and Ross [9], and a new variety of specific ion electrodes is just emerging, based upon the specific sequestration of cations by neutral macrocyclic molecules (typically cyclic antibiotics and polyethers) which offer the possibility of exquisite selectivity, entirely comparable to the very high selectivities characteristic of biological membranes [10-12]. The mechanism by which these uncharged molecules produce such highly specific electrodes in ultra-thin (100 Å) phospholipid bilayer membranes has been shown recently to be due to the action of these molecules as specific solubilizers of cations within the liquid-like interior of these membranes [13,14]. Bulk solvents containing such materials have also been reported to produce highly specific responses for ions such as K^+ and Rb^+ [12], but with sub-ideal slopes. The above types of membranes can be conveniently categorized into three general types which share a number of common features but have important theoretical and practical differences: (A) solid ion exchangers, (B) liquid ion exchangers, and (C) neutral sequestering agents.

I will begin by summarizing the principle theoretical expectations from the analysis of the origin of the membrane potential for each of these three types of electrodes, referring the reader to appendices for details, but explicitly examining in the test the parameters determining the ionic selectivity in each. The similarities and differences between these mechanisms as well as their particular advantages and limitations will then be discussed. Only monovalent cations will be considered, as a parallel line of argument applies in the case of monovalent anions.

II. Solid Ion Exchangers (e.g., The Glass Electrode)

When a thin membrane of glass is interposed between two solutions, an electric potential difference is observed which depends on the ions present in the solution in a simple and reproducible manner [3-6]. Depending on the composition of the glass, the response may be to H^+ chiefly [2] or it may be to other cations such as the alkali metal cations [3], the alkaline earths cations [5], or even certain organic cations [5]. The experimental evidence is now overwhelming that such glass electrodes are simply cation exchange membranes having a particularly high degree of selectivity among the various monovalent cations [15].

The theory of the origin of the membrane potential of such electrodes begins with the solution of the flux equations for liquid junctions by Planck [16] and Nernst [17]. This was first applied to semipermeable membranes by Teorell [18,19] and by Meyer and Sievers [20] by including the effects of Donnan equilibria at the membrane-solution interfaces. Helfferich [21] and Mackay and Meares [22] extended the analysis to include boundary conditions appropriate to ion exchangers. Karreman and Eisenman [23] postulated that glass electrodes were simple cation exchange membranes characterized by "n-type" non-ideal behavior (for which the derivative of the logarithm of the activity with respect to the derivative of the logarithm of the concentration is a constant) and obtained analytical expressions for the glass electrode potential in terms of the ion exchange equilibrium constants and mobilities of the cation species characteristic of the glass. This work was extended and generalized by Conti and Eisenman [24,25] with the results summarized in Appendix Section A. Nicolsky and his colleagues [26], as well as Doremus [27] and Isard [28] have recently carried out a theoretical treatment in agreement with these; and the theory is now generally accepted [6].

Glass electrodes are made from mixtures of oxides of elements of oxidation state 3 or greater (e.g., Si, Al) with oxides of elements of oxidation state 1 or 2 (e.g., Na, Ca). When melted and subsequently cooled, such oxides form a three-dimensional solid in which the most mobile charged species are the monovalent cations. A membrane made of glass is therefore permeable almost solely to cations and functions as a cation exchanger with the consequence that a Nernst potential is observed when such a membrane separates two solutions of a single salt at two different concentrations:

$$E = \frac{RT}{F} \ln \frac{a_i'}{a_i''},$$ (1)

where a_i' and a_i'' represent the activities of the cation I^+ in the two aqueous solutions designated by $(')$ and $('')$, on either side of the membrane. R is the gas constant, T is the absolute temperature, and F is the faraday constant.

If an electrode is constructed by filling a thin walled glass bulb with a solution of a salt of constant composition, the electric potential measured using such a half cell depends only on the activity of I^+ in the external solution $(')$ and can be written simply as:

$$E = \text{Const} + \frac{RT}{F} \ln a_i'.$$ (2)

This provides a means of measuring the activity of cation I^+ in different solutions provided only that an appropriate reference electrode is used to complete the electric circuit.

If a number of species of cations are present simultaneously, the theoretical analysis of Appendix Section A as well as experimental studies on certain hydrated glass compositions [15] as well as dry glass [29] inform us that the membrane potential depends on the weighted contributions of each ionic species according to the equation:

$$E = \frac{RT}{F} \ln \frac{a_i' + \left[\frac{u_j^*}{u_i^*} K_{ij}\right] a_j'}{a_i'' + \left[\frac{u_j^*}{u_i^*} K_{ij}\right] a_j''}.$$ (3)

For simplicity, I have restricted considerations to two species of cations, I^+ and J^+, and also considered only the case in which ideal behavior exists (i.e., $n = 1$). Equation (3) is time independent, applying at all times subsequent to the establishment of equilibria at the membrane-solution interfaces [24].

The parameter $[(u_j^*/u_i^*)K_{ij}]$ in Equation (3) is a weighting factor characteristic of the selectivity of a given membrane composition. A value of $[(u_j^*/u_i^*)K_{ij}] = 10$ implies that ion J^+ is 10 times as effective on a mole for mole basis as ion I^+ in determining the electrode potential. The selectivity between I^+ and J^+ is determined by the product of the mobility ratio of these species in the membrane (u_j^*/u_i^*) and the ion exchange equilibrium constant (K_{ij}) characteristic of their exchange between the aqueous phase and the membrane:

$$J^+ \text{ (aqueous)} + I^{+*}\text{(membrane)} \overset{K_{ij}}{\rightleftharpoons} J^{+*} \text{ (membrane)} + I^+ \text{ (aqueous)}. \quad (4)$$

[In Eqs. (3-4), and henceforth, asterisks are used to denote quantities characteristic of the membrane phase; while quantities relating to the aqueous phase will either be unmarked or will be designated by (') and ('') when it is necessary to distinguish between the solutions on two sides of the membrane.]

III. Liquid Ion Exchangers

Membranes composed of a water-immiscible solvent interposed between two aqueous solutions were among the first membranes whose electric properties were characterized [30]; their history has recently been summarized by Shean and Sollner [31]. When such membranes contain an appreciable concentration of an ionizable species which is preferentially soluble within the membrane phase (*e.g.*, a fatty acid or an aliphatic amine), they function as liquid ion exchangers [32], which differ from solid ion exchangers in that the ion exchange sites are free to move within the membrane. The situation in such a membrane is diagrammed in Figure 1, where the arrows indicate that the cation species, I^+, is freely permeable across the membrane-solution interfaces whereas the organophilic anion, S^-, is "trapped" within the membrane phase. As a consequence of this, the aqueous anion species, X^-, is excluded from the membrane phase.

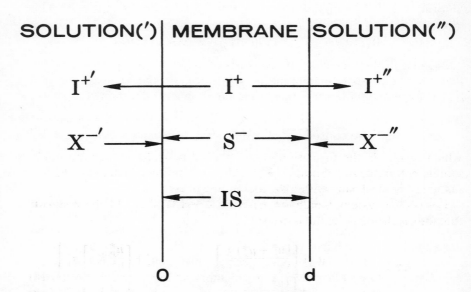

Figure 1.   Diagram of a liquid ion exchanger membrane (reproduced from Fig. 1 of [34]). I^+, S^-. and X^- refer to the counterions, the site, and the co-ion species, respectively. Asterisks for the species in the membrane have been omitted for simplicity.

A. Limiting Case of Complete Dissociation

Conti and Eisenman [33] have shown that, in the limiting case of negligible association, the membrane potential is given by:

$$E = \frac{RT}{F} \ln \frac{a_i' + \left[\frac{u_j^*}{u_i^*}\frac{k_j}{k_i}\right] a_j'}{a_i'' + \left[\frac{u_j^*}{u_i^*}\frac{k_j}{k_i}\right] a_j''} \qquad (5)$$

Equation (5) is valid both in the steady state and also instantaneously subsequent to a step change in solution conditions [34] and can be seen to be identical **in form** to Equation (3) characteristic of solid ion exchangers; here u_i^* is the mobility of the dissociated I^+ species in the solvent phase and k_i is the partition coefficient of I^+ between water and the solvent of the membrane:

$$I^+ \text{ (aqueous) } \underset{}{\overset{k_i}{\rightleftharpoons}} I^{+*} \text{ (membrane)} \qquad (6)$$

Equation (5) indicates that the selectivity between species I^+ and J^+ is determined by the partition coefficients and mobilities of the **dissociated ions**. The selectivity is therefore determined **entirely by the solvent** and is independent of the particular organophilic exchanger, which is not surprising since dissociation between the liquid ion exchanger molecules and their counterions is complete.

B. Limiting Case of Strong Association

Because of the low dielectric constant of the solvents typically used for liquid ion exchange membranes, association of the species I^{+*} and S^{-*} is expected within the membrane phase according to reaction:

$$I^{+*} + S^{-*} \overset{K_{is}^*}{\rightleftharpoons} IS^* \qquad (7)$$

which results in the formation of the neutral pairs $IS^{\cdot}$, which are freely mobile within the membrane. K_{is}^* is the association constant for the formation of neutral pairs within the membrane phase.

For such a system, Sandblom, Eisenman, and Walker [34] have shown that the electrode potential is given by:

$$E = \frac{RT}{F}\left\{ (1-\tau)\ln\frac{a' + \left[\frac{(u_j^*+u_s^*)\,k_j}{(u_i^*+u_s^*)\,k_i}\right] a'}{a_i'' + \left[\frac{(u_j^*+u_s^*)\,k_j}{(u_i^*+u_s^*)\,k_i}\right] a_j''} + \tau \ln\frac{a_i' + \left[\frac{u_{js}^*}{u_{is}^*}K_{ij}\right] a_j'}{a_i'' + \left[\frac{u_{js}^*}{u_{is}^*}K_{ij}\right] a_j''} \right\} \qquad (8)$$

both "instantaneously" and in the steady-state (see Appendix Section B).

The electrode potential of a liquid ion exchanger membrane in which strong association occurs is seen to consist of two logarithmic terms, each of the form of the previous electrode equations. The relative contributions of these terms are governed by the parameter:

$$\tau = \frac{u_s^* \, (u_{js}^* K_{js}^* - u_{is}^* K_{is}^*)}{(u_i^* + u_s^*) \, u_{js}^* K_{js}^* - (u_j^* + u_s^*) \, u_{is}^* K_{is}^*} \, ; \; 0 \leqslant \tau \leqslant 1. \qquad (9)$$

The selectivity in the first term of Equation (8) depends on the product of the partition coefficient ratio of the dissociated ion species (k_j/k_i) and the ratio of the summed mobilities of the dissociated ions and the dissociated sites $[(u_j^* + u_s^*)/(u_i^* + u_s^*)]$. It therefore depends predominantly on the solvent and only depends on the chemical nature of the liquid exchanger through its effect on u_s^*. On the other hand, the selectivity in the second term of Equation (8) is determined by the product of the mobility ratio of the neutral pairs (u_{js}^*/u_{is}^*) and the ion exchange equilibrium constant (K_{ij}) of the reaction:

$$J^+ \;(\text{aqueous}) + IX^* \;(\text{membrane}) \xrightleftharpoons{\; K_{ij} \;} JX^* \;(\text{membrane}) + I^+ \;(\text{aqueous}),$$

$$(10)$$

which is formally identical to the reaction shown as Equation (4). K_{ij} can alternatively be expressed as the product of the partition coefficient ratio of the ions and the association constants in the membrane phase as:

$$K_{ij} = \frac{k_j K_{js}^*}{k_i K_{is}^*}. \qquad (11)$$

The selectivity of K_{ij} depends on the properties not only of the organophilic ion exchanger molecule but also on the solvent in which it is dissolved, as will be examined in Section V. The value of τ, which lies between 0 and 1, depending on the properties of the solvent and of the ion exchanger, determines the relative importance of the two logarithmic terms of Equation (8).

For certain systems, Equation (8) is largely determined by either the first or the last term, depending on whether τ is zero or one. For example, if the association constant for the I^+ species is much larger than that for J^+, and if the mobilities of all neutral pairs are approximately equal so that $u_{is}^* = u_{js}^*$, Equation (9), reduces to:

$$\tau = \frac{u_s^*}{u_j^* + u_s^*} \qquad (12)$$

from which $(1 - \tau)$ is seen to be simply the transference number of the most dissociated counterion species and τ is identifiable as the transference number of the dissociated site species relative to the most dissociated counterion species. This means that, if the dissociated site species is more mobile than the most dissociated counterion, the second term will determine the potential predominantly, as appears to be the case experimentally for H^+ and Na^+ with the exchanger bis-2-ethylhexyl phosphoric acid in amyl alcohol [32]. The similarities and differences between solid and liquid exchangers are given by comparison of Equations (3), (5), and (8).

IV. Neutral Sequestering Agents Which Act as Molecular Carriers of Ions

In 1964, Moore and Pressman [35] discovered that neutral macrocyclic antibiotics induced ion permeation in mitochondria, and comparable electrical effects of these compounds on artificial phospholipid bilayer membranes were demonstrated shortly thereafter by Lev and Buzhinsky [10] and by Mueller and Rudin [11]. Bulk solvent electrodes based on these molecules were developed by Stefanac and Simon [12]. More recently, the related, but structurally simpler cyclic polyethers synthesized by Pedersen [36] have been found to produce cation-selective membrane electrodes with selectivities entirely comparable to those characteristic of the antibiotics [13,14]. These molecules are devoid of charged groups but contain an arrangement of ring oxygens energetically suitable (through ion-dipole interaction) to replace the hydration shell around cations. These lipid-soluble molecules are thus able to solubilize cations in organic solvents, forming mobile charged complexes with the cations therein, and in this way providing a mechanism for cation permeation across such (normally insulating) media. Chemical formulas and space-filling models of two such molecular carriers of cations are illustrated in Figure 2.

The membrane system corresponding to this mechanism is diagrammed in Figure 3 and resembles liquid ion exchangers in its fluid nature. It differs from these, however, in that the complexed cation species (IS^+) bears the charge of the sequestered cation instead of being electrically neutral. As a consequence of this, the most interesting properties of such carriers in low dielectric constant solvents are manifested in ultra-thin (60Å) membranes [37] in which a sufficient excess of cations is brought into the membrane in the form of the sequestered species to lead to a substantial deviation from electroneutrality [38]. (Indeed, the excess of complexed-cations solubilized in the membrane is sufficient for the concentration of free cations and anions to be regarded as negligible in the membrane [38].) In solvents of higher dielectric constant these molecules produce useful electrodes of much greater thickness [12], but since the published data on such systems are scanty in comparison to that for the thin membranes, I will confine my comments to the latter case, noting that its essential features should bear on the thicker systems as well.

A. MEMBRANE POTENTIAL

A theory for neutral carriers has been developed by Ciani, Eisenman, and Szabo for dilute aqueous solutions in which the concentrations of the neutral macrocyclic molecules are identical on both sides of the membrane [13,14,38]; and the membrane potential [*i.e.*, the potential difference between solutions ('') and (')] at zero current in mixtures of two

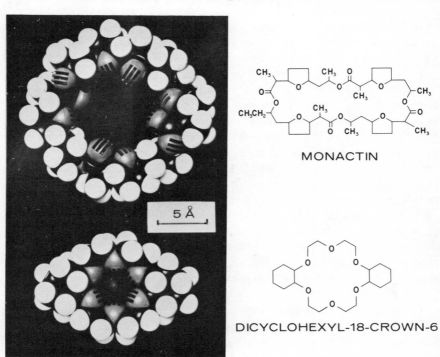

MONACTIN

DICYCLOHEXYL-18-CROWN-6

Figure 2.   Chemical formulas and space-filling models of the molecular carriers of ions, dicyclohexyl-18-crown-6 [36] and Monactin. (Reproduced from Fig. 1 of [13].) A sphere approximating the size of K^+ has been inserted in the ring of the CPK model of dicyclohexyl-18-crown-6 (abbreviated as XXXI). The monactin molecule is shown in an arbitrary open configuration. While neither of the molecules has a net charge, they both can, through their ring oxygens, provide an energetic environment for cations similar to that in water. Since the nonpolar exterior of the rings causes the molecules themselves to partition favorably into hydrocarbon solvents, they are expected to solubilize cations in low dielectric media. Note that while monactin is a flexible molecule capable of undergoing considerable configurational changes on interaction with cations, XXXI is more rigid and not susceptible to much deformation from a planar configuration.

cations I^+ and J^+ has been shown to be described by:

$$E = \frac{RT}{F} \ln \frac{a_i' + \left[\dfrac{u_{js}^* K_j}{u_{is}^* K_i}\right] a_j'}{a_i'' + \left[\dfrac{u_{js}^* K_j}{u_{is}^* K_i}\right] a_j''} \tag{13}$$

where K_j/K_i is the ratio of the equilibrium constants of the salt extraction reactions

$$I^+ + X^- + S^* \xrightleftharpoons{K_i} IS^{+*} + X^{-*} \tag{14}$$

$$J^+ + X^- + S^* \xrightleftharpoons{K_j} JS^{+*} + X^{-*}, \tag{15}$$

which measure the extent to which the neutral molecules, $S^{\cdot}$, can extract the salt, I^+X^-, from water into an organic solvent phase [14].

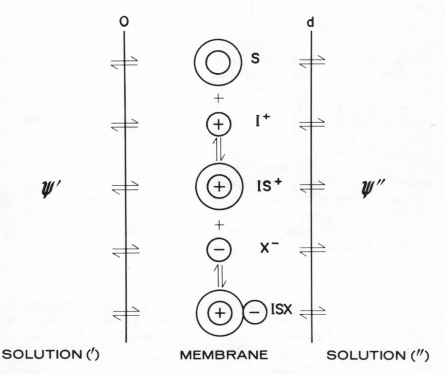

Figure 3.   Diagram of a neutral-carrier membrane (reproduced from Fig. 2 of [13]). I^+, S, IS^+, X^-, and ISX refer to the free ion, the neutral molecular carrier, the complexed cations, the free anion and the neutral complex, respectively. Asterisks for the membrane species have been omitted for simplicity.

Note that K_j/K_i is formally identical to K_{ij}, the equilibrium constant of the reaction:

$$J^+ \text{ (aqueous) } + IS^{+\,*}\text{(membrane)} \underset{}{\overset{K_{ij}}{\rightleftharpoons}} JS^{+\,*} \text{ (membrane) } + I^+ \text{ (aqueous)}.$$

(16)

Although Equation (13) is identical in form to Equation (3), characteristic of solid ion exchange membranes, it must be emphasized that the physical meaning of the selectivity parameters is quite different. In many practical instances the size and charge of the complexed-cation appears to be virtually independent of the particular cation sequestered [39,40] so that the ratio $(u_{js}^*/u_{is}^*)=1$. In these cases we have the very simple result that the electrode selectivity depends solely on the ratio, K_j/K_i, of equilibrium constants.

V. The Factors Determining Selectivity for Each of These Types of Membranes

The factors determining the relative ion selectivities for these various types of electrodes can be compared most easily with the aid of Table 1, which summarizes the selectivity parameters from Equations (3), (5), (8), and (13) for solid ion exchangers, dissociated liquid ion exchangers, associated liquid ion exchangers, and neutral carriers, respectively. From the column labelled "Exact Representation" it should be clear that mobility, as well as equilibrium factors, determine the electrode potential selectivity for each of these mechanisms. However, from the column labelled "Approximate Representation" it can be seen that mobility terms contribute only slightly to the selectivity of certain liquid ion exchange membranes, and not at all to neutral carrier membranes. The physical reasons for this will become more clear from examining each of these mechanisms in greater detail now; while the factors underlying the equilibrium ion exchange selectivity of these electrodes will be considered in Section VI.

A. Solid Ion Exchangers

Scrutiny of Equation (3) indicates that the relative effects of species I^+ vs. J^+ on the electrode potential of a given membrane depend on the relative mobilities of these species in the membrane (u_j^*/u_i^*) as well as on their ion exchange equilibrium constant (K_{ij}). It is expected, and observed [15,25], that the more strongly an ion is preferred by such an ion exchanger, the more poorly does it move within the membrane; since the more difficult it is for it to jump from site to site. For this reason, there are opposing effects between mobilities and affinities of ions in solid ion

Table 1. Selectivity parameters for the various types of membranes.

	Exact representation	Approximate representation	Comments
Solid ion exchangers	$\dfrac{u_{j^+}^*}{u_{i^+}^*}\,K_{ij}$	$\dfrac{u_{j^+}^*}{u_{i^+}^*}\,K_{ij}$	mobility opposes equilibrium selectivity
Liquid ion exchangers			
Dissociated	$\dfrac{u_{j^+}^*\ k_{j^+}}{u_{i^+}^*\ k_{i^+}}$	$\dfrac{u_{j^+}^*\ k_{j^+}}{u_{i^+}^*\ k_{i^+}}$	u^* and k depend only on solvent, are independent of exchanger species
Associated ($\tau = 0$, poorly mobile sites)	$\dfrac{\left(u_{j^+}^*+u_s^{*-}\right)k_{j^+}}{\left(u_{i^+}^*+u_s^{*-}\right)k_{i^+}}$	$\dfrac{u_{j^+}^*\ k_{j^+}}{u_{i^+}^*\ k_{i^+}}$	$u_s^{*-} \ll u_{i^+}^*,\ u_{j^+}^*$
($\tau = 1$, highly mobile sites)	$\dfrac{u_{js}^*}{u_{is}^*}\,K_{ij}$	$\dfrac{u_{js}^*}{u_{is}^*}\,K_{ij}$	
Neutral carriers	$\dfrac{u_{js}^*+\ K_j}{u_{is}^*+\ K_i}$	$\dfrac{K_j}{K_i}$	$u_{js}^*+\ =\ u_{is}^*+$

exchangers, which constitute one of the principle limitations of such systems.

For example, the ten-fold electrode potential selectivity for K$^+$ over Na$^+$ of a typical K$^+$-selective glass electrode is the result of a nearly hundred-fold ion exchange preference of the glass for K$^+$ over Na$^+$ opposed by a nearly ten-fold lower mobility of K$^+$ than Na$^+$ [41]. The relatively low selectivities of such solid ion exchangers for divalent cations appears to be a consequence of the poor mobility of these species [41,42].

Part of this limitation is overcome when one allows the ion exchange sites to move by making the ion exchanger a liquid in which the (neutral) complex between the counterion and the mobile-site can move; but an

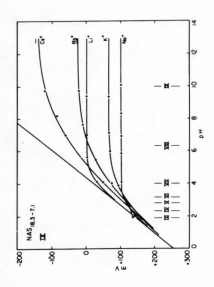

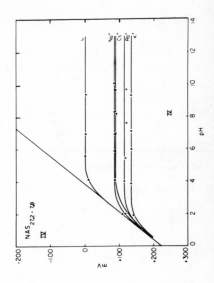

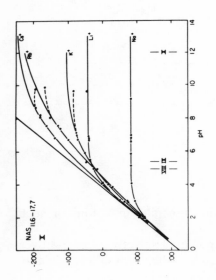

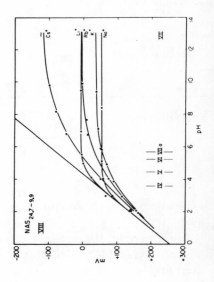

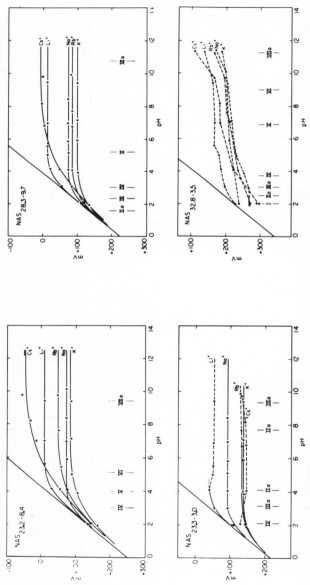

Figure 4. Representative sodium alumino-silicate glass electrode potential data at 22 ± 2 °C as a function of pH in $0.1\,N$ solutions of the indicated cations. (Reproduced from Fig. 3 of [4].) The points are experimentally measured by the indicated glass electrodes referred to a saturated KCl:calomel reference electrode (Beckman asbestos fiber type). The pH was measured simultaneously with a variety of commercial glass electrodes. The solid curves are drawn according to a theoretical equation extended from Equation (3) to include n-type non-ideal behavior. Dashed curves indicate data deviating significantly from the predictions of this equation. The composition of each glass is designated in the upper left of the subfigures in mole percent of Na_2O and Al_2O_3, respectively (SiO_2 equals the remainder). The Roman numerals below these designations indicate the selectivity rank order pertaining at the high pH limit. The Roman numerals below the curves indicate the rank orders characteristic of the indicated pH). (Note the dependence of the selectivity upon pH.) The six upper glasses are chemically durable and obey the theoretical equation well. The two lower glasses are soluble in H_2O and deviate significantly from the theoretical equation, although the deviations are least severe for Na^+ and K^+.

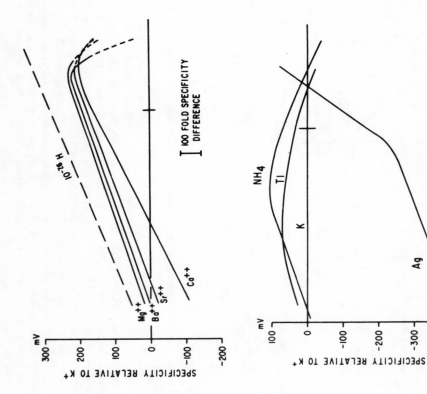

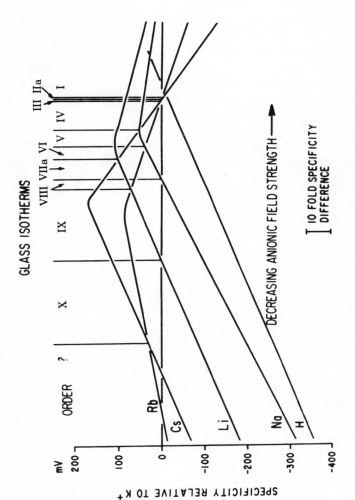

Figure 5. Selectivity of aluminosilicate glass electrodes. (Reproduced from Figs. 9-7 of [6].) The experimentally observed values of 58 log $[(u_j^*/u_i^*K_{ij}]$ for various cations relative to K$^+$ are plotted as a function of the observed Na$^+$-K$^+$ selectivity to illustrate the systematic relationship between Na$^+$-K$^+$ selectivity to the other cations.

even greater improvement will be seen to occur for the neutral carrier mechanism, in which the complex between the counterion and neutral carrier molecule is electrically charged. Despite this limitation, solid ion exchangers offer a variety of electrodes suitable for measuring monovalent cations such as H^+, Li^+, Na^+, K^+, Rb^+, Cs^+, Ag^+, Tl^+, NH_4^+, and even certain substituted ammonium, amines, and amino acids [3,5,6]. Typical data illustrating the kinds of selectivity characteristic of these electrodes are presented in Figures 4 and 5. The selectivity among ions is a function of the ion exchanger composition, as can be seen by the different magnitudes and sequences of selectivity observable in the various glass compositions of these figures, where the Roman numerals indicate the selectivity sequence (defined on page 30) characteristic of the electrodes under the indicated conditions.

At present, glass electrodes are the electrodes of choice for H^+, Na^+, Ag^+, and Li^+, for which their specificity is sufficiently high and their excellent stability characteristics are desirable. In addition, since these electrodes function well in organic solvents [6] they can be used in non-aqueous media, as well as in the presence of lipid-soluble or surface-active molecules [6,43].

B. LIQUID ION EXCHANGERS

Examination of Equation (5) and Table 1 indicates that for a strongly dissociated liquid ion exchanger (such as might be expected in solvents of sufficiently high dielectric constant) the selectivity among various ions should be **completely independent** of the chemical properties of the lipophilic ion exchanger molecule other than the sign of its charge. Thus, nitrobenzene or nitromethane can be caused to become a cation-selective electrode by adding oleic acid to them [32]. Such a membrane exhibits high specificities among cations, as illustrated by the data of Figure 6. The effect of oleic acid also occurs with long chain sulfonic or phosphoric acids; and the selectivities are the same [32]. It is therefore essentially independent of whether the ion exchanger is a carboxylate, phosphate, or sulfate, as would be expected from Equation (5). On the other hand, if a lipophilic anion exchanger molecule such as dodecylamine is used instead of oleic acid, the nitrobenzene membrane becomes an anion-selective electrode highly selective for $I^- > Br^- > Cl^- > F^-$ [44].

For a liquid ion exchanger in which association between counterion and site cannot be neglected (as for a solvent of low dielectric constant), the origin of selectivity is more complex and generally is a function of both the solvent and the exchanger since, even for the limiting case of strong association, separate contributions of the solvent and exchanger can be seen in the two terms of Equation (8).

In the first term, which dominates the properties of the system when $\tau = 0$ (as for example with sites which are poorly mobile compared to the

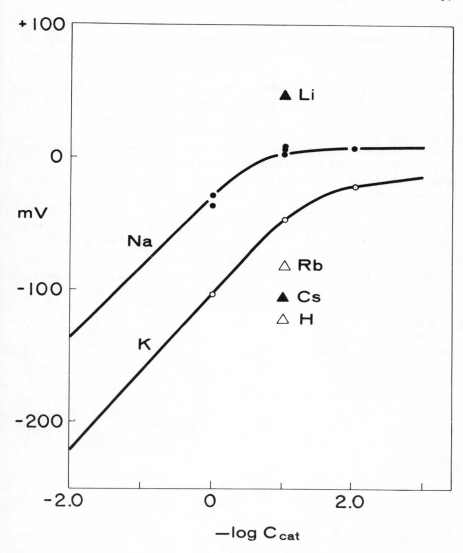

Figure 6. Cationic selectivity of liquid ion exchanger electrodes based on the solvent nitrobenzene. (Reproduced from Fig. 6 of [32].) The membrane is nitrobenzene containing 5% oleic acid. The points indicate the observed potentials at neutral pH. Note the large selectivity differences among the alkali cations. These are essentially independent of whether the added exchanger is a carboxylic, sulfonic, or phosphoric acid. Interestingly, the solid curves are drawn according to Equation (1) but the deviation from the Nernst behavior at the lowest cation concentrations is presumably the result of the dissolving of the sites rather than due to the effects of other cations because, at neutral pH, the H^+ effect is far too small to account for this deviation.

counterions), only the properties of the solvent appear in the "Approximate Representation" of Table 1. Since the mobility of the site species can be neglected in comparison to that of the counterions in this case, the parameters determining the selectivity become essentially the same as those for the completely dissociated case, namely u_j^*/u_i^* and k_j/k_i, both of which are independent of the chemical nature of the lipophilic exchanger since they represent properties of the **dissociated** ions alone.

The selectivity of the second term of Equation (8), on the other hand, which can dominate the properties of the membrane when $\tau = 1$ (as for example with sites which are highly mobile compared to the counterions), depends not only on the properties of the solvent but also on the chemical properties of the sites, since these affect both the ion exchange equilibrium constant (K_{ij}) and the mobility ratios (u_{js}^*/u_{is}^*) of the neutral complexes between the counterions and the sites. (For the usual ion exchangers like dodecylphosphoric acid, these mobilities should depend to some extent on the counterion, although for cyclic molecules like monensin [45] which can sequester cations in a manner similar to the neutral carriers discussed below [46], this ratio could approach unity.)

It will be instructive to examine the values of these parameters for a typical liquid ion exchange system consisting of bis-2-ethylhexyl phosphoric acid (abbreviated hereafter as "HBis") dissolved in n-amyl alcohol, for which these have been measured experimentally for H^+ and Na^+ [32]. The values of the association constant, single ion conductances, and distribution coefficients (S°) are presented in Table 2, together with the value calculated for these [32] for the ion exchange equilibrium constant K_{HNa}. These parameters should suffice in Equation (8) to deduce the selectivity to be expected for the electrode potential. Since τ is nearly unity, Equation (8) can be approximated by its second term alone, namely:

$$E = \frac{RT}{F} \ln \frac{a'_H + \dfrac{u^*_{HBis}}{u^*_{NaBis}} K_{HNa} a'_{Na}}{a''_H + \dfrac{u^*_{HBis}}{u^*_{NaBis}} K_{HNa} a''_{Na}} \cong \frac{RT}{F} \ln \frac{a'_H + 0.00005 a'_{Na}}{a''_H + 0.00005 a''_{Na}}, \qquad (17)$$

provided $u^*_{HBis} = u^*_{NaBis}$.

From Equation (17) and the data of Table 2, this membrane system is expected to be highly selective for H^+ to Na^+, which is in agreement with the experimental observations in Figure 7, where a large H^+ to Na^+ selectivity is seen. Thus, the selectivity characteristic of the equilibrium ion exchange appears to account for the principle selectivity observable as a membrane electrode.

Note that the selectivity of the ion exchange equilibrium constant K_{ij} of Equation (10) is not solely a property of the ion exchanger molecule but

Table 2. Association constants, single ion conductances, distribution coefficients, and the calculated ion exchange equilibrium constant for bis–2–ethylhexyl phosphoric acid in wet n–amyl alcohol.[a]

$$K^*_{HBis} \qquad 4.4 \times 10^8 \text{ cm}^3 \text{ mol}^{-1}$$

$$K^*_{NaBis} \qquad 1.8 \times 10^6 \text{ cm}^3 \text{ mol}^{-1}$$

$$\lambda^\circ_{Na} \qquad 1.47 \text{ ohm}^{-1} \text{ cm}^{-1} \text{ mol}^{-1}$$

$$\lambda^\circ_{H} \qquad 18.56 \text{ ohm}^{-1} \text{ cm}^{-1} \text{ mol}^{-1}$$

$$\lambda^\circ_{Bis} \qquad 9.99 \text{ ohm}^{-1} \text{ cm}^{-1} \text{ mol}^{-1}$$

$$\tau = \frac{\lambda^\circ_{Bis}}{\lambda^\circ_{Na} + \lambda^\circ_{Bis}} = 0.88$$

$$S^\circ_{HCl} = 0.022$$

$$S^\circ_{NaCl} = 0.0025$$

$$K_{HNa} = \left[\frac{S^\circ_{NaCl}}{S^\circ_{HCl}}\right]^2 \frac{K_{NaBis}}{K_{HBis}} = 0.00005$$

---

[a] K^*_{HBis} and K^*_{NaBis} are the association constants of Eq. (7) in wet n–amyl alcohol; λ°_{Na}, λ°_{H}, λ°_{Bis} are the single ion conductances; S°_{HCl} and S°_{NaCl} are the limiting partition coefficients of HCl and NaCl between H_2O and wet n–amyl alcohol. For further details, see reference [32].

depends also on the solvent of which the membrane is made. This can be seen by writing K_{ij} explicitly in terms of standard chemical potentials:

$$RT \ln K_{ij} = \mu^\circ_{ir} \text{ (membrane)} - \mu^\circ_{jr} \text{ (membrane)} + \mu^\circ_{j^+} \text{ (aqueous)} - \mu^\circ_{i^+} \text{ (aqueous).} \qquad (18)$$

Since $\mu^\circ_{j^+}$ (aqueous) and $\mu^\circ_{i^+}$ (aqueous) depend only on the aqueous

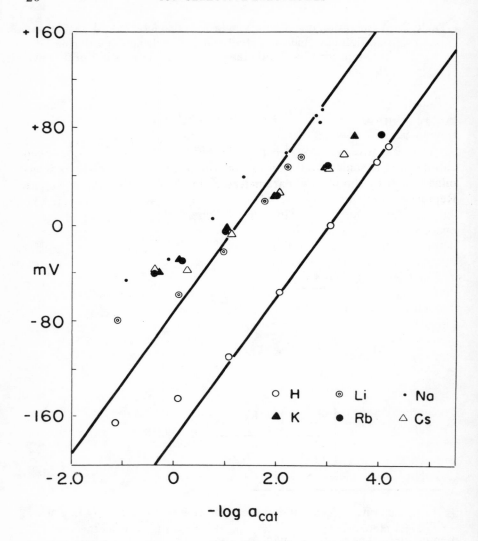

Figure 7. Electrode response to the indicated alkali metal cations of wet n-amyl alcohol
containing 10% bis-2-ethylhexyl phosphoric acid. (Reproduced from Fig. 5 of [32].)
The reference solution on one side of the membrane was $0.001N$ HCl in all cases; while
that on the other side had the concentrations of the chlorides indicated for each cation
on the abscissa.

phase, the only terms depending on the membrane are μ_{ix}° (membrane)
and μ_{jx}° (membrane). As the energy of taking the pairs IX and JX from
a convenient reference state (*e.g.*, in a dilute gas) into the membrane depends on the dielectric constant of the solvent and the electric field of the
ion-site dipole, which is a function of the ion exchanger molecule, [μ_{ix}°

(membrane)$-\mu^{\circ}_{jx}$ (membrane)] depends on both the properties of the solvent and of the exchanger.

C. NEUTRAL CARRIERS

Equation (13) and Table 1 present the extremely simple selectivity expectations for the neutral carrier mechanism typified by a variety of neutral macrocyclic molecules [14]. For these molecules, I have pointed out above that it is reasonable to expect that the mobilities of the complexed cations are the same for all cations, for which situation **selectivity is determined solely by equilibrium parameters**, as indicated in the "Approximate Representation" of Table 1, where only the ratio K_j/K_i appears. The neutral carrier mechanism differs from that of the ion exchangers in that charged ion exchange sites are not present. Instead, the "sites" are neutral molecules which form stoichiometric complexes with cations and function as carriers for these, the complex being charged.

Typical data for such a membrane are presented in Figure 8 which demonstrates the electrode potentials characteristic of the antibiotics nonactin and trinactin in mixtures of K^+ with Li^+, Na^+, Rb^+, and Cs^+ [14]. The points represent experimental observations; while the curves have been drawn according to Equation (13) with the values for the selectivity parameters labelled on the figures, designated as P_i/P_k:

$$P_i/P_K = (u^*_{is}K_i)/(u^*_{Ks}K_K) \tag{19}$$

The agreement of the data with Equation (13) is seen to be excellent; and the selectivity among the cations is very high (note that the K^+ to Na^+ selectivity of nonactin is better than 130 to 1). The sequence of selectivity among the group Ia cations for both nonactin and trinactin is $K > Rb > Cs > Na > Li$ (which is selectivity order IV to be defined below), but it is clear that systematic quantitative changes in selectivity occur as a function of increased methylation of the antibiotic (trinactin has 3 more methyl groups than nonactin). The significance of these will be commented on further in the following section.

Entirely comparable data are also characteristic of Pedersen's cyclic polyether, dicyclohexyl-18-crown-6 [36], as is illustrated in Figure 9, although it should be noted that the electrode slope is slightly sub-Nernstian, being only 50 mV in this case. Nevertheless, the selectivity of K^+ to Na^+ is again very high, being 125 to 1 for this molecule [13].

High selectivities of neutral carriers have been reported for considerably thicker membrane systems, such as monactin in CCl_4 [12], valinomycin in hexane [47], and valinomycin in octanol [48]. Tosteson has also found high K^+ over Na^+ selectivities for valinomycin, a mixture of monactin-dinactin, as well as for a cyclic polyether using thick

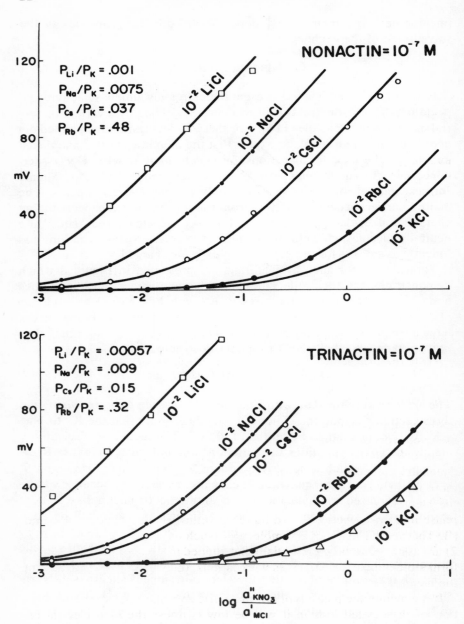

Figure 8.   Membrane potentials of lecithin bilayers in the presence of Nonactin and Trinactin. (Reproduced from Fig. 8 of [14].) The points represent the experimentally observed values of potential; while the curves are drawn according to Equation (13) with the indicated values of $P_i/P_k = (u_{is}^* K_i)/(u_{ks}^* K_k)$.

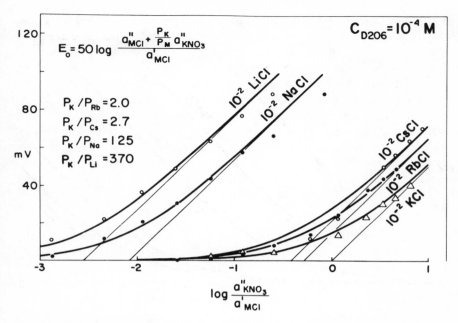

Figure 9. Membrane potentials in alkali chloride-potassium nitrate mixtures containing 10^{-4} molar Pedersen's cyclic polyether XXXI [36], labelled here D206 in the terminology of [13]. (Reproduced from Fig. 4 of [13].) The membrane was formed in an aqueous $10^{-2}M$ solution of the indicated alkali chloride containing $10^{-4}M$ XXXI. The points are experimental; while the curves have been drawn according to the equation indicated on the figure.

lipid-containing membranes [49]. Clearly the mixture need not be as thin as the bilayers of Figures 8 and 9.

Because of the relative newness of this system, I will describe its chemistry and properties in somewhat greater detail than was done for the more familiar ion exchangers examined above. Recall Figure 3, in which the membrane is represented by a thin (*e.g.*, 60 Å) liquid hydrocarbon phase interposed between two aqueous solutions, designated by (') and ("). The neutral macrocyclic molecules (such as those illustrated in Fig. 2) are assumed to be preferentially partitioned in the organic phase and to form stoichiometric complexes with cations, thereby solubilizing them in the membrane.[1]

If the membrane phase is of low dielectric constant, then the concentration of dissociated ions in it will be low (witness the high electric re-

---

[1]The membrane need not be thin, although I will restrict myself to this situation here since it is only for this case that a rigorous membrane theory has been derived and tested [13,38]. Indeed, in order to characterize the equilibrium properties for comparison with the electrical properties of bilayers, the membrane phase has been expanded into a bulk liquid and the salt extraction properties of the macrocyclic molecules characterized.

sistance of artificial bilayer membranes in the absence of added materials [37] and the low salt uptake characteristic of pure hydrocarbon solvents [39]). However, in the presence of lipid-soluble neutral macrocyclic molecules, both the electric conductance of thin membranes and the salt uptake by bulk phases are increased markedly [13] because of the ability of such molecules to solubilize the cations by providing an energetic environment for these comparable to that in water.

Three independent types of species exist in the aqueous as well as in the organic phases: the free cations (I^+), the free anions (X^-) and the free neutral macrocyclic molecules (S). For n species of monovalent cations, n reactions of the type

$$I^+ + S \underset{K_{is}^+}{\rightleftharpoons} IS^+, \tag{20}$$

occur between the cations I^+ and the macrocyclic compound S, leading to the formation of the positively charged lipid-soluble complexes IS^+, as indicated by the equilibrium between the upper three species in Figure 3.

Also indicated in Figure 3 is the possibility of further association between the IS^+ species and the anions X^- according to the reaction:

$$IS^+ + X^- \underset{K_{isx}}{\rightleftharpoons} ISX \,; \tag{21}$$

which is usually negligible in its effects on the electrical properties of the membrane [14].

When an aqueous solution is in contact either with a bulk organic solvent or with the membrane, viewed simply as a thin membrane-like portion of the solvent, the equilibrium distribution for each species between the two phases can be described by heterogeneous reactions of the type:

$$S \underset{k_s}{\rightleftharpoons} S^*, \quad k_s = a_s^*/a_s, \tag{22}$$

for the neutral species (S and ISX) and of the type:

$$l \underset{k_l}{\rightleftharpoons} l^* \qquad k_l = \frac{a_l^* \exp\left[\dfrac{z_l F \psi^*}{RT}\right]}{a_l \exp\left[\dfrac{z_l F \psi}{RT}\right]}, \tag{23}$$

for the charged species ($l = I^+$, IS^+, X^-) where z_l is the oxidation number of l.

For the species $l = IS^+$, subtracting Equation (22) from Equation (20) and adding Equation (23) we get:

$$I^+ + S^* \underset{\dfrac{k_{is} K_{is}^+}{k_s}}{\rightleftharpoons} IS^{+*}, \tag{24}$$

which is a heterogeneous reaction expressing the formation of the complexed-cation species IS^{+*} within the organic phase in terms of the aqueous concentration of I^+ and the concentration of S^* in the organic phase. By simply adding Equation (23) for $l = X^-$ to Equation (24), we get:

$$I^+ + S^* + X^- \underset{k_s}{\overset{k_{is}K_{is}^+k_x}{\rightleftharpoons}} IS^{+*} + X^{-*}, \tag{25}$$

which expresses the extraction of the salt I^+X^- from the aqueous phase into the organic phase.

When the partition coefficients, k_{is}, of the complexed cations are much higher than those of all the other ions, electroneutrality does not hold in the thin membrane; and the IS^+ complexes are present in excess as a "space charge" [38]. Since they then constitute the predominant charged species in the membrane, its electrical properties can be described solely in terms of the parameters appearing in the equilibrium constant of Equation (24):

$$K_i' = \frac{k_{is}K_{is}^+}{k_s}. \tag{26}$$

This constant can normally not be measured directly since its determination requires a knowledge of the (unmeasurable) electrical potential difference between the two phases.

On the other hand, when studying partition equilibria in bulk phases where the electroneutrality condition governs all chemically detectable concentrations, the equilibrium constant of reaction, Equation (25)

$$K_i = \frac{k_{is}K_{is}^+k_x}{k_s}, \tag{27}$$

is directly measurable. This constant differs from K_i' only in its dependence on k_x, the partition coefficient of the anion X^-; but, of course, k_x drops out when the ratios of K_i are compared for two cation species I^+ and J^+ (and a common anion X^-), so that a simple relationship is expected between the constants of Equations (24) and (25).

Comparing the ratio of Equation (26) for two different cations I^+ and J^+ with the corresponding ratio of Equation (27), it can be seen that

$$\frac{K_j'}{K_i'} = \frac{K_j}{K_i} = \frac{k_{js}K_{js}^+}{k_{is}K_{is}^+}, \tag{28}$$

showing that the ratio of the equilibrium constants of the reaction, Equation (24), for two different cations I^+ and J^+ is identical to the corresponding ratio for Equation (25). This is the argument from which we have shown elsewhere [14] that the equilibrium ratio K_j/K_i enters into the selectivity of Equation (13) for the membrane potential. The value of this ratio is easily measurable from studies of the equilibrium salt extraction by these molecules into organic solvents [13,14,39].

From Equation (28), it can be seen that the factors contributing to the ratio K_j/K_i are the ratio of the partition coefficients of the complexed species (k_{js}/k_{is}) and the ratio of the formation constants of the complexes in the **aqueous solutions.**

A further simplification is possible for those molecules for which the complexed species are expected to have the same approximate size. In this case, for species of the same valence type, the ratio (k_{js}/k_{is}) should be approximately unity and independent of the solvent since the complexed species are indistinguishable from each other in size and charge. For this reason the selectivity of the system depends solely on the chemical properties of the macrocyclic molecule, as these are reflected in the formation constant of the complex in the aqueous phase. It is therefore expected to be totally independent of the solvent (or lipid) of which the membrane is made! This theoretical expectation has been verified experimentally both for bulk solvent extraction equilibrium and for membrane electrical properties [14]. We therefore can reach the important conclusion that the selectivity of the neutral carrier mechanism should be a characteristic solely of the molecules themselves, under these conditions. The selectivity is a measure of the extent to which the macrocyclic molecules can sequester cations in competition with the hydration of these cations in the aqueous phases. The physical factors underlying this competition are similar to those previously analyzed for equilibrium ion exchange [4,50,51] but differ because the sequestering molecule does not bear a net charge, as will be outlined in the following section.

D. SUMMARY

It is possible to summarize the above comparison of selectivity by noting that there is an hierarchy of increasing simplicity of the factors involved in the membrane selectivity. (1) For **solid ion exchangers**, not only is equilibrium selectivity involved but so are the mobilities of the individual ion species within the exchanger. This mobility normally varies greatly from one species to another and partially opposes any attempt to increase electrode selectivity by increasing ion exchange selectivity. (2) For **liquid ion exchangers** some of the mobility limitations are circumvented but at the price of a considerably more complex behavior. (3) Membranes based on **neutral carriers** are the simplest in that their selectivity is principally a function of equilibrium properties and, moreover, determined largely by the specificity of the interactions with the neutral sequestering molecules. This system therefore offers the possibility of designing a particular molecule specifically to bind a particular cation most effectively, without undue concern for the properties of the solvent in which one chooses to disperse it. The versatility offered by this probably will make it worth accepting the technical difficulties of working with such systems when developing electrodes for species to which solid ion exchangers or liquid ion exchangers are not adaptable satisfactorily.

VI. The Origin of Equilibrium Specificity

From examination of Table 1, it should be apparent that equilibrium selectivity factors not only control the selectivity of neutral carrier membranes but also contribute importantly to the selectivity of ion exchanger membranes. It is therefore of interest to analyze the atomic factors involved in the origin of equilibrium specificity. This will be done first for the case of negatively charged (monopolar) ion exchange sites, in terms of a simple electrostatic model examined in detail elsewhere [4,50,51]. This model will then be extended by a heretofore unpublished analysis of the selectivity expected for neutral dipolar "sites," bearing zero net charge.

A. FREE ENERGY AND EQUILIBRIUM SPECIFICITY

The equilibrium specificity of a given phenomenon, such as an ion-exchange reaction, is directly related to the value of the standard free-energy change of the ion exchange of the reactions [Equations (4), (10), or (16)] through

$$\Delta F_{ij}^\circ = -RT \ln K_{ij} \tag{29}$$

where for neutral carriers it will be recalled that K_{ij} of Equation (16) is equal to K_j/K_i.

This free energy change can be expressed as the difference between ion-water interactions and ion-membrane interactions by

$$\Delta F_{ij}^\circ = (\bar{F}_{i+}^{hyd} - \bar{F}_{j+}^{hyd}) + (\bar{F}_{j+}^* - \bar{F}_{i+}^*) \tag{30}$$

where $(\bar{F}_{i+}^{hyd} - \bar{F}_{j+}^{hyd})$ represents the difference in partial molal free energies of hydration of the ions I^+ and J^+, and $(\bar{F}_{j+}^* - \bar{F}_{i+}^*)$ represents the difference of their free energies in the membrane phase. The hydration energy differences are accurately known constants for each pair of cations; but the free energies of interaction with the membrane phase depend upon the interaction energies therein. The problem of analyzing the origin of equilibrium specificity thus simplifies to the problem of characterizing the affinities of the various cations for an ion exchange site or neutral carrier molecule as a function of its chemical composition.

B. Ion Exchangers

The rigorous calculation of the energies of cation interaction with molecular anionic groups for a solid ion exchanger such as glass, or for a liquid ion exchanger molecule dissolved in a given solvent, has not yet been accomplished; although an approximate calculation for silicate and aluminosilicate models has successfully accounted for their selectivity properties [4]. I will consider here only a highly simplified model in which the ion exchange site is approximated by a monopolar (e.g., halide) model.

Consider first the simplest case in which we compare the selectivity expected for the competition for a given cation between such a site and a single water molecule as outlined diagrammatically in Figure 10 [50]. The energies of interaction of a monovalent cation I^+ of radius r_+ with a singly charged anionic site of radius r_- referred to the ions at rest in a vacuum are given by Coulomb's law as:

$$\bar{F}_{i+}^* \cong \frac{-332}{r_+ + r_-} \tag{31}$$

While its energy of interaction with the indicated tripolar model of a water molecule is given by:

$$\bar{F}_{i+}^{hyd} \cong -332\left(\frac{q^-}{r_4} - \frac{2q^+}{r_3}\right) \tag{32}$$

representing the net attractions between the cation and the effective charge of the oxygen ($q^- = -0.64$) at a distance r_4 from the center of the cation and the repulsions between the cation and the effective charge ($q^+ = +0.32$) of the two protons at the greater distance r_3 from the center of the cation. The energies are in kcal/mol for distances in angstroms, and charges are expressed as fractions of the electronic charge.

Calculating the values of these energies for the various naked (Goldschmitt) radii of the cations and inserting these in Equation (30), one obtains the selectivity isotherms, referred to Cs^+, plotted on the ordinate in Figure 10 (where ΔF_{ij}° is labelled ΔU_{ij}^R). This simple procedure leads to a pattern of selectivity in which, for an anion site of largest radius (i.e., lowest electrostatic field strength), the cations are preferred in the sequence $Cs > Rb > K > Na > Li$; while for an anionic site of sufficiently small radius the sequence of preference is reversed, being $Li > Na > K > Rb > Cs$. Between these extremes, the cations are

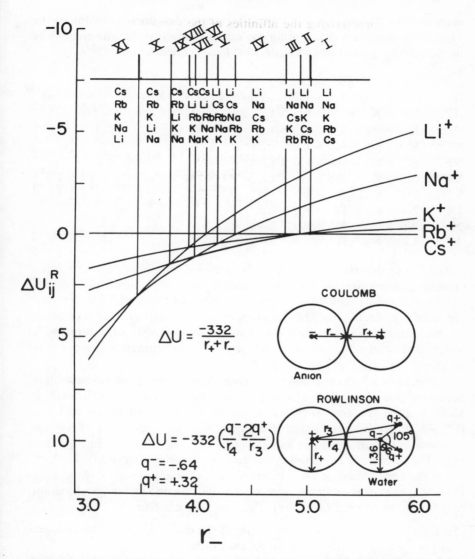

Figure 10. Selectivity pattern for the hypothetical cation exchange between a monopolar anion and a single multipolar water molecule. (Reproduced from Fig. 1 of [50].) The cation most strongly selected from water by the anionic "site" is the lowest on the chart. Above the graph are tabulated the cationic sequences (increasing specificity downwards), defining eleven rank order designations, as a function of decreasing site radius r_-. Units in kcal/mole and angstroms.

seen to pass through eleven selectivity sequences, corresponding to the
11 Roman numerals designating the regions between the interactions of
the selectivity isotherms of Figure 10. These sequences are:

I	Cs > Rb > K > Na > Li	
II	Rb > Cs > K > Na > Li, or IIa	Cs > K > Rb > Na > Li
III	Rb > K > Cs > Na > Li, or IIIa	K > Cs > Rb > Na > Li
IV	K > Rb > Cs > Na > Li	
V	K > Rb > Na > Cs > Li	
VI	K > Na > Rb > Cs > Li	
VII	Na > K > Rb > Cs > Li, or VIIa	K > Na > Rb > Li > Cs
VIII	Na > K > Rb > Li > Cs	
IX	Na > K > Li > Rb > Cs	
X	Na > Li > K > Rb > Cs	
XI	Li > Na > K > Rb > Cs	

Examining the data of Figure 4, it is clear that this simple model is sufficient to account for the observed selectivities of glass electrodes; and it
can be made more realistic by replacing the model interactions with a simple water molecule by the differences of free energies of hydration
of the cations in water, recalling that the interactions of cations with
water are constant, being given by the experimental values for
$(\bar{F}_{i+}^{hyd} - \bar{F}_{j+}^{hyd})$ [52].

If the sites of the exchanger are assumed in one limit to be widely
separated and the water molecules are assumed to be excluded from their
vicinity, then the free energies of interaction between cation and site
$(\bar{F}_{j+}^{*} - \bar{F}_{i}^{*})$ needed to solve Equation (30) are given in first approximation by the energies as calculated by Coulomb's law in Equation
(31). The selectivity expected in this case is plotted in Figure 11 [4].

On the other hand, if the ion exchanger sites are assumed to be very
closely spaced (for example, with 6 sites coordinated around each cation
and 6 cations around each site), then the free energies will be given by

$$\bar{F}_{i+}^{*} \cong 1.56\left(\frac{-332}{r_{+}+r_{-}}\right) \tag{33}$$

where the factor 1.56 appears as a consequence of the Madelung constant
(1.75) for this coordination state and a factor of 8/9 due to the Born repul-
sion energy [50]. Equation (33) is the classical Born-Lande equation for
the internal energy of an alkali halide crystal lattice and also depends only
on r_{-}. The expected selectivities in this case are plotted in Figure 12.

Inspection of Figures 10-12 yields the following conclusions. (1) The
selectivity among cations in each of these states depends upon the radius
of the anion r_{-} (i.e., upon anionic field strength). (2) A particular pattern
is seen for the selectivity among group Ia cations in that essentially only

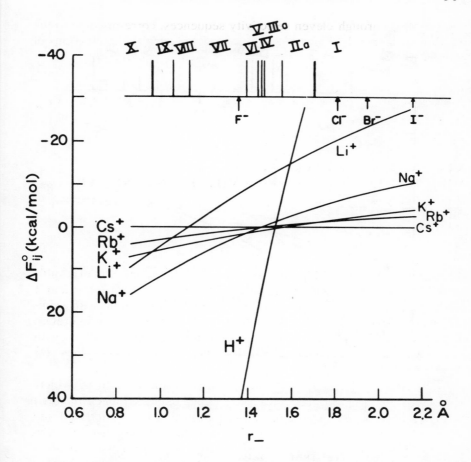

Figure 11. Selectivity isotherms for widely separated monopolar ion exchange sites. (Reproduced from Fig. 16 of [4].) Negative values of free energy change of reaction (30) are plotted as a function of r_- for the case of widely separated sites (see text). The Roman numerals above the figure indicate the sequences of ionic selectivity pertaining in the regions separated by the vertical lines drawn to the intersections of the various cation isotherms. The more strongly an ion is preferred by the exchanger the lower its position on the figure.

11 sequences of cation effectiveness are predicted out of a possible 120. These sequences are indicated by the Roman numerals I to XI above Figures 10-12, with only the minor variations indicated by subscript "a". The generality and usefulness of this model has recently been critically assessed for ion exchangers by Reichenberg [53], for zeolites by Sherry [54], and for biological membranes by Diamond and Wright [55]. In all of these diverse systems it has been remarkably successful.

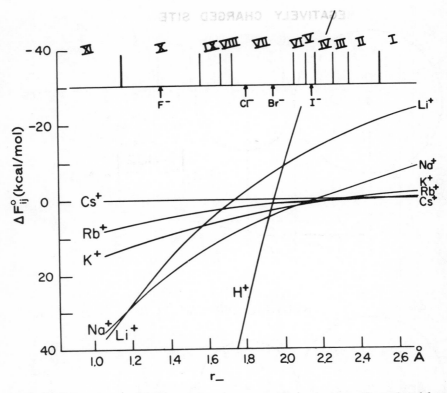

Figure 12. Selectivity isotherms for closely spaced monopolar sites. (Reproduced from Fig. 17 of [4].) Plotted in the same manner as Figure 11.

C. NEUTRAL SEQUESTERING MOLECULES

An understanding of the elementary factors underlying the specificity of neutral molecules which bind cations can be gained from a completely analogous analysis in which the negatively charged ion exchange site considered above is replaced by a neutral dipole, as illustrated in Figure 13. This is more appropriate as a model for the carbonyl or ether oxygens which are the ligands in such typical neutral carrier molecules as the macrocyclic antibiotics or the macrocyclic polyethers illustrated in Figure 2.

The partial molar free energy of the complexed ion is given for the case of such a neutral dipolar site by

$$\bar{F}_i^* = \left[\frac{-332}{r_+ + r_n} + \frac{332}{r_+ + r_p} \right] (q \cdot N) \tag{34}$$

where q is the fractional value of electronic charge, N is the coordination

NEGATIVELY CHARGED SITE

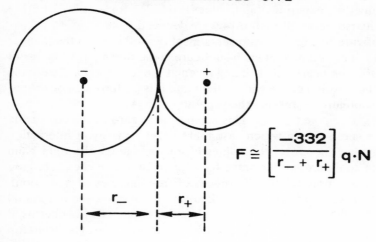

$$F \cong \left[\frac{-332}{r_- + r_+} \right] q \cdot N$$

NEUTRAL DIPOLAR SITE

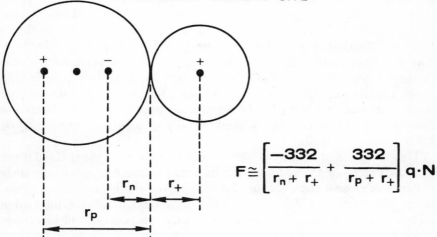

$$F \cong \left[\frac{-332}{r_n + r_+} + \frac{332}{r_p + r_+} \right] q \cdot N$$

Figure 13. Models for a negatively charged ion exchange site and a neutral dipolar ligand. Described in text.

number of the ligands, r_+ is the (Goldschmitt) cationic radius, and r_n and r_p are the distances from the surface of the dipole of the negative and positive charges, respectively. (This calculation lumps all repulsions between ligands as an effective diminution of coordination number or of effective charge.)

Calculating values for these energies and inserting in Equation (30), using Latimer's experimental values [52] for $(\bar{F}_{i+}^{hyd} - \bar{F}_{j+}^{hyd})$,[2] the selectivity isotherms of Figure 14 were deduced.

Each subfigure in Figure 14 presents a set of isotherms in the manner of Figure 11. The ordinate of each subfigure is the free energy change of Equation (30), the energy scale being given at the lower left in kcal/mole (the lower the position of the cation, the more it is preferred). The abscissa of each subfigure represents the separation (in Å) of the positive pole from the negative pole $(r_p - r_n)$. This separation is zero at the right hand side of each subfigure, in which case there is zero energy of interaction with the dipole. Therefore, the values of energies along the right hand edge of each subfigure are the same for a given cation on each subfigure (corresponding simply to the differences of free energies of hydration). The individual isotherms are not labelled; but in all cases the horizontal line represents the reference ion Cs^+, while the sequence of isotherms at the right hand edge of each subfigure is Li^+, Na^+, K^+, Rb^+, Cs^+ from top to bottom (corresponding to the differences of free energies of hydration).

The horizontal sets of isotherms are calculated for a given (constant) distance of the negative pole of the dipole from the surface (i.e., "0.8" means $r_n = 0.8$Å); while the vertical sets of isotherms correspond to a particular product of charge times coordination number $(q \cdot N)$. Thus a value $(q \cdot N)$ equal to 3 would correspond to dipoles of unit charge in three-fold coordination or to dipoles of charge 0.5 in six-fold coordination. The family of isotherms for the value $(q \cdot N)$ of 2.56 represents a particularly reasonable case of a tetrahedral coordination of oxygens having a net negative charge of -0.64 corresponding to the Rowlinson-type water molecule of Figure 10. These ranges of $(q \cdot N)$ and of r_n should encompass all values of dipoles likely to be encountered for carbonyl or ether oxygens in nature.

This model examines what sort of specificity would be expected if the ligand oxygens of the sequestering molecules were free to assume their distance of closest approach around each cation with negligible configurational differences of the molecule from one cation to another. Under these circumstances, a very crude approximation of the energies of binding is given by the attractive energy of interaction between cations and dipolar models for the ligand oxygens, neglecting differences in deformation energy and entropy among cations.

Not surprisingly, when the dipole separation is sufficiently large $(r_p - r_n \gg r_n)$, the selectivities approach those calculated for the simple

---

[2]In these calculations, free energies of hydration were taken from Latimer's compilation [52] as the most accurate source. Referred to Cs^+ these are: 53.8 ± 1.4 kcal/mole for Li^+, 28.9 ± 0.9 for Na^+, 12.7 ± 0.9 for K^+, and 6.7 ± 1.1 for Rb^+. My previous calculations [4] were based on values of 54.3, 30.4, 12.7, and 7.7, respectively, which are in good agreement except for Rb^+.

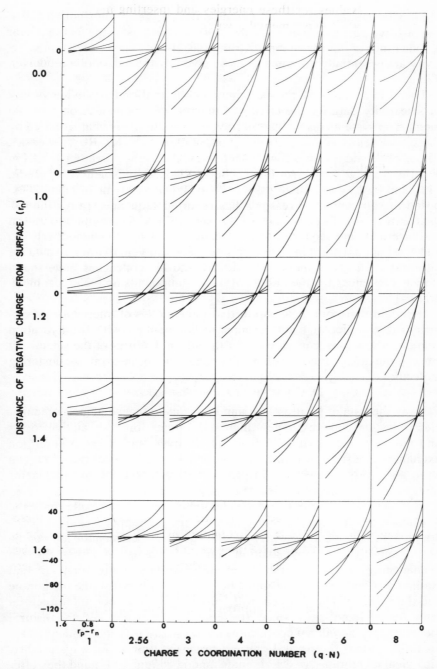

Figure 14.   Selectivity isotherms for a neutral dipolar site as a function of various charge
distributions and ligand coordination numbers. Described in text.

monopolar model, since in this situation the energetic contribution due to the positive pole becomes negligible. Of more interest is the fact that over a wide range of dipolar charge distributions, the sequences of cation selectivity are essentially the same as those given by the monopolar model (*cf.* Fig. 10).

This is in accord with the experimental observation that a wide variety of selectivity data for the effects of macrocyclic molecules on artificial membrane systems (as well as on solvent extraction) are characterized by these very selectivity sequences. Thus, sequence IV (K^+, Rb^+, Cs^+, Na^+, Li^+) is observed for nonactin, trinactin, and the cyclic polyether XXXI in Figures 8 and 9. Sequence III has been reported by Mueller and Rudin [11] and by Lev and Buzhinsky [10] to be characteristic of bilayers exposed to valinomycin. Pressman has reported sequence IIa for the solvent extraction of compound X-537, sequence V for compound X-206 and nigericin, and sequence VII for dianemycin [46]. Sequences III, IV, and VIII are apparent in Pedersen's published solvent extraction data for different cyclic polyethers [56]; Lardy and his colleagues have found similar sequences for the effects of these compounds on biological membranes [57].

It should therefore be apparent that the energies of interaction of cations with the dipolar ligand groups, in competition with the hydration energies of the ions, can account for the salient features of the selectivity among the alkali metal cations characteristic of neutral sequestering molecules.

D. PRACTICAL CONSIDERATIONS

From the data of Figures 5, 6, and 8, it is clear that solid ion exchanger electrodes can have extremely high selectivities for Na^+ relative to K^+ and moderate selectivities in favor of K^+ over Na^+. Typical liquid ion exchangers, best known for their usefulness as Ca^{++} electrodes [7], can show a K^+ to Na^+ selectivity in excess of 30 to 1. Neutral carrier systems offer K^+ to Na^+ selectivities substantially greater than 100 to 1.

From a practical point of view, solid ion exchanger electrodes have the advantage that the ion-detecting sites are truly "trapped," and one does not have to be concerned with partition equilibria between the membrane phase and the aqueous solution. Liquid systems, of either the ion exchanger or neutral carrier type, suffer from the disadvantage that equilibrium for these species must be established between the membrane and the solution. This problem will probably be less important for neutral than for charged sites since transient readjustments of the **neutral** molecules *per se* will not contribute directly to the potential. Indeed, it appears likely that the neutral carriers represent one of the ways used by biological membranes to discriminate among cations [14]; and they offer the possibility that the exquisite selectivities characteristic of living cells can therefore be duplicated in an artificial electrode.

VII. Appendix

Derivation of the Equations for the Membrane Potential at Zero Current

Although it should be possible to present a general derivation for the membrane potential, of which each of the three types of membrane electrodes discussed in this paper would be a particular case, the three types of electrodes are physically so distinct that it is more useful to present separate derivations appropriate to each.

A. SOLID ION EXCHANGER MEMBRANES

This appendix deduces the expression of the difference of electric potential between two solutions separated by an ion exchange membrane with fixed monovalent sites and follows the treatment of Conti and Eisenman [24,25]. The results are valid not only in the steady state for zero net current but also in the non-steady state, being independent of time once equilibria are established at the boundaries of the membrane. The membrane is assumed to be solely permeable to cations or anions, depending on whether the charge of the sites is -1 or $+1$, and not to permit any flow of solvent. Under the assumptions that the difference of standard chemical potentials of any pair of permeant monovalent species and the ratio of their mobilities are constant throughout the membrane, explicit expressions are derived for the diffusion potential and total membrane potential as functions of time and of solution activities. The expressions are valid for ideal behavior for any number of permeant monovalent species and for two permeant monovalent species having "n-type" non-ideal behavior.

Consider an ion exchanger membrane interposed between solution (') and solution ('') in which the membrane properties vary only in the x direction, perpendicular to the membrane sufraces. Under the assumption that the only driving force acting on each species is due to the gradient of its electrochemical potential, we have at any point in the interior of the membrane phase:

$$J_i = -C_i u_i \frac{\partial}{\partial x} (\mu_i^0 + RT \ln a_i + z_i F \psi), \quad i = 1, 2, \ldots N, \qquad (A1)$$

where J is the flux per unit area in moles $cm^{-2}sec^{-1}$, C is the concentration in moles cm^{-3}, u is the mobility, μ^0 is the standard chemical potential, a is the activity, ψ is the electric potential, z is the valence, F the faraday constant, R the gas constant, T the absolute temperature, and the subscript i refers to any one of the N permeant species present.

Since any excess space charge is negligible compared to the number of ion exchange sites at any point:

$$\sum_{i=1}^{N} z_i C_i \cong -z_0 C_0, \qquad (A2)$$

where the subscript 0 refers to the sites. Moreover, conservation of mass requires:

$$\frac{\partial J_i}{\partial x} = -\frac{\partial C_i}{\partial t}; \quad i = 0, 1, \ldots N. \tag{A3}$$

The electric current, I, per unit area, is related to the fluxes of the counterions and sites through:

$$F \sum_{i=1}^{N} z_i J_i = I \tag{A4}$$

In writing Equation (A4), we assume that there is no electronic contribution to the current.

To find the time-dependent solution of Equations (A1) and (A3) under conditions of current flow is a difficult mathematical problem; but the behavior of the electric potential at zero membrane current can be deduced easily as is done below. Non-zero current cases are considered elsewhere [25].

For ion exchanger electrodes such as glass, it is reasonable to assume that:

$$\frac{d\mu_i^0}{dx} = \frac{d\mu_j^0}{dx}; \quad i, j = 1, \ldots N \tag{A5}$$

and

$$\frac{d}{dx}\left(\frac{u_i}{u_j}\right) = 0; \quad i, j = 1, \ldots N. \tag{A6}$$

Assumptions (A5) and (A6) are certainly satisfied if the standard chemical potentials and mobilities[3] are constant.

I will distinguish two cases now. In the first, any number of counterion species may be present, but their behavior is assumed to be ideal. In the second, the possibility of a certain type of non-ideal behavior is allowed; but considerations are restricted to only two different species present.

In an ideal system, the activity of any component is equal to its concentration:

$$a_i = C_i; \quad i = 1, \ldots N. \tag{A7}$$

On the other hand, for "n-type" non-ideal behavior [24]:

$$d \ln a_1 / d \ln C_1 = n \tag{A8}$$

$$d \ln a_2 / d \ln C_2 = n \tag{A9}$$

where

$$\frac{dn}{dx} = 0 \tag{A10}$$

---

[3]For simplicity of nomenclature the asterisks, denoting quantities characteristic of the membrane phase, have been omitted in this Appendix.

for membranes whose chemical properties are uniform.

Equation (A1), for the ideal behavior of Equation (A7), reduces to:

$$J_i(x, t) = -C_i(x, t)u_i(x) \frac{\partial}{\partial x} [\mu_i^0(x) + RT \ln C_i(x, t)$$
$$+ zF\psi(x, t)], \ i = 1, \ldots N, \quad (A11)$$

where $z = +1$ or -1, depending on whether a cation exchange or anion exchange membrane is considered. For zero current, Equation (A4) becomes:

$$\sum_{i=1}^{N} J_i(x, t) = 0 \quad (A12)$$

Addition of Equation (A11), taking into account Equation (A5), gives

$$\left[\sum_{i=1}^{N} u_i(x)C_i(x, t) \right] \frac{\partial}{\partial x} [\mu_1^0(x) + zF\psi(x, t)] = -RT \sum_{i=1}^{N} u_i(x) \frac{\partial C_i(x, t)}{\partial x}. \quad (A13)$$

Dividing both sides of Equation (A13) by $\left[\sum_{i=1}^{N} u_i(x)C_i(x, t) \right]$ gives:

$$\frac{\partial}{\partial x} [\mu_1^0(x) + zF\psi(x, t)] = -RT \left[\sum_{i=1}^{N} \frac{u_i}{u_1} \frac{\partial C_i(x, t)}{\partial x} \right] \Big/ \left[\sum_{i=1}^{N} \frac{u_i}{u_1} C_i(x, t) \right] \quad (A14)$$

where numerator and denominator of the right-hand side of Equation (A14) have been divided by u_1.[4] Recalling Equation (A6):

$$\frac{\partial}{\partial x} [\mu_1^0(x) + zF\psi(x, t)] = -RT \frac{\partial}{\partial x} \ln \sum_{i=1}^{N} \frac{u_i}{u_1} C_i(x, t). \quad (A15)$$

Equation (A15) can be seen to be a total differential which is immediately integratable, having a value which depends only on the values of $C_i(x,t)$ between which it is integrated. Let us take the origin of the x axis at the boundary between solution (') and the membrane, and let d be the thickness of the membrane. The electric potential, the standard chemical potential, and the concentrations, have discontinuities at $x = 0$ and $x = d$. I shall indicate by $\psi(0,t)$, $\mu_1^0(0)$, $C_i(0,t)$ and $\psi(d,t)$,

---

[4] The expression $[\Sigma u_i(x)C_i(x,t)]$ is positive when the mobility of at least one of the species is not zero. In Equation (A14), $u_i(x)$ is assumed to be non-zero.

$\mu_1^0(d)$, $C_i(d,t)$ the values of these quantities at the two boundaries inside the membrane; whereas by $\psi'(t)$, $\mu_1^{0'}$ and $\psi''(t)$, $\mu_1^{0''}$, I shall indicate the values of the electric potential and standard chemical potential in solutions (') and (''), respectively. Integration of Equation (A15) with respect to x from 0 to d gives the expression of the diffusion potential, $E_d = \psi(d,t) - \psi(0,t)$:

$$zFE_d = \mu_1^0(0) - \mu_1^0(d) + RT \ln \left\{ \frac{\sum_{i=1}^{N} \frac{u_i}{u_1} C_i(0, t)}{\sum_{i=1}^{N} \frac{u_i}{u_1} C_i(d, t)} \right\}. \qquad (A16)$$

At the boundary between the membrane and each solution, thermodynamic equilibrium requires for each species the equality of the electrochemical potentials across the interface:

$$\mu_i^{0(sol)} + RT \ln a_i^{(sol)} + zF\psi^{(sol)} = \mu_j^{0(m)} + RT \ln a_i + zF\psi^{(m)}; \ i = 1, \ldots N \qquad (A17)$$

where the superscripts (sol) and (m) refer to solution and membrane. Disregarding concentration gradients in the solution due to diffusion, a_i is constant throughout the solution.

Subtraction, term by term, of the first part of Equation (A17) from the others gives:

$$\frac{a_i a_1^{(sol)}}{a_1 a_i^{(sol)}} = \exp \left\{ \frac{\mu_1^{0(m)} - \mu_i^{0(m)} + \mu_i^{0(sol)} - \mu_1^{0(sol)}}{RT} \right\} = K_{1i}; \ i = 1, \ldots N \qquad (A18)$$

where K_{1i} is the thermodynamic equilibrium constant of the ion exchange reaction represented by Equation (4).

For $i = 1$, Equation (A18) together with Equation (A7) gives, as soon as thermodynamic equilibrium is established at the two boundaries:

$$\mu_1^0(0) + RT \ln C_1(0, t) + zF\psi(0, t) = \mu_1^{0'} + RT \ln a_1' + zF\psi'(t), \qquad (A19)$$

$$\mu_1^{0''} + RT \ln a_1'' + zF\psi''(t) = \mu_1^0(d) + RT \ln C_1(d, t) + zF\psi(d, t), \qquad (A20)$$

where a_1' and a_1'' are the activities of component 1 in solutions (') and (''), respectively.

Addition of Equations (A16), (A19), and (A20) gives the expression for the total potential E:

$$E = \psi'' - \psi' = \frac{\mu_1^{0'} - \mu_1^{0''}}{zF} + \frac{RT}{zF} \ln \frac{a_1'}{a_1''}$$

$$+\frac{RT}{zF}\ln\left\{\left[\sum_{i=1}^{N}\frac{u_i}{u_1}\frac{C_i(0,\,t)}{C_1(0,\,t)}\right]\bigg/\left[\sum_{i=1}^{N}\frac{u_i}{u_1}\frac{C_i(d,\,t)}{C_1(d,\,t)}\right]\right\}. \tag{A21}$$

Equation (A18) at the two boundaries, together with Equation (A7), gives:

and

$$\frac{a_1'}{a_i'}\frac{C_i(0,\,t)}{C_1(0,\,t)}=K_{1i}';\; i=1,\,\ldots\,N \tag{A22}$$

$$\frac{a_1''}{a_i''}\frac{C_i(d,\,t)}{C_1(d,\,t)}=K_{1i}'';\; i=1,\,\ldots\,N \tag{A23}$$

as soon as thermodynamic equilibrium is established at the boundaries. K_{1i}' and K_{1i}'' refer to the equilibrium constants at the two boundaries.

Taking account of Equations (A22) and (A23), Equation (A21) becomes:

$$E=\frac{\mu_1^{0'}-\mu_1^{0''}}{zF}+\frac{RT}{zF}\ln\frac{\displaystyle\sum_{i=1}^{N}\frac{u_i}{u_1}K_{1i}'\,a_i'}{\displaystyle\sum_{i=1}^{N}\frac{u_i}{u_1}K_{1i}''\,a_i''}. \tag{A24}$$

All expressions through (A24) are valid for two different solvents on the two sides of the membrane. If the solvent is the same for solution (') and solution (''), then:

$$\mu_i^{0'}=\mu_i^{0''} \tag{A25}$$

and, taking into account Equations (A18) and (A5):

$$K_{1i}'=K_{1i}''=K_{1i},\,i=1,\,\ldots\,N \tag{A26}$$

so that Equation (A24) becomes simply:

$$E=\frac{RT}{zF}\ln\left\{\frac{\displaystyle\sum_{i=1}^{N}\frac{u_i}{u_1}K_{1i}\,a_i'}{\displaystyle\sum_{i=1}^{N}\frac{u_i}{u_1}K_{1i}\,a_i''}\right\}, \tag{A27}$$

which is the desired expression for the membrane potential under ideal conditions.

This equation is time-independent for time-independent solution conditions, once the membrane-solution interfaces have reached equilibrium. However, it should be noted that if the activities of the ions in solution are varied with time, the total potential will reproduce these time variations, provided they are slow compared to the velocity of establishing the boundary equilibria.

For systems obeying n-type non-ideal behavior, a way of proceeding similar to that used above gives, taking account of Equations (A8-A10):

$$E_d = \frac{\mu_1^0(0) - \mu_1^0(d)}{zF} + \frac{RT}{zF} \ln \frac{p(0)}{p(d)} - \frac{nRT}{zF} \ln \frac{C_1(d,t) + \frac{u_2}{u_1} C_2(d,t)}{C_1(0,t) + \frac{u_2}{u_1} C_2(0,t)}, \qquad (A28)$$

for the diffusion potential. For the same solvent in solutions (') and ('') the total potential is given by:

$$E = \frac{nRT}{zF} \ln \frac{a_1'^{1/n} + \frac{u_2}{u_1} [K_{12} a_2']^{1/n}}{a_1''^{1/n} + \frac{u_2}{u_1} [K_{12} a_2'']^{1/n}}. \qquad (A29)$$

Equation (A29) is identical in form to that found characteristic of glass electrodes by Eisenman [3-6].

B. LIQUID ION EXCHANGER MEMBRANES

This appendix deduces the steady-state properties of a homogeneous, ideally permselective, liquid ion-exchange membrane in which sites and counterions are incompletely dissociated and is based on the analysis of Sandblom, Eisenman, and Walker [34]. Dissociated species are assumed to be in chemical equilibrium with neutral ion pairs at every point in the membrane, their concentrations being interconnected by the law of mass action. The flux equations, which describe the complete behavior of the system, are derived by considering the free ions and their combined forms as separately flowing entities, and the boundary conditions are obtained by assuming the sites to be completely trapped in the membrane phase (although free to move within it) while the counterions are free to undergo ion exchange. Under the restriction of zero membrane current, an expression for the membrane potential is deduced in terms of external solution conditions and membrane parameters which is valid not only for the steady state but for certain transient situations as well.

The system has been diagrammed in Figure 1 and consists of a membrane separating two homogeneous (*e.g.*, aqueous) solutions whose electric potentials are ψ' and ψ''. The membrane is composed of a single liquid phase immiscible with the external solutions. In the membrane is dissolved a "site" species, S, bearing a charge $z_s = \pm 1$ (given a negative sign of Fig. 1).[5] The sites are assumed to be completely reflected at the boundaries, 0 and d, (as indicated by the arrows), but are free to move within the interior of the membrane. The system also contains n number of

---

[5] Again, asterisks denoting membrane quantities will be omitted in this Appendix.

permeable univalent counterion species I whose charge z_i is opposite to that of the sites and which are free to cross the membrane-solution interfaces as indicated by the arrows in Figure 1. Any number of co-ion species may be present in the external solutions although the co-ions are assumed to be completely excluded from the membrane.

Even species which behave as strong electrolytes in aqueous solutions will in general not be completely dissociated in a liquid ion-exchange membrane. Species I and S will therefore be assumed to be in chemical equilibrium at every point in the membrane with the associated species IS

$$I^+ + S^- \rightleftharpoons IS \tag{B1}$$

assuming that the only reactions occuring in the membrane are those in which electrically neutral complexes are formed. For simplicity, considerations are restricted to the smallest complex possible (*i.e.*, the ion pair).

The chemical potentials corresponding to Equation (B1) are related everywhere in the membrane through

$$\mu_i + \mu_s = \mu_{is}; \ i = 1, \ . \ . \ . \ n \tag{B2}$$

where μ_i, μ_s, and μ_{is} are the chemical potentials of the counterions, sites, and ion pairs, respectively. For simplicity, activities will be assumed to be equal to concentrations. Under this assumption, the concentrations of the species (C_i, C_s, C_{is}) are related to the association constant, K_{is}, through a simple law of mass action

$$K_{is} = \frac{C_{is}}{C_i C_s}; \ i = 1, \ . \ . \ . \ n \tag{B3}$$

which, in effect, describes a chemical coupling between the various species within the membrane. In addition, the concentrations of the charged species are coupled electrically through the condition of electroneutrality

$$C_s = \sum_i C_i \tag{B4}$$

It is useful to consider separately the flows of associated and dissociated species. The total flux, J^{Tot}, of each species through the membrane can be written as a sum of partial fluxes

$$J_i^{\text{Tot}} = J_i + J_{is} \tag{B5a}$$

$$J_s^{\text{Tot}} = J_s + \sum_i J_{is} \tag{B5b}$$

where J_i^{Tot}, and J_s^{Tot} are the total fluxes of counterions and sites, J_i and J_s are the fluxes of the species in their dissociated state, and J_{is} are the fluxes of the ion pairs.

Since counterions, sites, and associated pairs are treated as separately flowing entities, it is possible to write separate linear relationships between the forces and fluxes of each of the species. By the Curie principle, the chemical reactions introduce no additional driving forces since the membrane is assumed to be isotropic, and assuming diffusion only in the x direction, the flux equations can therefore be written in the classical manner as:

$$J_i = -u_i C_i \frac{\partial}{\partial x} (RT \ln C_i + z_i F \psi) \tag{B6a}$$

$$J_s = -u_s C_s \frac{\partial}{\partial x} (RT \ln C_s + z_s F \psi) \tag{B6b}$$

$$J_{is} = -u_{is} C_{is} \frac{\partial}{\partial x} (RT \ln C_{is}) \tag{B6c}$$

where u_s, u_i, and u_{is} are the mobilities of sites, counterions, and ion pairs, respectively; u_s, u_i and u_{is} will be assumed to be constant.

The continuity equations for the total fluxes and concentrations are:

$$\operatorname{div} J_i^{\text{Tot}} = \frac{\partial J_i^{\text{Tot}}}{\partial x} = \frac{\partial C_i^{\text{Tot}}}{\partial t} \tag{B7a}$$

$$\operatorname{div} J_s^{\text{Tot}} = \frac{\partial J_s^{\text{Tot}}}{\partial x} = \frac{\partial C_s^{\text{Tot}}}{\partial t} \tag{B7b}$$

where the superscript "Tot" refers to total quantities

$$(C_i^{\text{Tot}} = C_i + C_{is}; C_s^{\text{Tot}} = C_s + \sum_i C_{is}).$$

At steady state, the total fluxes are constant, a conclusion which is not necessarily valid for the partial fluxes. In fact, the partial fluxes are generally functions of distance; and the membrane may be thought of as containing local sources and sinks. Because the continuity equations apply only for the total fluxes, the number of variables is increased by n (the number of partial fluxes J_{is}) over than in the usual Nernst-Planck treatment. The n additional equations needed to solve the problem are given by Equation (B2).

Assuming that boundary processes are not rate limiting, the boundary conditions for the counterions follow from the continuity of electrochemical potentials. Hence we may equate the electrochemical potentials of the counterions across each of the two boundaries 0 and d as

$$RT \ln a_i' + \mu_i^0 + z_i F \psi' = RT \ln C_i(0) + \mu_i^0(m) + z_i F \psi(0);$$
$$i = 1, \ldots n \quad \text{(B8a)}$$

and

$$RT \ln a_i'' + \mu_i^0 + z_i F \psi'' = RT \ln C_i(d) + \mu_i^0(m) + z_i F \psi(d);$$
$$i = 1, \ldots n \quad \text{(B8b)}$$

respectively. The quantities on the left-hand sides of Equations (B8a) and (B8b) refer to the solution phases, while the quantities on the right-hand sides refer to the membrane phase, μ_i^0 and $\mu_i^0(m)$ being the standard chemical potentials in the solution and membrane phases, respectively.

Subtracting any pair of Equations (B8a) and rearranging gives

$$\frac{a_i' k_i}{C_i(0)} = \frac{a_j' k_j}{C_j(0)} \quad \text{(B9)}$$

where the constants k_i and k_j are defined as

$$k_i = \exp\left(\frac{\mu_i^0 - \mu_i^0(m)}{RT}\right); \; k_j = \exp\left(\frac{\mu_j^0 - \mu_j^0(m)}{RT}\right). \quad \text{(B10)}$$

Equation (B9) can be written for all the ions

$$\frac{a_1' k_1}{C_1(0)} = \frac{a_2' k_2}{C_2(0)} = \cdots = \frac{a_n' k_n}{C_n(0)} = \frac{\sum_i a_i' k_i}{C_s(0)}, \quad \text{(B11)}$$

where the condition of electroneutrality, Equation (B4), has been used to obtain the last term. From Equation (B11), the membrane concentrations $C_i(0)$ can be expressed in terms of the solution activity a_i' as

$$C_i(0) = C_s(0) \times \frac{a_i' k_i}{\sum_i a_i' k_i} \quad \text{(B12)}$$

Similar expressions hold for the other membrane boundary.

Subtracting Equation (B8a) from Equation (B8b) gives the expression for the total membrane potential $[E = \psi'' - \psi']$ in terms of internal potential $[\Delta\psi = \psi(d) - \psi(0)]$ and the concentrations at the boundaries as

$$z_i F E = z_i F \Delta\psi + RT \ln \frac{a_i' k_i}{C_i(0)} - RT \ln \frac{a_i'' k_i}{C_i(d)} \quad \text{(B13)}$$

Combining Equations (B12) and (B13) yields an expression in terms of the activities of the counterions in the solutions and ratio of the site concentrations at 0 and d:

$$E = \Delta\psi + \frac{RT}{z_i F} \ln \frac{C_s(d)}{C_s(0)} + \frac{RT}{z_i F} \ln \frac{\sum_i a_i' k_i}{\sum_i a_i'' k_i} \quad \text{(B14)}$$

This equation will be used to express the total potential in terms of external conditions and membrane parameters.

The boundary conditions for the sites follow from the assumption that the sites are completely reflected at the membrane boundaries, which leads directly to the equations:

$$\frac{1}{d} \int_0^d C_s^{\text{Tot}} \, dx = \bar{C}_s^{\text{Tot}} \tag{B15}$$

and

$$J_s^{\text{Tot}} = 0. \tag{B16a}$$

Equation (B16a) is valid for all values of x at steady state, but in the non-steady state it is only valid at the boundaries where

$$J_s^{\text{Tot}} (t, 0) = J_s^{\text{Tot}} (t, d) = 0. \tag{B16b}$$

Equation (B15) expresses the condition that the total number of sites contained in the membrane is constant, regardless of their concentration profile. Expressed per unit area, this number is equal to the average total concentration $\bar{C}_s^{\text{Tot}}$ times the membrane thickness d. Equation (B16a) states that the total flow of sites must be zero at all points in the membrane in the steady state, whereas Equation (B16b) indicates that for the non-steady state J_s^{Tot} is zero only at the membrane-solution interfaces.

Equations (B1) to (B16) describe the total behavior of the system. The special case of the membrane potential at zero current will now be considered. Non-zero current cases are considered elsewhere [58].

Since the electric current I is carried only by the charged species, it is given by

$$I = F \sum_i z_i J_i + F z_s J_s = F z_i \left(\sum_i J_i - J_s \right) \tag{B17}$$

substituting Equation (B5) in Equation (B17) yields

$$I = F \sum_i z_i J_i^{\text{Tot}} + F z_s J_s^{\text{Tot}} \tag{B18}$$

from which it is seen that the electric current is also given by the sum of the total flows. The potential gradient at zero current can now be expressed by inserting Equations (B6a) and (B6b) into Equation (B17) for $I = 0$ and rearranging to yield

$$\frac{\partial \psi}{\partial x} = -\frac{RT}{z_i F} \frac{1}{\sum_i u_i C_i + u_s C_s} \frac{\partial}{\partial x} \left(\sum_i u_i C_i - u_s C_s \right) \tag{B19}$$

which can be recognized as the usual expression for the potential gradient in a "Planck" liquid junction. However, when Equation (B19) is integrated, the presence of ion pairs influences the profiles of C_i and C_s. In order to perform this integration it is necessary to derive another expression containing $\partial C_s/\partial x$.

Combining Equations (B5b), (B6b), and (B6c),

$$J_s^{\text{Tot}} = -u_s C_s \frac{\partial}{\partial x}(RT \ln C_s + z_s F \psi) - \sum_i u_{is} C_{is} \frac{\partial}{\partial x}(RT \ln C_{is}),$$ (B20)

and inserting the mass law of Equation (B3),

$$J_s^{\text{Tot}} = -RT u_s \frac{\partial C_s}{\partial x} - F u_s z_s c_s \frac{\partial \psi}{\partial x} - RT \sum_i \frac{u_{is} K_{is} C_s \partial C_i}{\partial x}$$

$$- RT \sum_i \frac{u_{is} K_{is} C_i \partial C_s}{\partial x}$$ (B21)

Equation (B21) is now combined with Equation (B19) to eliminate $\partial C_s/\partial x$ and solving for the potential gradient,

$$\frac{z_i F}{RT} \frac{\partial \psi}{\partial x} = -\frac{\left(u_s + \sum_i u_{is} K_{is} C_i\right) \sum_i u_i \frac{\partial C_i}{\partial x} + u_s C_s \sum_i \frac{u_{is} K_{is} \partial C_i}{\partial x} - \frac{u_s J_s^{\text{Tot}}}{RT}}{\left(u_s + \sum_i u_{is} K_{is} C_i\right) \sum_i u_i C_i + u_s C_s \sum_i u_{is} K_{is} C_i}$$ (B22)

By rearranging this equation, the expression is obtained

$$\frac{z_i F}{RT} \frac{\partial \psi}{\partial x} = -\frac{\sum_i u_i \frac{\partial C_i}{\partial x}}{\sum_i u_i C_i} - t \left[\frac{\sum_i u_{is} K_{is} \frac{\partial C_i}{\partial x}}{\sum_i u_{is} K_{is} C_i} - \frac{\sum_i u_i \frac{\partial C_i}{\partial x}}{\sum_i u_i C_i}\right]$$

$$- \frac{\frac{u_s J_s^{\text{Tot}}}{RT}}{\left(u_s + \sum_i u_{is} K_{is} C_i\right) \sum_i u_i C_i + u_s C_s \sum_i u_{is} K_{is} C_i}$$ (B23)

where

$$t = \frac{u_s C_s}{\left(\frac{u_s C_s}{\sum_i u_{is} C_{is}} + 1\right) \sum_i u_i C_i + u_s C_s}$$ (B24)

When Equation (B23) is integrated between the two boundaries 0 and d, the internal potential at zero current, $\Delta\psi_o$, is obtained as:

$$\frac{z_iF}{RT}\Delta\psi_0 = -\ln\left[\frac{\sum_i u_iC_i(d)}{\sum_i u_iC_i(0)}\right] - \int_0^d t\,d\ln\left[\frac{\sum_i u_{is}K_{is}C_i}{\sum_i u_iC_i}\right]$$

$$-\int_0^d \frac{\dfrac{u_sJ_s^{\text{Tot}}}{RT}\,dx}{\left(u_s + \sum_i u_{is}K_{is}C_i\right)\sum_i u_iC_i + u_sC_s\sum_i u_{is}K_{is}C_i} \tag{B25}$$

In order to arrive at an expression for the total membrane potential at zero current, Equation (B25) is combined with the boundary conditions (B12) and (B14) to yield:

$$\frac{z_iF}{RT} = -\ln\frac{\sum_i u_ik_ia_i''}{\sum_i u_ik_ia_i'} - \int_1 - \int_2 \tag{B26}$$

where $\int_1, \int_2$ are the two integrals appearing in Equation (B25).

The membrane potential of a liquid ion exchange membrane is therefore seen from Equation (B26) to be composed of three terms, only the first of which is independent of site distribution. Since no assumption as to steady state has been necessary in the derivation of Equation (B26), this expression is valid for nonstationary as well as stationary states.

In the steady state when, according to Equation (B16a), $J_s^{\text{Tot}}=0$, E_o is described by the two first terms in Equation (B26). Examining the parameter t, given by Equation (B24) and which determines the behavior of the second term in Equation (B25), it is seen that the degree of dissociation enters through the quantity:

$$\frac{u_sC_s}{\sum_i u_{is}C_{is}}. \tag{B27}$$

The second term is therefore affected by the total concentration of sites, $\bar{C}_s^{\text{Tot}}$, since C_{is} and C_s do not vary proportionally when the total number of sites is changed. This fact is most easily illustrated by adding the mass laws (B3) and inserting the condition of electroneutrality (B4). We get

$$C_s^2 = \sum_i C_{is}/K_{is} \tag{B28}$$

and from this it is seen that the quantity given by Equation (B27) varies inversely as the concentration of free sites, C_s. As the degree of dissociation is varied, for example by varying C_s from zero to infinity keeping all K_{is} constant, the quantity t varies from zero to t_s, where t_s, the transference number of free sites, is given by:

$$t_s = \frac{u_s C_s}{\sum_i u_i C_i + u_s C_s}.$$ (B29)

Consequently, the membrane potential at zero current depends on the site concentrations at intermediate degrees of dissociation. However, when the degree of dissociation is small and the quantity given in Equation (B27) is small compared to unity, the potential becomes independent of the degree of dissociation.

In the limiting case of complete dissociation, $\int_1$ is zero ($t = 0$) and since $\int_2$ is also zero in the steady state, the potential is described by the first term of Equation (B26) as

$$\frac{z_i F}{RT} E = -\ln \left[\frac{\sum_i u_i k_i a_i''}{\sum_i u_i k_i a_i'} \right].$$ (B30)

In the special case of strong association for two counterion species, Equation (B27) is much less than unity; and the integral $\int_1$ in Equation (B26) can be written as

$$\int_1 = \int_0^d \frac{u_s \left(\frac{C_1}{C_2} + 1 \right)}{(u_1 + u_s) \frac{C_1}{C_2} + u_2 + u_s} \, d \ln \left[\frac{\frac{u_{1s} C_1 K_{1s}}{C_2} + u_{2s} K_{2s}}{u_1 \frac{C_1}{C_2} + u_2} \right],$$ (B31)

where the condition of electroneutrality has been taken into account and where we have divided through by C_2. The only independent variable is now C_1/C_2 and the integral can be solved explicitly to give:

$$\int_1 = (1 - \tau) \ln \frac{\sum_{i=1}^{2} (u_i + u_s) C_i(d)}{\sum_{i=1}^{2} (u_i + u_s) C_i(0)} + \tau \ln \frac{\sum_{i=1}^{2} u_{is} K_{is} C_i(d)}{\sum_{i=1}^{2} u_{is} K_{is} C_i(0)} - \ln \frac{\sum_{i=1}^{2} u_i C_i(d)}{\sum_{i=1}^{2} u_i C_i(0)}$$

(B32)

where

$$\tau = \frac{u_s (u_{2s} K_{2s} - u_{1s} K_{1s})}{(u_1 + u_s) u_{2s} K_{2s} - (u_2 + u_s) u_{1s} K_{1s}}$$ (B33)

Equation (B32) depends only on the values of C_i of the boundaries and is therefore profile independent, which has important consequences to be discussed below.

When the boundary conditions are inserted in Equation (B32) combined with Equation (B26), taking into account that $\int_2 = 0$ in the steady state since $J_s^{\text{Tot}} = 0$, then the total potential is:

$$\frac{z_i F}{RT} E = (1 - \tau) \ln \frac{\sum\limits_{i=1}^{2} (u_i + u_s) k_i a'}{\sum\limits_{i=1}^{2} (u_i + u_s) k_i a_i''} + \tau \ln \frac{\sum\limits_{i=1}^{2} u_{is} K_{is} k_i a'_i}{\sum\limits_{i=1}^{2} u_{is} K_{is} k_i a_i''}. \qquad (B34)$$

Note that Equation (B34) has been derived using only the condition that $J_s^{\text{Tot}} = 0$ and does not require the counterions to be in a steady state.

Despite the many studies of the electrode properties of liquid ion exchangers, none of the measurements published to date appear to correspond to the convection-free steady state considered to this point. This is because the membrane phase has either been deliberately stirred or because precautions to prevent convective mixing in its interior have not been taken (the membrane phase being so thick that steady states have generally not been reached and because, moreover, stable concentration gradients can only be established in the relatively static layers just internal to the solution interfaces).

From Equations (B11), (B15), and (B16), it is seen that a simple dilution of the external solution on one side of the membrane will not alter the interior concentrations. The first two terms in Equation (B14) are therefore unaltered by such a dilution; and the potential will vary with the Nernst slope as given by the third term. This behavior is a consequence of assuming complete co-ion exclusion and completely trapped sites. Since Equation (B14) is valid at all times, this has the practical consequence that the membrane potential will respond in a step fashion to a step change in solution conditions whenever this corresponds to a simple dilution.

Except for the above case, however, a step change in external solution conditions will be accompanied by a redistribution of the sites until a new steady state is reached. However, when a step change is made from a previous steady state, the profiles are initially unaltered. J_s^{Tot} is therefore zero in the interior of the membrane at zero time. At the boundaries, J_s^{Tot} is zero at all times by virtue of the boundary conditions (B16b). Therefore $\int_2$ of Equation (B26) is zero instantaneously following a step change in solution conditions. Since in the limit of complete dissociation, $\int_1$ of Equation (B26) is zero; while in the limit of strong association, $\int_1$

is a profile independent [being given by Eq. (B32)], we reach the important practical conclusion that the instantaneously observed potential is given by the steady state expression (B26) for the case of complete dissociation as well as by Equation (B34) for the case of strong association. This conclusion is true not only for convection-free systems but also for stirred systems because $\int_1$ is independent of the concentration profiles.

If the membrane interior is deliberately stirred, a quasi-steady state of potential will be rapidly established [again described by Eqs. (B26) and (B34)] since in this case $\int_2$ is zero because the uniform distribution of sites in the stirred interior reduces J_s^{Tot} to zero therein.

C. Neutral Carriers

This appendix deduces the electrical properties of a thin liquid (*e.g.*, hydrocarbon) membrane, interposed between two aqueous solutions, and containing uncharged molecular carriers for ions and is based upon the theoretical treatment of Ciani, Eisenman, and Szabo [13,38]. The analysis is carried out within the framework of classical electrochemistry but without making any assumptions as to electroneutrality or as to profiles of concentration or electric potential within the membrane.

The system and its reactions has been diagrammed in Figure 3. For the reaction, Equation (19), of a neutral macrocyclic molecule, S, with a positive monovalent cation, I^+, to form a charged complex, IS^+, the equilibrium constant in a given homogeneous phase (*e.g.*, aqueous or organic) is defined by:

$$K_{is}^+ = \bar{v} \exp\left[\frac{\mu_i^0 + \mu_s^0 - \mu_{is}^0}{RT}\right] = \frac{a_{is}}{a_i a_s} \tag{C1}$$

where $\bar{v}$ is the mean molal volume; a_i, a_s, and a_{is} denote the activities at equilibrium in moles per liter; and μ_i°, μ_s°, and μ_{is}° are the standard chemical potentials of the cation, neutral site, and charged complexes, respectively. The charged complex IS^+ can react further with a monovalent anion, X^-, to give a neutral compound ISX through reactions, Equation (21), whose equilibrium constant is:

$$K_{isx} = \bar{v} \exp\left[\frac{\mu_{is}^0 + \mu_x^0 - \mu_{isx}^0}{RT}\right] = \frac{a_{isx}}{a_{is} a_x} \tag{C2}$$

Therefore, if n species of monovalent cations and m species of monovalent anions are present in a homogeneous solution containing a given concentration of neutral compound, the chemical reactions occurring in the system will be characterized by n constants K_{is} ($i = 1,2,\ldots,n$) and $n \cdot m$ constants K_{isx} ($i = 1,2 \ldots,n; x = 1,2,\ldots,m$). If the activities are known functions of the concentrations, the system of Equations (C1) and (C2) allows us to determine the composition of the phase in terms of the equilibrium constants of the reactions and of the given amounts of electrolytes and neutral carriers initially contained in the system.

When considering the equilibrium between two separate phases, it is convenient to define the partition coefficient of each component h, bearing a charge z_h, namely:

$$k_h = \frac{\bar{v}}{\bar{v}^*} \exp\left[\frac{\mu_h^0 - \mu_h^{0*}}{RT}\right] = \frac{a_h^*}{a_h} \exp\left[\frac{z_h F(\psi^* - \psi)}{RT}\right] \tag{C3}$$

where a_h^* and a_h designate activities, $\bar{v}$ and $\bar{v}^*$ are the mean molal volumes, and $\psi^* - \psi$ is the potential difference between the two phases (the * being used for the organic phase). Note that each component h corresponds to one of the species of ions or complexes in the system (e.g., I+, S, IS+, ISX, X−) and that for uncharged species (for which $z_h = 0$) the third term of Equation (C3) reduces to a_h^*/a_h.

For a planar membrane diagrammed in Figure 3 interposed between two solutions of differing composition with the x-axis directed perpendicularly to the interfaces and parallel to the direction of the fluxes, we denote the x-coordinates of the membrane boundaries by 0 and d. An asterisk will be used to denote the membrane phase, while superscripts (′) and (″) will refer to the aqueous solutions. It is assumed that: (i) the rate of diffusion is controlled by the diffusion across the membrane; (ii) the ionic complexes IS+ are the predominant charged species in the membrane so that the contribution to the electric current due to the partial fluxes of free ionic species (e.g., I+, X−) can be neglected; and (iii) the activities of the species IS+ in the membrane are assumed equal to concentrations.

The validity of assumption (ii) and the consequent lack of electroneutrality in the membrane is justified from the theory of interaction between double layers when the partition coefficients of the ionic complexes are much higher than those of the free ionic species and when the thickness of the membrane is on the order of or less than the Debye length of the membrane phase [38].

From assumptions (i), (ii), and (iii) and recalling the definition, Equation (C3), the continuity of the electrochemical potentials of the species IS+ at the interfaces gives:

$$C_{is}^*(O) = a_{is}' k_{is} \exp\frac{F[\psi' - \psi^*(O)]}{RT}; \; i = 1, 2, \ldots n \tag{C4}$$

and

$$C_{is}^*(d) = a_{is}'' k_{is} \exp\frac{F(\psi'' - \psi^*(d))}{RT}; \; i = 1, 2, \ldots n. \tag{C5}$$

Describing the fluxes of the species IS^+ by the Nernst-Planck equations, the condition of zero current requires:

$$0 = \frac{I}{F} = \sum_{i=1}^{n} J_{is}^* = -RT \sum_{i=1}^{n} u_{is}^* \left(\frac{dC_{is}^*}{dx} + C_{is}^* \frac{F}{RT} \frac{d\psi^*}{dx} \right) \qquad (C6)$$

where u_{is}^* are the mobilities of the charged complexes in the membrane in moles cm^2 sec^{-1} joules^{-1}. Assuming constant mobility ratios, Equation (C6) can be integrated immediately, without further assumptions to give an explicit expression for the "internal potential" of the membrane:

$$\psi^*(d) - \psi^*(0) = -\frac{RT}{F} \ln \frac{\sum_{i=1}^{n} u_{is}^* C_{is}^*(d)}{\sum_{i=1}^{n} u_{is}^* C_{is}^*(O)}. \qquad (C7)$$

Substituting $C_{is}^*(0)$ and $C_{is}^*(d)$ by the right-hand sides of Equations (C4) and (C5) we find that it is not necessary to solve explicitly for the internal potential since the (observable) total membrane potential $\psi'' - \psi'$ is given directly by:

$$E = \psi'' - \psi' = -\frac{RT}{F} \ln \frac{\sum_{i=1}^{n} k_{is} u_{is}^* a_{is}''}{\sum_{i=1}^{n} k_{is} u_{is}^* a_{is}'} \qquad (C8)$$

which shows the simple dependence of E on the aqueous activities of the complexed cations, a_{is}' and a_{is}''.

Since these activities are not known, it is desirable to express this result explicitly in terms of the (given) aqueous concentrations of salts and complexing molecules. For the case in which only two species of cations, I^+ and J^+, are present, both at higher concentrations in the aqueous phases than the neutral species

$$a_i > C_s^{\text{Tot}} \text{ and } a_j > C_s^{\text{Tot}} \qquad (C9)$$

where C_s^{Tot} indicates the total concentration of S in the aqueous phase and the inequalities (C9) are assumed to be satisfied in both solutions. Recalling that

$$C_s = C_s^{\text{Tot}} - C_{is} - C_{js} - \sum_{x=1}^{m} C_{isx} - \sum_{x=1}^{m} C_{jsx}, \qquad (C10)$$

restricting considerations to the same total concentration of S in both aqueous solutions, and solving the system of Equations (C1) and (C2) under the additional assumptions that: (iv) the species S and IS^+ behave ideally in the aqueous solutions, and (v) that the concentration of the neutral complexes ISX and JSX are negligible in water, Equation (C8) becomes:

$$E = \frac{RT}{F} \ln \frac{a_i' + \left[\dfrac{u_{js}^* k_{js} K_{js}^+}{u_{is}^* k_{is} K_{is}^+}\right] a_j'}{a_i'' + \left[\dfrac{u_{js}^* k_{js} K_{js}^+}{u_{is}^* k_{is} K_{is}^+}\right] a_j''} + \frac{RT}{F} \ln \frac{1 + K_{is}^+ a_i'' + K_{js}^+ a_j''}{1 + K_{is}^+ a_i' + K_{js}^+ a_j'}, \quad (C11)$$

where a_i and a_j are the activities of two monovalent cations, I^+ and J^+ in solutions (') and ('').

The second term of Equation (C11) is negligible when there is negligible complex formation in the aqueous solutions (as, for example, when the ionic concentrations in solutions are sufficiently low). In this situation, Equation (C11) reduces to the very simple form:

$$E = \frac{RT}{F} \ln \frac{a_i' + \left[\dfrac{u_{js}^* k_{js} K_{js}^+}{u_{is}^* k_{is} K_{is}^+}\right] a_j'}{a_i'' + \left[\dfrac{u_{js}^* k_{js} K_{js}^+}{u_{is}^* k_{is} K_{is}^+}\right] a_j''} \quad (C12)$$

Note that the bracketed selectivity parameter depends on such parameters as the mobilities of the charged complexes in the membrane (u_{js}^*, u_{is}^*) their partition coefficients (k_{js}, k_{is}) and their association constants in the aqueous solutions (K_{js}^+, K_{is}^+).

VIII. Acknowledgment

This work has been carried out under the generous support of the National Science Foundations (Grants GB 4039, and GB 6685) and of the National Institutes of Health (Grant GM 14404-01/02/03).

IX. References

[1] Cremer, M., Z. Biol. 47, 562 (1906).
[2] Haber, F., and Klemensiewicz, Z., Z. Physik. Chem. (Leipzig) 67, 385 (1909).
[3] Eisenman, G., Rudin, D. O., and Casby, J. U., Science 126, 831 (1957).
[4] Eisenman, G., Biophys. J. 2, part 2, 259 (1962).
[5] Eisenman, G., in Advances in Analytical Chemistry and Instrumentation 4, C. N. Reilley, Ed., Wiley-Interscience, N. Y., 1965, p. 215.
[6] Eisenman, G., Ed., Glass Electrodes for Hydrogen and Other Cations: Principles and Practice, Marcel Dekker, N. Y., 1967.
[7] Ross, J. W., Jr., Science 155, 1378 (1967).
[8] Ross, J. W., Jr., Orion Research Inc., Bulletin 92-81.
[9] Frant, M., and Ross, J. W., Science 154, 1553 (1966); Orion Research Bulletin 94-09 and 94-16.
[10] Lev, A. A., and Buzhinsky, E. P., Cytologia (U.S.S.R.) 9, 106 (1967).
[11] Mueller, P., and Rudin, D. O., Biophys. Biochem. Res. Comm. 26, 398 (1967).

[12] Stefanac, Z., and Simon, W., Microchem. J. **12**, 125 (1967).
[13] Eisenman, G., Ciani, S., and Szabo, G., Fed. Proc. **27**, 1289(1968).
[14] Eisenman, G., Szabo, G., and Ciani, S., Proc. of the Coral Gables Conf. on the Physical Principles of Biological Membranes, Dec. 18-20, 1968, Gordon and Breach, Science Publisher (in press).
[15] Eisenman, G., Ann. N. Y. Acad. Sci. **148**, 5 (1968).
[16] Planck, M., Ann. Physik. Chem. **39**, 161 (1890); **40**, 561 (1890).
[17] Nernst, W., Z. Physik. Chem. **2**, 613 (1888); **4**, 129 (1889).
[18] Teorell, T., Proc. Soc. Exp. Biol. Med. **33**, 282 (1935).
[19] Teorell, T., "Transport processes and electrical phenomena in ionic membranes" in Progr. in Biophys. & Biophysical Chem. **3**, J. A. V. Butler and J. T. Randall, Eds., Pergamon, N. Y., 1953.
[20] Meyer, K. H., and Sievers, J. F., Helv. Chim. Acta **19**, 649 (1936).
[21] Helfferich, F., Disc. Faraday Soc. **21**, 83 (1956).
[22] Mackay, D., and Meares, P., Kolloid-Z. **171**, 139 (1960).
[23] Karreman, G., and Eisenman, G., Bull. Math. Biophys. **24**, 413 (1962).
[24] Conti, F., and Eisenman, G., Biophys. J. **5**, 247 (1965).
[25] Conti, F., and Eisenman, G., Biophys. J. **5**, 511 (1965).
[26] Stephanova, O. K., Shultz, M. M., Materova, E. A., and Nicolsky, B. P., Vestn. Leningr. Univ. **4**, 93 (1963).
[27] Doremus, R. H., "Diffusion Potentials in Glass" (Chapt. 4 of Ref. [6]).
[28] Isard, J. O., "The Dependence of Glass-Electrode Properties on Composition" (Chapt. 3 of Ref. [6]).
[29] Doremus, R. H., "Ion Exchange in Glasses" in Ion Exchange **2**, J. A. Marinsky, Marcel Dekker, N. Y., 1969.
[30] Haber, F., Ann. Physik. **26**, 927, (1908).
[31] Shean, G. M., and Sollner, K., Ann. N. Y. Acad. Sci. **137**, 759 (1966).
[32] Eisenman, G., Anal. Chem. **40**, 310 (1968).
[33] Conti, F., and Eisenman, G., Biophys. J. **6**, 227 (1966).
[34] Sandblom, J. P., Eisenman, G., and Walker, J. L., Jr., J. Phys. Chem. **71**, 3862 (1967).
[35] Moore, C., and Pressman, B. C., Biochem. Biophys. Res. Commun. **15**, 562 (1964).
[36] Pedersen, C. J., J. Amer. Chem. Soc. **89**, 7017 (1967).
[37] Mueller, P., Rudin, D. O., Tien, H. T., and Wescott, W. C., Circulation **26**, 1167 (1963).
[38] Ciani, S., Eisenman, G., and Szabo, G., "A Theory for the Effects of Neutral Carriers such as the Macrotetralide Actin Antibiotics on the Electrical Properties of Bilayer Membranes", J. Membrane Biol. **1**, 1 (1969).
[39] Eisenman, G., Ciani, S., and Szabo, G., "The Effects of the Macrotetralide Actin Antibiotics on Equilibrium Extraction of Alkali Metal Salts into Organic Solvents" J. Membrane Biol. (in press).
[40] Szabo, G., Eisenman, G., and Ciani, S., "The Effects of the Macrotetralide Actin Antibiotic on the Electrical Properties of Phospholipid Bilayer Membranes", J. Membrane Biol. (in press).
[41] Eisenman, G., "The Origin of the Glass Electrode Potential" (Chapt. 5 of Ref. [6]).
[42] Truesdell, A. H., and Christ, C. L., "Glass Electrodes for Calcium and Other Divalent Cations" (Chapt. 11 of Ref. [6]).
[43] Rechnitz, G. A., "Cation-Sensitive Glass Electrodes in Analytical Chemistry" (Chapt. 12 of Ref. [6]).
[44] Eisenman, G., unpublished data.
[45] Lardy, H. A., Graven, S. N., and Estrada-O, S., Fed. Proc. **26**, 1355 (1967).
[46] Pressman, B. C., Fed. Proc. **27**, 1283 (1968).

[47] Lev, A. A., Buzhinsky, E. P., and Grinfeldt, A. E., Proc. 24th Int. Congr. of Physiol. Sci. 6, 39 (1968).

[48] Simon, W., personal communication.

[49] Tosteson, D. C., personal communication.

[50] Eisenman, G., in Symposium on Membrane Transport and Metabolism, A. Kleinzeller and A. Kotyk, Eds., Academic Press, N. Y., 1961, p. 163.

[51] Eisenman, G., Proc. 23rd Int. Congr. of Physiol. Sci.; Exerpta Medica 87, 489 (1965).

[52] Latimer, W. M., The Oxidation States of the Elements and Their Potentials in Aqueous Solutions, 2nd Ed., Prentice-Hall, N. Y., 1952.

[53] Reichenberg, D., "Ion-Exchange Selectivity" in Ion Exchange 1, J. A. Marinsky, Ed., Marcel Dekker, N. Y., 1968, p. 227.

[54] Sherry, H. S., "The Ion-Exchange Properties of Zeolites" in Ion Exchange 2, J. A. Marinsky, Ed., Marcel Dekker, N. Y., 1969, p. 89.

[55] Diamond, J. M., and Wright, E., Ann. Rev. Physiol. 31, 581 (1969).

[56] Pedersen, C. J., Fed. Proc. 27, 1305 (1968).

[57] Graven, S. N., Lardy, H. A., Johnson, D., and Rutter, A., Biochem. 5, 1729 (1966).

[58] Sandblom, J. P., Eisenman, G., and Walker, J. L., Jr., J. Phys. Chem. 71, 3871 (1967).

CHAPTER 2

SOLID-STATE AND LIQUID MEMBRANE ION-SELECTIVE ELECTRODES

James W. Ross, Jr.

Orion Research, Incorporated
Cambridge, Massachusetts 02139

I. Introduction

In this paper I will summarize the work, carried out in our laboratory by myself and Dr. Martin S. Frant, which has been directed toward developing useful new ion-sensing devices. I will not attempt to give a complete survey of the ion-selective electrode field and will omit the important class of glass membrane electrodes and the newer heterogeneous membrane devices, which are discussed in Chapter 3.

II. The Practical Importance of Ion Activity Measurement

Our work was undertaken in response to a change in the type of question being asked of an analytical chemist. Historically, the analyst was expected only to count atoms of a given kind in a sample; *i.e.,* to determine concentration. The bulk of the subject matter of classical chemical analysis has been concerned with this problem. Concentration data is, of course, very useful and will continue to be needed. In many cases, however, when one is interested in positions of chemical equilibria or rates of chemical reaction, predictions based on concentration information can be misleading.

To take a particularly simple case, zinc dissolves rapidly in hydrochloric acid, but is relatively unaffected by an acetic acid solution of the same concentration. Attempts to correlate acid concentration with corrosion rates will be disappointing. If, instead of acid concentration, the pH — that is, the hydrogen ion activity in the acid solution — is measured, the correlation with corrosion rates will be excellent. The role of hydrogen ion activity in acid-base chemistry has been appreciated for years, and its importance led to the development of the first ion-selective electrode, the familiar glass membrane pH electrode.

In recent years, there has been a growing awareness that activity measurements are equally important for other chemical species. The hardness of water depends on the calcium ion activity in the sample, and not on the total calcium concentration. The role of calcium in biological processes

57

such as nerve conduction, muscle contraction, and blood clotting is determined by the free calcium ion activity in the system, which may vary by several hundred percent from the total calcium concentration. Other examples involving other ions are easy to find. In general, if an analysis is being performed in order to answer a question relating to a rate of a chemical reaction or the position of a chemical equilibrium, it is an activity measurement, rather than a concentration measurement, which will be most significant.

III. The Ideal Nernst Electrode

Practical measurement of ion activities can be accomplished by several techniques. One method is to measure the effect of an ion on the rate of some calibrated process. Calcium ion activities, for example, have been measured in serum samples by noting the beating rate of a freshly excised frog heart immersed in the sample. In principle, pH could be determined by measurement of rates of hydrogen evolution from a standard metal surface. Apart from the inherent inconvenience of such methods, they are invariably subject to numerous interferences, and the fact that they have been used at all underscores the importance of ion activity measurement.

Oxidation-reduction processes occurring at the surface of metal electrodes permit activity measurements of a limited number of ions. Such electrodes are subject to many interferences and have not found wide application as sensing devices. They are widely used as reference electrodes, however, in the form of the familiar calomel and silver-silver chloride half cells.

The only device capable of determining ion activities which is both convenient and at the same time sufficiently free from interferences to be of general usefulness is the ion-selective membrane electrode (Fig. 1). The sensing membrane allows only the ion of interest to pass from the sample solution at the outer membrane surface to an internal solution in contact with the inner membrane surface. The internal solution contains a fixed activity of the ion to which the membrane is permeable.

When such an electrode is placed in a sample solution, there is a momentary flux of ions across the membrane in the direction of the solution containing the lower activity of the mobile ion. Since the ions carry a charge, an electrical potential is set up which opposes further ion migration, and eventually an equilibrium is established in which the potential across the membrane is exactly that required to prevent further net movement of ions.

Changes in this membrane potential can be measured by making electrical contact to the inner solution with a suitable reference electrode, and at the same time contacting the sample solution with a second reference

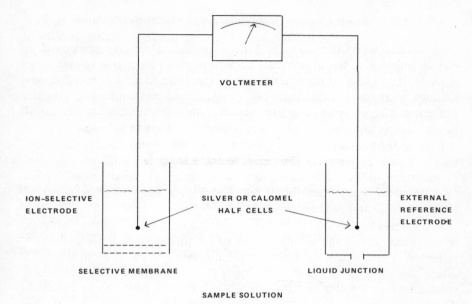

Figure 1.   Schematic diagram of the apparatus used in ion-selective electrode measurement.

electrode *via* a salt bridge. A high input impedance voltmeter connected across the two reference electrode leads will indicate a potential given by the Nernst equation:

$$E = \text{constant} + \frac{2.3RT}{zF} \log A \tag{1}$$

Here E is the potential, in millivolts, developed by the system. The constant term depends on the particular choice of reference electrodes used, on the choice of ion activity in the inner solution, and also includes a small potential associated with the liquid-liquid junction at the salt bridge connection. RT/F is the Nernst factor, which depends on the temperature, and has a value of 59.16 millivolts at 25 °C. A is the activity (in the sample solution) of the ion to which the membrane is permeable, and z is its charge, including sign.

In use, the electrode pair must first be calibrated with standard solutions of known activity (the calibrating buffer solutions, in the case of pH measurement). A plot of electrode potential *vs.* log A of the standard solutions can then be used as a working curve to determine unknown sample activities. Instruments are also available with which direct activity readings can be obtained from the meter scale, eliminating the need of plotting a working curve.

348–381 O–69—6

IV. Advantages and Disadvantages of Electrode Methods

Compared with other analytical techniques, an electrode measurement has an impressive list of advantages. Although an electrode senses ionic activity, it can also be used to determine free ion and total concentrations through methods such as titration, standard addition, and ionic strength buffering. These approaches to concentration measurement are discussed in subsequent chapters, and I mention them here only in passing.

Electrode measurements are rapid – virtually instantaneous in many cases. Time responses are frequently as fast as ten milliseconds, and even under unfavorable conditions, a reading can be obtained within two minutes. They therefore find ready application in such areas as kinetic studies and process control.

An electrode measurement is nondestructive. The number of ions transported across the membrane in order to establish the equilibrium potential is infinitesimal relative to the number present even in the most dilute samples. In addition, with appropriate electrode geometry, very small samples amounting to a few tenths of a milliliter can be handled. These advantages can be very important in biological applications, where several determinations must be performed on a single small sample.

In most cases, no sample pretreatment is necessary. Opaque solutions and even viscous slurries can be measured directly. Time-consuming filtration and distillation operations are eliminated. Automated analytical methods based on electrode measurements are therefore extremely simple to design.

Finally, the equipment required is simple and, at least when compared with most analytical methods of analysis, relatively inexpensive. Portable battery-operated meters are available which can be used in such applications as geological prospecting, oceanography, and water pollution control.

Unfortunately, at their present state of development, electrodes are not highly accurate devices. All electrodes exhibit a drift in the magnitude of the constant term in the Nernst equation at a rate which depends primarily on the temperature variation in the surroundings. An electrode in an average laboratory will show a noncumulative drift of about two millivolts per day. Under field conditions or in process control applications, even larger fluctuations can occur. The presence of drift requires periodic restandardization at a frequency which depends on the accuracy required and the rate of temperature variation. Under the most favorable conditions, in an air-conditioned laboratory with samples and standards all at the same temperature, a precision of 0.2 millivolt can be obtained on replicate measurements of the same sample. Under typical field conditions, a precision of 4.0 millivolts is more usual. The following table trans lates the uncertainty in potential into the corresponding percent uncertainty in ion activity as determined from the Nernst equation.

Precision in E	Percent uncertainty monovalent ion	Percent uncertainty divalent ion
0.1 mV	0.4	0.8
2.0 mV	7.5	15.0

For a given uncertainty in E, the precision of a divalent ion measurement is poorer than that of a monovalent ion because of the appearance of the charge, z, in the Nernst equation. These figures apply only to direct electrode measurements. When electrodes are used as end-point detectors in titrations, precisions of better than one part per thousand are possible. Being a logarithmic device, an electrode gives a constant precision throughout its dynamic range. Trace ion levels in very dilute solutions can therefore be determined with just as high accuracy as for concentrated solutions.

Another problem in electrode measurements is the uncertainty associated with the definition of ion activity. By ion activity, we intuitively mean the "effective concentration" of the free ion in solution. This "effective concentration" is different from the total concentration because of the presence of complexes and ion-pairs, and also because of the effect of sample ionic strength. At the present time, there is no known way by which the activity of an ion in a solution of known composition can be calculated or measured to a high degree of accuracy. In other words, it is presently impossible to formulate with accuracy the standard solutions necessary to calibrate an electrode without making some arbitrary assumptions. The problem has already been faced in the case of pH measurements, and resulted in the development of the conventional NBS pH scale and standard buffer solutions. Similar work must also be carried out for the other ions for which electrodes are now available. This problem is the subject of Chapter 6, and I shall say no more about it here, except to emphasize the importance of this work to the field of applied electrode analysis.

V.   Liquid Membrane Systems

A.   GENERAL PROPERTIES

From the preceding discussion, it is evident that all ion-selective electrodes are similar in mechanism and in the way that they are used. They differ only in the details of the process by which the ion to be determined moves across the membrane and by which other ions are forbidden access to the membrane phase.

In discussing membranes, it is useful to separate the transport process of an ion through the membrane into two steps; the movement of the ion within the membrane phase, and the process by which the ion enters the membrane. It is obviously necessary that the ion to which the membrane is permeable be able to both enter the membrane and move. Rejection by the membrane of other ions can be achieved by blocking either the movement or the ability to pass the membrane-solution interface, or both.

A liquid phase offers one approach to a membrane material. The problem of insuring mobility of the sought-for ion is immediately solved, since if the ion is capable of existence in the membrane at all, it will be free to move by diffusion. Any selectivity of the liquid phase will, of necessity, have to be based on entering restrictions at the interface. Since the liquid phase will be in contact with aqueous solutions, it must be water-insoluble, and it must also have a low enough vapor pressure to prevent significant evaporation. The liquid phase, in effect, should be a relatively low dielectric-constant, high molecular-weight organic liquid.

Two solutions to the mechanical problem of providing a stable liquid membrane separating two aqueous solutions are shown in Figure 2. In the first configuration, which was used in our earlier work [1], the membrane liquid is held inside a glass tube sealed across the end with cellulose dialysis membrane. The dialysis membrane is equally permeable to all ions and serves only to prevent loss of the organic liquid phase. The internal aqueous electrolyte solution is provided in the form of a small tube filled with an agar gel and provided with a silver-silver chloride reference electrode.

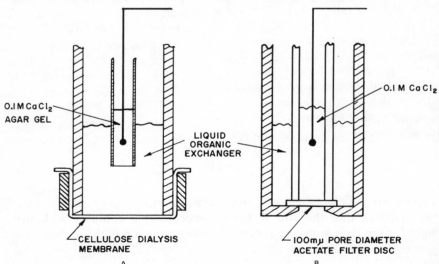

Figure 2. Liquid membrane electrodes. (a) A simple configuration suitable for work where high resistance and long time response are not important. (b) A thin layer configuration with low resistance and fast time response.

The actual electrode membrane, across which changes in cell potential arise, is represented by the organic liquid in the region between the dialysis membrane and the agar gel. Such electrodes are characterized by a high resistance and a relatively long time-response, due principally to the thick layer of the organic phase.

An improved but more complicated assembly is also shown, in which the organic liquid is held in the pores of a thin (0.076 mm) disc of Millipore filter membrane of about 100 nanometer (millimicron) pore diameter. If treated to render the filter material hydrophobic, the organic liquid will wick into the pores of the membrane from a reservoir provided in the annular space indicated in the diagram. The central chamber is filled with the internal aqueous electrolyte and a reference electrode. An electrode of this type has the advantage of a very thin membrane phase, while at the same time it is able to tolerate pressure differentials of greater than one atmosphere without rupture or displacement of the organic phase from the pores.

Since an ion cannot exist by itself in the liquid membrane phase without violating the requirements of electroneutrality, it is necessary to provide a charged "site" of opposite sign as an addition to the solvent liquid. The ion and the site are dissolved as neutral, essentially undissociated salt molecules in the base solvent. The site ion must have a relatively high molecular weight to insure that the resulting salt will be substantially insoluble in water. In addition, the salt must be soluble in the low dielectric constant solvent. Organic phase solubility can usually be obtained by providing long hydrocarbon-chain groups on the site ion.

In a liquid membrane system, the site and the ion move together through the membrane phase. At the membrane interface, a process of ion exchange can take place between the ions of the ion-site salt in the organic phase and the free ions in the aqueous phase. The selectivity of the electrode depends primarily on the selectivity of this ion exchange process. In order for the electrode to display Nernstian response to an ion A^{++} in the presence of an interfering ion B^{++}, it is necessary that the position of the following equilibrium lie far to the left.

$$B^{++}_{aq} + AR_{2_{org}} \rightleftarrows BR_{2_{org}} + A^{++}_{aq} \tag{2}$$

R represents the charged "site" group. Putting this in other terms, selectivity requires that the site R form a more stable complex with the sought-for ion than with any potentially interfering ion in the sample. To the extent that B^{++} enters the membrane phase (and this will always be the case if the activity of A^{++} in the sample is sufficiently low relative to the activity of B^{++}), then the electrode potential will be affected; *i.e.*, B^{++} will be an interference.

The theoretical treatment of a liquid membrane system in which two or more ions are simultaneously transported is difficult. Eisenman [2] has solved the problem for a few special cases, but it should be pointed out that the analytically useful systems which will be discussed in this section are much more complicated than the systems which have been accessible to mathematical analysis. Any theoretical equations based on integration of the Nernst-Planck flux equations applied to monomeric site-ion molecules of symmetrical charge type will be approximate at best when applied to real electrodes.

Fortunately, the analytical chemist is only interested in electrodes which behave in a simple Nernstian manner in response to the ion activity levels present in his sample. The absence of exact equations describing non-Nernstian mixed-ion potentials is not a serious disadvantage. It is important, however, to be able to predict in advance if a given electrode will be subject to interference in a given sample. For this purpose, the following empirical equation is useful:

$$E = \text{constant} + \frac{2.3\,RT}{z_A F} \log \left[A + \sum_i k_i B_i^{z_B/z_A} \right] \tag{3}$$

Here A and B represent the sample activity levels of the sought-for ion and an interfering ion, respectively. The activity of each interfering ion in the sample, raised to a power equal to the charge ratio, is multiplied by a weighting factor, the selectivity constant k_i. If the resulting terms are negligible compared to the activity of A, then the electrode may be used with confidence. The equation has been tested with a wide variety of electrodes and a large number of interfering ions, and agrees quite well with experiment at low levels of interference. However, the equation is only approximate when the interference levels are high, and it should not be used in an attempt to correct a potential measurement for interferences when the activity levels in the sample are known. However, it does permit the analyst to calculate in advance, given a table of selectivity constants, the maximum level of interfering ions which can be tolerated before interference becomes serious.

In attempting to develop a new electrode for a given ion, it is first necessary to find a site group which displays the required selectivity, given the interfering ions which are likely to be present in the sample. The best guide in searching for a new site type is the value of the complex ion stability constant for various ligands with the ion of interest. For a given ligand, the ratio of the stability constant for the ion of interest to that of a potentially interfering ion in aqueous solution will be approximately the same as the ratio in an organic phase. If the ratio is large, then the ligand, suitably substituted to confer organic-phase solubility to the ion-ligand salt, will in all probability make an electrode showing good selectivity in the presence of the interference. In addition to selectivity requirements, the site group must also be capable of entering into a rapid, mobile ion exchange equilibrium with the ion of interest. Many groups which are potentially interesting from a selectivity standpoint, such as most multi-dentate chelating sites, equilibrate too slowly to give electrodes with reasonable time responses. In addition, most of these chelating groups form mixed complexes with the ion of interest and hydrogen ion over the pH range which is of major analytical interest. Hydrogen ion in this situation will be transported across the membrane, producing a large hydrogen ion interference.

With these guides in mind, it is usually possible to find several site groups among the vast number of known complexing ligands showing the required selectivity, provided that the number of potential interferences is reasonably small. It is unlikely that a completely selective electrode will ever be found that can be used in every sample solution. The chances of finding a system which will be sufficiently selective in a given restricted application are, however, quite good.

A few comments regarding the solvent should be made. Most of the ion-site complexes of practical interest are bulky molecules in which the ion is well shielded from interaction with the solvent. As a result, the choice of the solvent has little effect on electrode selectivity. In the case of divalent ion selective systems based on phosphoric acid ester groups, we have found that some differences of selectivity among the various alkaline-earth ions can be achieved by varying the polarity of the solvent. In general, however, the solvent is merely an inert vehicle for site-ion diffusion, and its selection is made on the basis of the physical properties mentioned earlier.

B. Phosphate Ester Systems

Some of the first systems we studied were ion-site salts derived from diesters of phosphoric acid [1]. We were searching for an electrode which would show good selectivity for calcium ions in the presence of large amounts of sodium and lower levels of potassium and magnesium. An electrode of this description was needed for biological research and in water quality analysis. The choice of the phosphate ester was made because phosphate and polyphosphate ions form stable complexes with calcium, while no such complexes are known with sodium and the alkali metals. In addition, esters of phosphoric acid containing long hydrocarbon chains are easy to synthesize. A diester, rather than a monoester, group is necessary to avoid the problem of mixed complex formation with hydrogen ion mentioned earlier. Electrodes made from diesters with hydrocarbon chains in the C_8-C_{16} range showed good selectivity for calcium in the presence of sodium, as expected. In solvents with very polar substituent groups, such as dioctylphenylphosphonate, the electrodes also showed good selectivity for calcium relative to magnesium and other alkaline-earth ions. Selectivity in the presence of other divalent ions — Zn^{++}, Pb^{++}, Fe^{++}, etc.—was poor, but these ions are not normally present in the samples in which the electrode was intended to be used. Using less polar solvents, such as decanol, electrodes were obtained which showed virtually identical response to all the alkaline-earth ions, while still preserving good rejection of monovalent ions. Electrodes of this type are useful for the determination of water hardness.

A calibration curve of an electrode in $CaCl_2$ solutions is shown in Figure 3. This particular electrode was made from a liquid phase containing $0.1M$ calcium salt of didecyl phosphoric acid in dioctylphenylphosphonate. In converting calcium ion concentrations into activities, we have used the ionic activity coefficients of Kielland [3], which were obtained by the use of an extended Debye-Hückel equation.

Over the range 10^{-1} to $10^{-5}M$, this electrode behaves in a completely Nernstian manner. Below $10^{-6}M$, the calibration curve forms a plateau, and the electrode no longer responds to changes in sample calcium ion activity. This lower limit of detection is caused by the small solubility of the calcium-phosphate ester salt in the aqueous phase. In very dilute sample solutions, the electrode saturates the sample, raising the level of calcium ion to a point which depends on the concentration of the salt in the organic phase and the partition coefficient of the salt between the aqueous and the organic phase.

In general, the lower limit of useful electrode response can be improved by increasing the molecular weight of the site group and by working with lower loadings of the salt in the organic phase. Unfortunately, increasing the molecular weight beyond a certain point may cause precipitation or gelling in the organic membrane phase. Reducing the concentration of the salt in the organic phase can also lead to problems associated with higher membrane resistance and longer time response. A practical electrode is always a result of compromise between these factors.

The effect of hydrogen ion interference on the same calcium electrode is shown in Figure 4. The electrode potential at constant calcium ion concentration is independent of pH until the hydrogen ion activity increases to a point where $k_H A_H^{1/2}$, as defined by Equation (3), becomes appreciable compared with A_{Ca}. The hydrogen ion then contributes to the charge transport process across the membrane and produces a positive increase in the electrode potential. With still further increase in A_H, a point is reached where the contribution of Ca^{++} to the charge transport in the membrane is overwhelmed by hydrogen ion, and the electrode now responds in a Nernstian manner as a pH electrode.

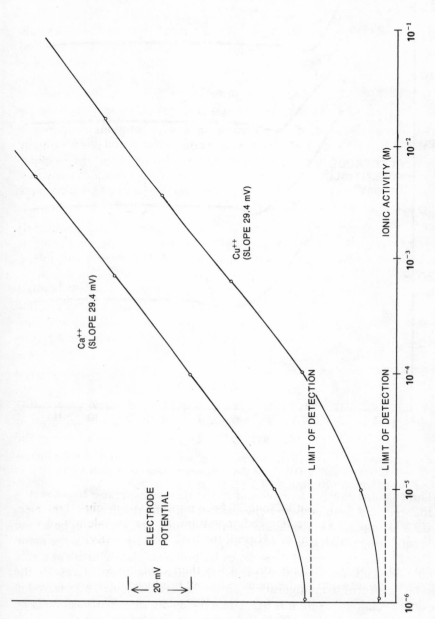

Figure 3.   Calibration curves for a cupric and a calcium ion-selective electrodes.

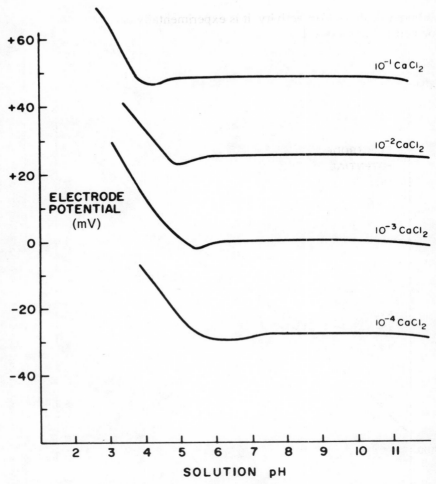

Figure 4.   Effect of H⁺ on calcium ion measurements. pH has been varied with increments of HCl and NaOH at the CaCl₂ molarity indicated on each curve.

The calcium-phosphate ester salt in the membrane phase is converted
to the free acid form in these acid regions, with the result that, if the electrode is then placed in a calcium solution of high pH, there will be a time
interval during which calcium ions displace the hydrogen ions in the membrane. During this period, the electrode potential slowly drifts at a rate
which depends on the thickness of the membrane. As a result, the
thin-layer electrode configuration shown in Figure 2 is to be preferred in
those applications where it is likely that the electrode will occasionally be
exposed to excessively high concentrations of interfering ions.

Sodium ion interference is shown in Figure 5. Because the calcium
electrode does not respond at all to sodium, except at very high ratios of

sodium to calcium ion activity, it is experimentally easier to vary calcium ion activity in the presence of high background levels of sodium chloride.

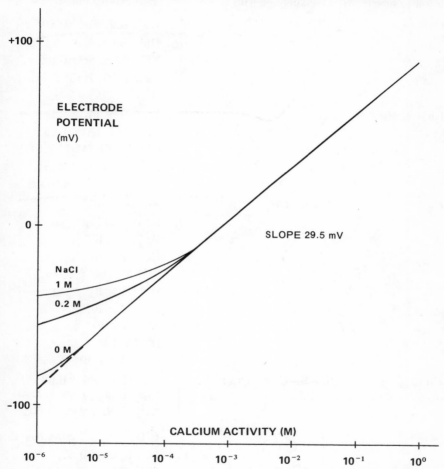

Figure 5. Effect of Na+ in calcium ion activity measurements. CaCl₂ varied in the presence of the indicated background molarity of NaCl.

Again, it can be seen that Equation (3) is obeyed with respect to the major features of the curves. The curve corresponding to the highest background level of sodium chloride (1.0M) is displaced from the others by a small amount. This is caused by a junction potential at the salt bridge and does not represent sodium ion interference. Selectivity constants calculated from Figures 4 and 5, together with constants for other ions, are summarized in Table 1.

In discussing interferences for liquid membrane electrodes, it is necessary to reemphasize that a selectivity constant is an approximate number,

Table 1. Liquid membrane systems.

Ion measured	Exchange site	Selectivity constants
Ca^{++}	$(RO)_2PO_2^-$	Zn^{++} 3.2, Fe^{++} 0.80, Pb^{++} 0.63, Cu^{++} 0.27, Ni^{++} 0.08, Sr^{++} 0.02, Mg^{++} 0.01, Ba^{++} 0.01, H^+ 10^7, Na^+ 0.0016
Ca^{++} & Mg^{++}	$(RO)_2PO_2^-$	Zn^{++} 3.5, Fe^{++} 3.5, Cu^{++} 3.1, Ni^{++} 1.35, $(Ca^{++}$ 1.0), $(Mg^{++}$ 1.0), Ba^{++} 0.94, Sr^{++} 0.54, Na^+ 0.01
Cu^{++}	$R-S-CH_2-COO^-$	Na^+ 5×10^{-4}, K^+ 5×10^{-4}, Mg^{++} 1×10^{-3}, Ca^{++} 2×10^{-3}, Sr^{++} 1×10^{-3}, Ba^{++} 1×10^{-3}, Zn^{++} 3×10^{-2}, Ni^{++} 1×10^{-2}, H^+ 1×10^1, Fe^{++} 1.4×10^2
Pb^{++}	$R-S-CH_2-COO^-$	Cu^{++} 2.6, Fe^{++} 0.08, Zn^{++} 0.003, Ca^{++} 0.005, Ni^{++} 0.007, Mg^{++} 0.008
NO_3^-		ClO_4^- 10^3, I^- 20, ClO_3^- 2, Br^- 0.9, $S^=$ 0.57, NO_2^- 6×10^{-2}, CN^- 2×10^{-2}, HCO_3^- 2×10^{-2}, Cl^- 6×10^{-3}, OAc^- 6×10^{-3}, $S_2O_3^=$ 6×10^{-3}, $SO_3^=$ 6×10^{-3}, F^- 9×10^{-4}, $SO_4^=$ 6×10^{-4}, $H_2PO_4^-$ 3×10^{-4}, $PO_4^{\equiv}$ 3×10^{-4}, $HPO_4^=$ 8×10^{-5}

Table 1. Liquid membrane systems (continued).

Ion measured	Exchange site	Selectivity constants
ClO_4^-	$\left[\text{Fe} \left(\text{N} \bigcirc \text{N} \right) R \right]_3^{++}$	OH^- 1.0, I^- 1.2×10^{-2} F^- 2.5×10^{-4}, NO_3^- 1.5×10^{-3}, Cl^- 2.2×10^{-4}, Br^- 5.6×10^{-4}, $SO_4^=$ 1.6×10^{-4}, OAc^- 5.1×10^{-4}
Cl^-	NR_4	ClO_4^- 32, I^- 17, NO_3^- 4.2, Br^- 1.6, OH^- 1.0, OAc^- 0.32, HCO_3^- 0.19, $SO_4^=$ 0.14, F^- 0.10
BF_4^-	$\left[\text{Ni} \left(\text{N} \bigcirc \text{N} \right) R \right]_3^{++}$	OH^- 10^{-3}, I^- 20, NO_3^- 0.1, Br^- 4×10^{-2}, OAc^- 4×10^{-3}, HCO_3^- 4×10^{-3}, F^- 10^{-3}, Cl^- 10^{-3}, $SO_4^=$ 10^{-3}

and can be used only to estimate orders of magnitude of interferences to be used in a given application. It cannot be used to make corrections to electrode readings obtained in solutions in which the level of interference is appreciable. In Figure 6 are shown some experimental values of k_{Mg} obtained with an electrode using a calcium-phosphate ester salt in a mixed alcohol-phosphonate solvent. As can be seen for this typical case, the value of k_{Mg} depends to some extent on solution composition.

If calculation shows that the maximum expected value of an interference term in Equation (3) is small, say less than 2% of the minimum value of the activity of the sought-for ion, then an electrode can be used with confidence. For borderline situations, it is best to determine the pertinent selectivity constants in a solution of ionic composition similar to the samples to be analyzed.

C. OTHER CATION-SELECTIVE LIQUID SYSTEMS

Charged site groups containing sulfur would be expected to show selectivity toward heavy metal ions which form insoluble sulfides and stable mercapto complexes. The use of mercaptan groups by themselves has not proved fruitful because of their sensitivity to oxidation and the difficulty of eliminating hydrogen ion interference due to the very weakly acid na-

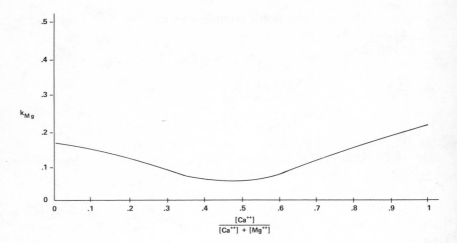

Figure 6. Variation of k_{Mg} with solution composition for an experimental divalent ion electrode. Data obtained at constant $CaCl_2 + MgCl_2$ concentration of 0.01 M.

ture of the site. Site groups of the type $R-S-CH_2COO^-$, in which the sulfur and the carboxylate groups are in a position to form a chelate ring with a heavy metal ion, do show good selectivity and are sufficiently stable to form useful electrodes [4].

A calibration curve for a copper electrode based on a thio-acid site is shown in Figure 3. The plateau at low copper levels has the explanation given previously for the calcium electrode. Selectivity constant data for this copper electrode, as well as for a lead-selective electrode utilizing the same site group, are given in Table 1. From a practical point of view, liquid electrodes for heavy metals are now obsolete due to the recent development of solid-state membranes, which in almost all applications show better selectivities than the liquid systems.

D. ANION-SELECTIVE LIQUID SYSTEMS

By making use of a positively charged site group, it would be expected that anion-selective electrodes could be fabricated. The most important class of site groups in this category are complexes of positively charged transition metal complexes with a bulky organic ligand containing the orthophenanthroline chelating group. Salts of the type $FeL_3(NO_3)_2$, where L is a substituted phenanthroline ligand, function as anion exchangers.

This metal ion complex is non-labile, and the rate of transition metal cation exchange at the membrane interface is too slow relative to the rate of anion exchange to have any effect on the electrode potential. The positive charge in sites of this type is largely delocalized because of the aromatic ring system in the ligand. It would be expected that such low charge density sites would form more stable complexes with large polarizable anions than with small "hard" ions, such as fluoride and hydroxide.

Calibration curves for electrodes making use of complex metal sites and selective to nitrate and perchlorate ions are shown in Figure 7. The only notable difference in these curves compared with the cation-selective electrodes is the change in the sign of the slope. This is to be expected, since it is a negatively charged species which is being transported across the membrane, and the sign of the logarithmic term in the Nernst equation changes accordingly. Also, the slope has twice the absolute value of the divalent cation curves, since we are now dealing with a monovalent ion. Selectivity constants for these electrodes are shown in Table 1.

An electrode for fluoroborate ion is also listed in Table 1. This electrode resulted from the observation by Carlson [5] that the nitrate electrode just described could also be used to measure BF_4^- in solutions containing no nitrate ion, provided that the liquid phase of the nitrate electrode membrane was first extracted with a solution of $NaBF_4$, thereby converting the nitrate salt into the fluoroborate form. The internal reference solution of the nitrate electrode must, of course, be replaced with one containing a fixed concentration of fluoroborate ion.

Another liquid system which has some practical utility uses a high molecular weight tetraalkyl ammonium salt. A chloride electrode of this type using a dimethyl-distearyl ammonium cation can be used to measure chloride ion activities in the presence of sulfide and small amounts of bromide and iodide, all of which seriously interfere with the solid-state chloride electrodes. The properties of this electrode are also listed in Table 1.

VI. Solid-State Membrane Systems

A. GENERAL PROPERTIES

A few crystalline materials are known which exhibit ionic conductivity at room temperature. In most cases, only one of the lattice ions is involved in the conduction process, usually the lattice ion with the smallest ionic radius and the smallest charge. Provided that the crystal is mechanically stable, chemically inert in the sample solution, and of low solubility, it can be used in the form of a thin section as an electrode membrane.

A crystal membrane can be a highly selective device. Conduction in the crystal phase proceeds by a lattice defect mechanism in which a mobile ion adjacent to a vacancy defect moves into the vacancy. A vacancy for a particular ion is ideally tailored with respect to size, shape, and charge distribution to admit only the mobile ion; all other ions are unable to move

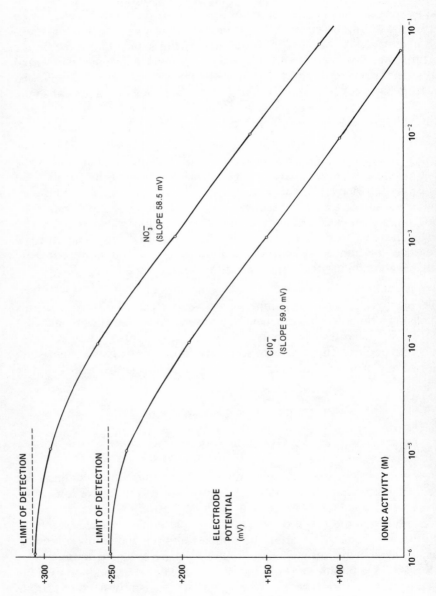

Figure 7. Calibration curves for a nitrate and perchlorate ion-selective electrode.

and cannot contribute to the conduction process. With liquid membrane electrodes, any ion capable of entering the membrane phase is able to move as a site-ion complex, and selectivity therefore must depend entirely on the ion-exchange process at the membrane-sample interface. Solid-state crystal membrane electrodes derive their selectivity by restricting the movement of all ions except the one to be detected.

Since no foreign ions can enter the crystal phase, the theory of the solid-state membrane is simple. It always behaves as a Nernstian device. Interferences can occur, but they arise from chemical reactions at the crystal surface and are of an entirely different type than in the case of the liquid membrane electrodes.

B. Rare-Earth Fluoride Membranes

It has recently been observed that electrodes can be made from fluorides of several of the rare earths, notably lanthanum, which are pure fluoride ion conducting systems at room temperature [6]. These materials in single crystal form have unusually low volume resistivities which can be reduced still further by doping the crystal with a divalent cation such as Eu^{++}.

A calibration curve of a LaF_3 membrane electrode is shown in Figure 8. Nernstian response is obtained over a range extending from saturated solutions to $10^{-7}M$ fluoride ion activity. Below $10^{-7}M$ fluoride levels, the calibration curve plateaus in a manner similar to the calibration curves of the liquid membrane electrodes. The reason for the plateau is the same: the solubility of lanthanum fluoride in the sample solution.

However, the lower limit of detection for the fluoride electrode is much smaller than one would calculate from the literature values for the solubility product of lanthanum fluoride [7]. Why this should be the case is still an open question. It may be due to a very slow rate of dissolution of the membrane in the sample solution, which does not permit equilibrium to be established in dilute samples during the time involved in making the measurement. An alternative explanation, and one which seems much more probable, is that the single crystal material may have a much smaller equilibrium solubility than the finely divided, freshly precipitated compound that has been used for the solubility product determinations.

In addition to being a Nernstian detector of fluoride ions, a lanthanum fluoride membrane electrode can be used to measure lanthanum ion levels in solutions which initially contain no fluoride. The electrode potential is given by the Nernst equation:

$$E = \text{constant} - \frac{2.3\,RT}{F} \log A_\text{F}. \tag{4}$$

If the sample solution is equilibrated with solid LaF_3, then the fluoride

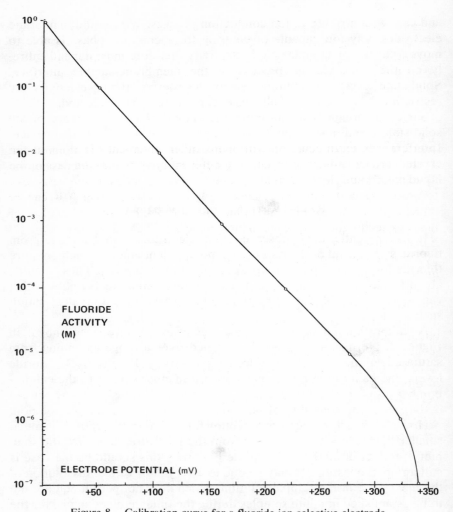

Figure 8.   Calibration curve for a fluoride ion-selective electrode.

level at the electrode surface in a solution containing La^{3+} is determined by the solubility product of LaF_3, *i.e.:*

$$K_{sp(LaF_3)} = A_{La} A_F^3. \tag{5}$$

Substitution of Equation (5) in Equation (4) gives:

$$E = \text{constant} + \frac{2.3\,RT}{3F} \log A_{La}. \tag{6}$$

The slow rate of equilibration of solid single crystal LaF_3 with aqueous solutions necessitates the separate addition of finely divided LaF_3 to the sample. Although the ability to detect an exotic ion such as lanthanum is of itself of little analytical importance, the fact that a crystal membrane electrode can be used to detect the other non-mobile ions of the membrane lattice has important practical implications, as will be shown in the following sections.

C. Systems Based on Silver Sulfide

Silver sulfide, in common with many other silver salts, is an ionic conductor of low resistance in which the silver ions are the mobile species. The exceedingly low solubility product of Ag_2S, its excellent resistance to oxidizing and reducing agents, and the ease with which it can be fabricated into dense polycrystalline membranes by conventional pellet pressing techniques, makes it an ideal material for electrode use. By itself, it can be used either to detect silver ions or to measure sulfide ion levels by the mechanism of the solubility product equilibrium already discussed under the fluoride electrode [8]. Because silver sulfide equilibrates very rapidly with the sample solution, it is not necessary to add additional solid silver sulfide to the sample. As a silver-ion detector, it is superior to a silver metal electrode, since it is not attacked by strong oxidizing agents, and it is not sensitive to redox couples in the solution. As a sulfide-sensing device, it is preferable to the silver metal-silver sulfide electrodes which have occasionally been used in the past, for the reasons just cited, and also because the membrane surface is dense and nonporous, resulting in very fast time responses to changes in sample sulfide levels.

Calibration curves obtained with silver sulfide membrane electrodes are Nernstian and are similar to the curves already described for the other ion-selective electrodes. The dynamic range of the electrode extends from saturated solutions down to silver and sulfide levels on the order of $10^{-8}M$. The lower limit of detection is far too high to be caused by the solubility of the membrane $[K_{sp(Ag_2S)} = 10^{-51}]$, and reflects instead the experimental difficulty of preparing extremely dilute solutions of ions without extensive ionic adsorption on and desorption from the surfaces of the containing vessels and the electrodes. This problem is identical to the difficulty faced by an analyst in attempting to obtain accurate pH readings in very dilute unbuffered solutions.

With solutions of higher levels of silver or sulfide in which extensive complexation is present, it is quite possible to obtain accurate measurements of very low levels of the free ions. Free sulfide ion levels on the order of $10^{-19}M$, for example, are easily determined in acid hydrogen sulfide solutions. Similarly, silver ion levels can be followed down to the $10^{-20}M$ level during the course of titrations of silver with a number of complexing and precipitating reagents.

D. Mixed Ag₂S-AgX Systems

Kolthoff reported, many years ago, that chloride and bromide electrodes could be made with membranes of fused silver chloride and silver bromide [9]. Both silver chloride and silver bromide are ionic conducting materials in which silver is the mobile species. Such electrodes sense the halide ion by a mechanism identical to that of the silver sulfide membrane in a sulfide solution. Although these electrodes were not affected by redox couples and were faster in response than the classical silver metal-silver halide electrodes, they were never widely used in chemical analysis. The principal disadvantages were associated with the rather high room-temperature resistance of silver chloride, and with the fact that both materials exhibit large photoelectric potentials requiring that they be used under conditions of constant illumination, difficult to achieve in the average laboratory.

We have found that these disadvantages can be eliminated by using electrode membranes of a silver sulfide matrix in which the appropriate silver salt is dispersed in a very finely divided form. Since silver halides are much more soluble than silver sulfide, the sulfide can be considered as a chemically inert matrix material through which silver ions are free to move. At the membrane-solution interface, the silver halide equilibrates with the sample solution, resulting in a silver ion level given by:

$$A_{Ag} = \frac{K_{sp(AgX)}}{A_X} .$$

(7)

Substitution into the Nernst equation for a silver ion conducting membrane gives the result that a mixed sulfide of this type behaves as though the membrane were a pure halide ion conductor.

The mixed silver sulfide-silver salt approach to membrane fabrication can also be used with silver iodide and silver thiocyanate respectively; other electrodes can also be visualized. The chief restriction on the silver salt is that its solubility must be much larger than that of silver sulfide (which will always be the case) and yet be sufficiently small so that the equilibrium solubility of the silver salt does not give an anion level which is higher than the expected sample activity.

It is not necessary that the salt AgX be a silver ion conductor, nor is it always necessary that the salt form a mechanically stable pressed pellet when present in the pure state. Silver iodide, for example, cannot be formed as a pure AgI pellet and used as an electrode membrane, even though it is a good silver ion conductor and has a sufficiently low room-temperature resistivity. Silver iodide undergoes several solid-phase transformations on heating or on increasing pressure above ambient values. A pellet prepared by fusion or by pressing slowly reverts to the stable room-temperature modification, fracturing in the process. When prepared as a mixed sulfide pellet, this does not take place, either because the kinetics of the process are too slow or because the silver iodide has been converted to the compound Ag_3SI, which does not exhibit a phase transition.

Calibration curves obtained using the mixed silver sulfide-silver salt membrane electrodes are identical to those which would be expected if the membranes were made from the pure silver salt. Lower limits of sensitivity are determined by the solubility products for the various silver salts. The properties of a number of examples of this class of electrodes are summarized in Table 2.

Table 2. Solid–state membrane electrodes.

Ion determined	Membrane	Principal interferences
F^-, La^{+++}	LaF_3	OH^-
Cl^-	$AgCl/Ag_2S$	Br^-, I^-, $S^=$, NH_3, CN^-
Br^-	$AgBr/Ag_2S$	I^-, $S^=$, NH_3, CN^-
I^-	AgI/Ag_2S	$S^=$, CN^-
SCN^-	$AgSCN/Ag_2S$	Br^-, I^-, $S^=$, NH_3, CN^-
$S^=$, Ag^+	Ag_2S	Hg^{++}
CN^-	AgI/Ag_2S	I^-, $S^=$
Cu^{++}	CuS/Ag_2S	Hg^{++}, Ag^+
Pb^{++}	PbS/Ag_2S	Hg^{++}, Ag^+, Cu^{++}
Cd^{++}	CdS/Ag_2S	Hg^{++}, Ag^+, Cu^{++}

E. MIXED SILVER SULFIDE-METAL SULFIDE MEMBRANE SYSTEMS

Silver sulfide can also be used as a matrix material in conjunction with a number of metal sulfides to give membranes selective to the metal ion of the second metal sulfide. As long as the membrane contains sufficient silver sulfide to provide silver ion conducting pathways through the membrane, it will function as a silver ion detector. The silver ion activity level at the sample/membrane interface, assuming that the sample contains no silver ion initially, is determined by the following two equilibria:

$$A^2_{Ag}A_S = K_{sp(Ag_2S)} \tag{8}$$

$$A_M A_S = K_{sp(MS)} \tag{9}$$

where MS is the metal sulfide present in a finely dispersed state in the silver sulfide matrix. Eliminating A_S and solving for A_{Ag} gives:

$$A_{Ag} = \left\{ \left[\frac{K_{sp(Ag_2S)}}{K_{sp(MS)}} \right] A_M \right\}^{1/2} \tag{10}$$

which, when substituted into the Nernst equation for a silver ion conducting system, yields:

$$E = \text{constant} + \frac{2.3\,RT}{2F} \log A_M. \tag{11}$$

The electrode therefore behaves, in solutions containing M^{++} but not Ag^+, as a Nernstian device selective for A_M.

There are several restrictions on the metal sulfide MS which must be satisfied. The solubility product $K_{sp(MS)}$ must be much larger than that of Ag_2S. If this were not the case, then it would not be possible to have silver sulfide present on the electrode surface, as the reaction

$$M^{++} + Ag_2S \rightleftharpoons MS + 2Ag^+ \tag{12}$$

would proceed completely to the right. At the same time, the value of $K_{sp(MS)}$ must be sufficiently small so that the level of M^{++} in the sample solution produced from the solubility of MS is small relative to the levels of the ion which are expected in the sample. In addition to solubility product restrictions, it is also necessary that the sulfides of the membrane phase equilibrate rapidly with the ions of the sample in order for the electrode to have a reasonable time response. Unlike the electrodes discussed earlier, two solid-phase equilibria must now be established. The resulting kinetic complications prevent a number of otherwise suitable sulfides from being used in electrodes.

Among the sulfides which we have found make useful electrodes are CuS, CdS, and PbS. Nernstian calibration curves are obtained in all cases, and the curves extend over a dynamic range from saturated solutions at the upper limit to a lower limit which is a strong function of pH. The pH dependence of the lower limit of sensitivity arises from the increased solubility of metal sulfides in acid solution, due to the formation of HS^- and H_2S. The effect of pH on the sensitivity range of a lead electrode is shown in Figure 9. Data for the other electrodes are summarized in Table 2.

Data of the type shown in Figure 9 are useful in determining in advance how dilute a sample may be and still permit a direct electrode measurement of the metal ion level. In titration applications involving relatively concentrated solutions of the metals in the 10^{-1} to $10^{-4}M$ range, Nernstian response to the free metal ion can be obtained down to very

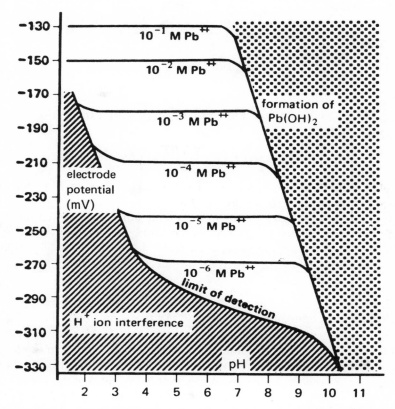

Figure 9.   Effect of pH on a lead-selective electrode. pH varied with $HClO_4$ and NaOH
at the indicated background level of $Pb(ClO_4)_2$.

low levels in the presence of excess reagent [10]. In this case, it is only necessary that the equilibrium solubility of the metal sulfide in the presence of the reagent be small compared with the **total** metal concentration in the solution being titrated. A titration curve obtained with a cadmium electrode showing the variation in free cadmium ion activity with added EDTA is shown in Figure 10.

F. INTERFERENCES AT SOLID-STATE MEMBRANE ELECTRODES

I have already pointed out that, because of the stringent requirements regarding size and charge of the mobile ion species in a crystal lattice, interference resulting from lattice penetration of the interfering ion is not to be expected with solid-state devices. Such penetration, if it occurred, would require the existence of stable solid solutions involving the mobile ion and the interfering ion. Among the compounds we have been discussing, very few solid solutions of this type are known which will

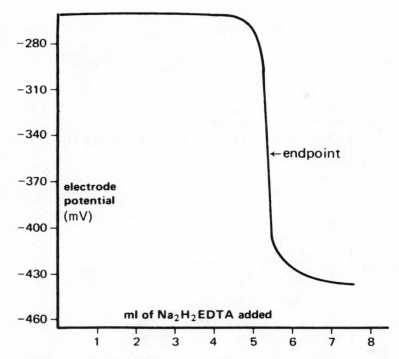

Figure 10.   Titration of Cd^{++} with EDTA. 100ml of $5\times10^{-3}M$ Cd(NO$_3$)$_2$ adjusted to pH
10 with NH$_3$. Titrated with 0.1M Na$_2$H$_2$EDTA.

form at room temperature. Glass electrode membranes, however, which
involve a lattice of much higher disorder than the crystalline materials, do
show lattice-penetration interference, and are more properly considered
as a special case of a liquid membrane system in which the sites have zero
mobility.

Nernstian response in a solid-membrane device requires that all the
solid phases of the membrane be in equilibrium with the sample solution.
This will not be the case if there are species present in the sample solution
which can react with the components of the membrane. The most common type of reaction, and one which is frequently observed with membranes containing a silver halide, involves reaction with an ion in the sample solution to form a more insoluble silver salt. Thiocyanate ion, for example, can interfere with bromide ion measurements if the reaction

$$SCN^- + AgBr(s) \rightleftharpoons AgSCN(s) + Br^- \tag{13}$$

takes place [11]. This reaction will not proceed to the right unless the
ratio of the thiocyanate ion activity to the bromide ion activity exceeds a
value given by the ratio of the solubility products of silver thiocyanate to

silver bromide. If this ratio is exceeded, then all the silver bromide on the membrane surface will be converted to silver thiocyanate. The silver ion activity at the electrode surface will then be determined by the thiocyanate ion activity, and the electrode will behave as a thiocyanate-sensing device.

An example of the abrupt onset of this type of interference is shown in Figure 11. This should be compared with Figure 5, which shows the gradual increase in the level of interference with increasing activity of the interfering ion. This latter response is typical of liquid membrane systems.

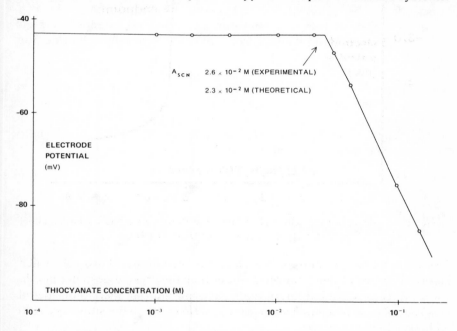

Figure 11.   Effect of SCN⁻ on a bromide electrode. Background solution $10^{-3}M$ NaBr with NaSCN added in the amount indicated on the horizontal axis.

A more complicated case of interference, resulting in the formation of a new solid phase, is found with the mixed cupric-silver sulfide membrane electrode. In samples containing both copper and chloride ions, the reaction:

$$Ag_2S(s) + Cu^{++} + 2Cl^- = 2AgCl(s) + CuS(s) \qquad (14)$$

may take place. The condition which must be satisfied, if the silver sulfide on the membrane surface is to be stable, is readily derived from equilibrium calculations, and may be expressed as:

$$A_{Cu}A_{Cl}^2 < \frac{K_{Ag_2S}}{K_{AgCl}^2 K_{Cus}} \qquad (15)$$

where K_{Ag_2S}, K_{AgCl}, K_{CuS} refer to the solubility products of the compounds indicated by the subscripts. If the sample activity product $A_{Cu}A_{Cl}^2$ exceeds the value given, then all the silver sulfide at the membrane surface is converted to silver chloride, accompanied by an abrupt change in electrode function from a Nernstian response to cupric ion to a response to chloride ion.

Fortunately, an electrode is not irreversibly harmed if it is inadvertently placed in a solution which results in the formation of a new solid phase. The reactions giving rise to the interferences are all reversible, and the electrode can be restored to normal operation by exposure to a high concentration of the appropriate ion (bromide in the first example cited), or to a reagent such as ammonia, which will remove the silver chloride from a contaminated cupric ion selective electrode.

Solid electrodes may also give problems if they are used in samples containing a species which forms a very stable complex with one of the component ions of the membrane. An example is the effect of citrate ion on a lanthanum fluoride electrode. Lanthanum ion forms a very stable soluble citrate complex, which has the effect of increasing the solubility of the membrane in the sample by the reaction:

$$LaF_3(s) + Cit^{3-} \leftrightarrows LaCit^0 + 3F^-. \qquad (16)$$

At equilibrium in a solution originally containing no fluoride, but an activity of citrate, A_{Cit}, the sample fluoride level in the vicinity of the membrane surface will be given by:

$$A_F^\circ = 4[K_f K_{LaF_3} A_{Cit}]^{1/4} \qquad (17)$$

where K_f refers to the formation constant of the lanthanum citrate complex. In most cases, the fluoride level given by this expression will be small compared with the sample fluoride level, and can therefore be ignored. In dilute fluoride solutions, however, the value of A_F° may be appreciable compared with the sample fluoride level, and the electrode will give too high a value for the analysis. The effect of the citrate is to increase the lower limit of detection of the fluoride electrode by an amount which increases with the one-fourth power of the sample citrate activity. Figure 12 shows a set of calibration curves obtained at various citrate background levels. Similar results are obtained in the presence of other strong complexing agents for lanthanum, such as EDTA.

With a mixed silver iodide-silver sulfide membrane in contact with a cyanide solution, a similar reaction occurs:

$$AgI(s) + 2CN^- = Ag(CN)_2^- + I^-. \qquad (18)$$

In this case, however, the reaction proceeds virtually to completion at equilibrium with the consumption of silver iodide from the membrane and

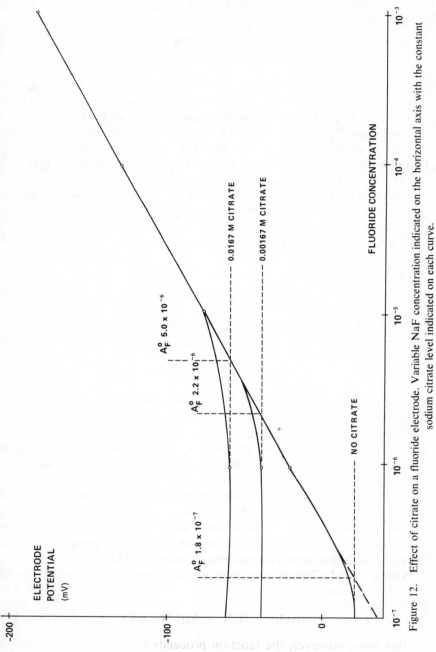

Figure 12.   Effect of citrate on a fluoride electrode. Variable NaF concentration indicated on the horizontal axis with the constant sodium citrate level indicated on each curve.

the production of iodide ions. The iodide and cyanide ions interdiffuse between the eroding electrode surface and the sample solution. If an appropriate diffusion barrier is placed on the membrane surface, then a steady state is quickly established in which the cyanide level at the solid membrane surface is virtually zero, while the iodide level is very nearly one-half the sample cyanide ion concentration. The silver ion activity at the membrane surface is fixed by the iodide level *via* the solubility product of silver iodide, and the electrode potential as a result depends in an almost Nernstian manner on the sample cyanide ion concentration.

We have found that the porous silver sulfide matrix left behind as the silver iodide is consumed provides an almost ideal diffusion barrier. The flux of iodide and cyanide ions is kept sufficiently low so that electrode lives of several months of continuous operation are possible. At the same time, the porous silver sulfide layer never becomes thick enough to adversely affect the electrode time response. The outermost silver sulfide layers are continuously sloughing off at a rate which keeps the effective diffusion barrier thickness a constant.

A pseudo-Nernstian electrode of this type is not as convenient a device as the other solid-state electrodes which have been discussed, because of its limited life. The precision with which analyses can be made, however, especially in dilute solutions, is as good as that obtained with other electrodes, and the cyanide electrode finds wide use in such applications as plating solution analysis and water pollution monitoring.

VII. Future Developments

In this presentation, I have discussed only two approaches to the construction of ion-selective devices — solid-state and liquid membrane electrodes. Glass and heterogeneous membranes are two other approaches which have received attention by other workers in recent years, and undoubtedly new and presently unsuspected materials will be uncovered in the future. I would like to close by giving my own, highly personal, estimation of what will be forthcoming during the next few years in each of these areas.

Glass membranes were the first ion-selective devices, and there is a history of at least thirty years of active research in the field of new and useful glass compositions for electrode use [12]. A large number of pH-sensitive compositions have been discovered, as well as several highly useful sodium ion-selective glasses. Unfortunately, the range of site types that can be incorporated in a silicate glass lattice is relatively small, due principally to the severe restrictions imposed by the high melting point of the glass. In view of the large amount of work that has already been devoted to this area and the limited range of available sites, I feel that there will be little forthcoming, at least as far as additions to the list of ions which can be detected. Undoubtedly though, new and better glass compositions, from the standpoint of chemical durability, strength, and absence of drift, will be discovered. Nonsilicate, organic glasses present an interesting alternative to silicate glasses, chiefly because of the much larger spectrum of sites that can be used, and this area deserves investigation.

In terms of the number of different ions that can be detected, the organic liquid membranes offer the most versatile approach to ion selectivity. Virtually any ion, mono- or polyvalent, cation or anion, can be determined with these systems. This versatility, however, is achieved at the expense of selectivity, which rarely reaches the high order of selectivity found in solid-state systems. Still, however, the selectivities are adequate for many analytical applications, and certainly many new electrodes of this type will become available in the near future. The principal problem in the liquid membrane field is, at present, the lack of data on complex ion stabilities in low dielectric constant solvents and on the mobilities of the various species which are formed in these solvents. These data are needed both for the intelligent selection of appropriate site groups for a given application and also for devising realistic models for the transport process and the testing of the theoretical equations which the models suggest.

Solid-state membranes made from crystalline materials have only recently received serious consideration. Development of new electrodes of this type will depend on finding new classes of ionically conducting materials. At the present time, only the rare-earth fluorides and the various silver salts show sufficient ionic mobility at room temperature to be useful as membrane materials, most crystals being good insulators. Unfortunately, our understanding of ionic conduction in the solid state and its relationship to crystal structure is very limited, making it impossible to predict if a known crystal will show useful electrode properties. The number of untried materials is vast, and the experimental process of evaluation is slow. Any large-scale breakthrough in this area will have to await a better theoretical understanding of solid-state ionic conduction, so that the intelligent screening of all the known insoluble crystalline materials can be made. It is probably safe to say that only small univalent ions can have a significant mobility in a crystal lattice at room temperature. Solid-state electrodes sensitive to polyvalent ions are unlikely to be found, and any advances in the search for solid-state sulfate or phosphate electrodes probably will be made *via* the establishment of a solubility equilibrium with a measurable monovalent ion.

Heterogeneous membrane electrodes in which a finely divided solid material is embedded in an inert, nonconducting matrix are difficult to classify. Membranes made from ionically conducting solids, such as the silver halides [13], are identical to the solid-state electrodes in both mechanism and electrode response to the mobile ion. For these membranes, the comments of the last paragraph apply. In addition, however, membranes have been described in which the suspended solid is a nonconductor, such as electrodes made with barium sulfate for which sulfate ion response has been reported [14]. Membranes made from nonconductive materials must operate by a surface conduction process on the interface between the dispersed solid and the inert matrix. Virtually nothing is known about this surface conduction process, and it is impossible to predict what further study will uncover. The surface conduction approach is an interesting one, and suggests also that ion diffusion in grain boundaries in other solid-state systems should be investigated.

In summary, I would point out that the past several years have seen the development of over twenty ion-selective electrodes. This represents the fruits of largely Edisonian research, and I would think that the rate of new electrode introduction will be much slower in the near future. Further advances must await a better theoretical understanding of the subject. This temporary hiatus can be used to good advantage by analytical chemists, however, since there remains much to be done in the application of the presently existing electrodes. These electrodes are currently being used in only a small fraction of the applications for which they have a potential use, both in research and in industry. The recent exponential increase in publication of electrode applications reflects this situation, and a still further increase is to be expected.

VIII. References

[1] Ross, J. W., Science **156**, 3780 (1967).

[2] Eisenman, G., Anal. Chem. **40**, 310 (1968).

[3] Kielland, J., J. Amer. Chem. Soc. **59**, 1675 (1937).

[4] Ross, J. W. and Frant, M. S., Liquid Ion Exchange Membrane Electrodes. Paper presented at Pittsburgh Conference on Analytical Chemistry and Applied Spectroscopy, March 1966.

[5] Carlson, R. M. and Paul, J. L., Anal. Chem. **40**, 1292 (1968).

[6] Frant, M. S. and Ross, J. W., Science **154**, 3756, (1966).

[7] Lingane, J. J., Anal. Chem. **39**, 881 (1967).

[8] Frant, M. S. and Ross, J. W., A New Electrode for Sulfide Activity. Paper presented at the Eastern Analytical Symposium, New York, November 1966. Rechnitz, G. A. and Hesu, T. M., Anal. Chem. **40**, 1054 (1968).

[9] Kolthoff, I. M. and Sanders, H. L., J. Amer. Chem. Soc. **59**, 416 (1937).

[10] Ross, J.W. and Frant, M. S. Use of New Ion-Selective Membrane Electrodes for Titrations of Copper, Lead and Cadmium Paper presented at Pittsburgh Conference on Analytical Chemistry and Applied Spectroscopy, March, 1969.

[11] Ross, J. W. and Frant, M. S., The Mechanism of Interference at Solid-State Ion-Selective Electrodes. Paper presented at Pittsburgh Conference on Analytical Chemistry and Applied Spectroscopy, March, 1968.

[12] Glass Electrodes for Hydrogen and Other Cations. G. Eisenman, Ed., Marcel Dekker, Inc., New York, 1967.

[13] Pungor, E., Havas, J., and Toth, K., Z. Chem. **1**, 9 (1965).

[14] Rechnitz, G. A., Lin, Z. F., and Zamochnick, S. B., Anal. Lett. **1**, 29 (1967).

CHAPTER 3

HETEROGENEOUS MEMBRANE ELECTRODES

Arthur K. Covington

Department of Physical Chemistry
School of Chemistry
University of Newcastle
Newcastle upon Tyne, England

I. Introduction

The subject of the development of electrical potentials across membranes has received much attention over the past seventy years, principally because of its importance in biological processes. The subject has been extensively reviewed recently from different standpoints [1-3] and it is not the intention to provide an extensive historical review here. It is important to realize, however, that a wide range of membrane types is possible, from material with pores of several times ionic dimensions, impeding the flow of solutions, to membranes in which equilibria are separately developed on two surfaces and electronic or ionic conduction processes in the solid are responsible for linking these. In between these extremes, the terms semipermeable and permselective are used to describe membrane behavior; the unqualified general use of the word membrane must not, however, be construed as implying any connotation as to the mechanism of its operation. As will be emphasized later, it is dangerous to make inferences about the operation of one particular type of membrane and the mechanism of the setting up of a potential difference across it, from the properties of another type.

Recent developments in ion-selective electrodes culminating in their commercial availability, can be directly traced to the work of Marshall on zeolite and clay membranes, of Tendeloo on natural heavy spar ($BaSO_4$) and fluorite (CaF_2) membranes, and of Michaelis and of Sollner on collodion membranes, to mention only a few of the principal workers in a vast literature.

II. The Development of Heterogeneous Membrane Electrodes

A useful distinction can be made between homogeneous and heterogeneous membranes. In the latter, which are our concern here, an inert binder material is used to form the membrane and give it the required mechanical properties. The new solid-state membrane electrodes, part of the subject of Chapter 2 [4], come into the first category, and perhaps are to be regarded as a more perfect form of the latter. However, it may not always be feasible to obtain a material in the requisite single crystal or fused form, and it may be possible to control more easily the properties of the dispersed material. The two types are therefore to be regarded essentially as complementary.

Although the role of the binder material is simply to provide an inert matrix in which the material of interest is embedded, its properties are obviously important. It must first be chemically inert, and provide the correct adhesion properties with the particles. Paraffin wax and collodion have already been mentioned as binder materials but polyvinyl chloride (PVC), polystyrene, polyethylene and most important, silicone rubber have been used. The latter has ideal hydrophobic qualities and its flexibility and resistance to cracking and to swelling in aqueous solution make it the most valuable material yet found. This fact, alone, has led to the commercial developments.

It is worth distinguishing between the types of material that have been dispersed in an inert matrix and the properties and uses of the electrodes thus formed:

A. ION-EXCHANGE RESINS

Wyllie and Patnode [5] were the first workers to embed ion exchange resins in an inert binder to achieve robust membranes. Since then, the technique has received much attention. Recent work includes that of Bose [6], Basu [7], Hale and McCauley [8], and Joshi and Suryanarayana [9]. Parsons [10] showed that Amberlite IR 120 dispersed in polystyrene and soaked in sodium chloride solution gave a sodium ion response. However, the most extensive studies have been those of Pungor and his collaborators [11-13] who have prepared ion-exchange resin electrodes based on silicone rubber which show response to sulfate, chloride, hydroxide, hydrogen, potassium, zinc and nickel. "Complexonite" (ion-exchange resin containing imino diacetic acid groups) membranes were also investigated in the case of zinc, nickel and aluminum. It was concluded [13] that all these membranes are selective to ion valence type only and not to individual ions. Some interesting experiments were carried out with silver, platinum or mercury between two rubber membranes which showed that diffusion potential effects could thereby be reduced.

B. PRECIPITATE TYPE

The materials used include sparingly soluble metal salts and a few metal chelates. Table 1 gives a summary of the principal developments in the field. The literature tends to be full of contradictory conclusions, and this is indicative of factors which are not known to, or fully under the control of, the investigators.

Table 1. Summary of the development of precipitate–type membrane electrodes.

Workers	Reference no.	Active material	Matrix	Sensitive to	Nernst slope and solution media	Selectivity	Comments
Tendeloo and Krips (1957)	[14, 15]	Calcium oxalate and other calcium salts	Paraffin + non-ionic detergent on gauze	Ca^{2+}	Calcium nitrate	"Fairly acceptable"	Criticised by Shatkay [19]
Tendeloo and Krips (1959)	[16]	Potassium tetraphenylborate	Polystyrene + gauze	K^+	Various	Not selective	
Tendeloo and van der Voort (1960)	[17]	Calcium stearate	Paraffin as above	Ca^{2+}		Stronger response to Ca^{2+} than oxalate electrode. No response to K^+	
Cloos and Fripiat (1961)	[18]	Calcium oxalate	Paraffin + detergent	Ca^{2+} ?	Various	Non-specific, porous	"Exhibit memory"
Fischer and Babcock (1958	[21]	Barium sulfate / Barium chromate	Paraffin without gauze	Ba^{2+} / SO_4^{2-}	Barium chloride and hydroxide, sulfuric acid	Not perfectly selective to either anions or cations	Slow to attain equilibrium
Pungor and Hollos-Rokosinyi (1961)	[26]	Silver iodide	Paraffin	I^-		Potassium chloride does not interfere	±5 mV reproducibility
Pungor, Toth and Havas (1964)	[11, 12]	Barium sulfate / Silver iodide	Silicone rubber	SO_4^{2-} / I^-	Potassium sulfate (24–30 mV) / Potassium iodide (56–60 mV)	Phosphate interferes 10^{-1} M KCl does not interfere	
Pungor, Havas and Toth (1965)	[25]	Silver halides / Manganese (III) phosphate / Aluminum oxine / Nickel DMG	Silicone rubber	Ag^+, X^- / PO_4^{3-} / Al^{3+}? / Ni^{2+}?			No details
Geyer and Syring (1966)	[23]	TiO_2, Fe_2O_3, SnO_2 / ZrO_2 / Al_2O_3 / K_2SiF_6 / $Ag_4Fe(CN)_6$ / $PbWO_4$	Polyethylene / Polypropylene / Paraffin / Agar or paper / Agar / Paraffin	H^+, OH^- / Na^+ / SiF_6^{2-} and K^+ both ions / both ions			Titrations only studied

Table 1. Summary of the development of precipitate–type membrane electrode (continued).

Workers	Reference no.	Active material	Matrix	Sensitive to	Nernst slope and solution media	Selectivity	Comments
Morazzani-Pelletier and Baffier (1965)	[24]	$Co_2(PO_4)_3$ NiDMG Mn(II) oxalate Ni(II) oxalate	Collodion Paraffin		20–23 mV in Cobalt chloride, bromide and nitrate. Poor response in sulfate and acetate	Levelled by Potassium chloride, Lithium sulfate	Porous membranes
Shatkay (1967)	[19]	Calcium oxalate	Paraffin + non-ionic detergent + gauze	Ca^{2+}	Calcium chloride (15–20 mV)	Not completely permselective; not specific	Gauze necessary for conduction. No difference between pure paraffin and paraffin + calcium oxalate
		thenoyltri-fluoroacetone	PVC + tributyl-phosphate	Ca^{2+}	Calcium chloride (27–28 mV)	Selective up to 0.1 M Mg, Na chlorides	Compared well with commercial liquid ion exchanger electrode
Buchanan and Seago (1968)	[20]	Barium sulfate	Paraffin, silicone rubber	Divalent ions	36 mV	Respond to total free cations	Conditioning very important, crystalline form, hydration, and anion not important
		NiDMG $Co_3(PO_4)_2$, $Ni_3(PO_4)_2$ $CuHPO_4$, $MnHPO_4$ $MnCO_3$			nil $\left.\right\}$ 20–30 mV		
Macdonald and Toth (1968)	[27]	CaF_2	Silicone rubber	F^-	35–50 mV	Selective response to F^-	
		ThF_4 LaF_3			— 53 mV in Potassium fluoride + Potassium chloride (pF 2–4 only)	Not reproducible Selective response to F^-	
Pungor, Schmidt and Toth (1968)	[46]	Ag_2S	Silicone rubber	Ag^+, S^{2-}	Na_2S in 0.1 M NaOH	Unaffected by Cl^-, Br^-, I^-	

Tendeloo and Krips [14-16] studied paraffin membranes incorporating calcium oxalate, a non-ionic detergent and gauze on which the membrane was supported. Some degree of calcium ion response was claimed, and the calcium stearate electrode [17] was investigated. Their conclusions about the specificity of these electrodes were challenged by Cloos and Fripiat [18] who found the calcium oxalate-paraffin electrode to be porous and non-specific. Shatkay confirmed this [19] and found a pure paraffin electrode to give the same response as the calcium oxalate-paraffin electrode. He found that gauze was necessary to make the membrane conducting and therefore played an important role in the mechanism. The conductance could also be increased by greatly increasing the proportion of calcium oxalate in the binder. Pungor [11] has suggested that Tendeloo's results were vitiated by the small amount of active material used. Pungor, Toth, and Havas [11] maintain, however, that paraffin and silicone rubber based electrodes have both proved to be perfectly permselective. Buchanan and Seago [20] considered that microcracks were responsible for the functioning of paraffin membrane electrodes. Fischer and Babcock [21], who also dispensed with the gauze in the preparation of barium sulfate-paraffin membranes, concluded that their membranes were not perfectly permselective to either cations or anions. Even so, they considered that such electrodes could be useful indicators for potentiometric titrations involving barium or sulfate ions. Radiochemical studies showed that barium ions were immobile but that sodium or chloride ions could migrate through the membrane in about 15 minutes. Hirsch-Ayalon [22] prepared barium sulfate cellophane membranes by placing barium hydroxide on one side of the membrane and sulfuric acid on the other.

Geyer and Syring [23] investigated the properties of some hydrated oxides dispersed in paraffin or polyethylene and their suitability as electrodes for potentiometric titrations. Transition metal salts such as phosphates of cobalt, nickel, copper and manganese in paraffin, collodion and silicone rubber have variously been studied by Morazzani-Pelletier and Baffier [24], and by Buchanan and Seago [20]. These latter workers found that the crystalline form, the degree of hydration and the anion of the active material had little or no effect on the membrane electrode response or selectivity. All the electrodes proved to be non-specific, responding to the total ion content whether this was divalent or univalent ions.

Results obtained using metal chelates as active material are discrepant. Geyer and Syring [23] were unable to repeat the work of Pungor and Toth [28] with nickel-responsive electrodes formed using nickel dimethylglyoxime (NiDMG), but the latter workers claimed theoretical response for only 6% of the electrodes prepared and only 30% showed any response at all. Buchanan and Seago [20] also found no response with NiDMG or with nickel acetylacetonate dihydrate. Geyer and Syring [23] report successful potentiometric titration experiments with membranes containing potassium hexafluorosilicate, silver ferrocyanide and lead tungstate.

The first studies of Pungor and his collaborators [26] were with silver iodide paraffin membranes, but since then he has exclusively used silicone-rubber based membranes containing, for example, silver halides, sulfide and barium sulfate. Macdonald and Toth [27] have studied the possibility of obtaining selective fluoride response from lanthanum, thorium or calcium fluoride impregnated silicone rubber electrodes. More details of the work mentioned in this paragraph will be given in Section C.

A study which may indicate a useful line for further research is that of Shatkay [19] with solid polymeric membranes of PVC containing tributyl phosphate and 2-thenoyltrifluoracetone (TTA). The latter is a chelating agent and perhaps surprisingly it does not seem that TTA is incorporated as its calcium enolate form. Shatkay found that the TTA polymeric membrane and the Orion liquid ion-exchanger electrode gave comparable results.

C. OTHER MATERIALS

It is appropriate to mention here silicone-rubber based electrodes containing graphite, carbides, borides and silicides which have recently received attention as possible improved-form electrodes for redox potentiometric titrations and voltammetry. The graphite impregnated electrode has been introduced by Pungor, Szepesvary and Havas [29] for voltammetry where it appears to offer advantages. It is commercially available. Some applications have been discussed by Farsang [30]. Weser and Pungor [31] have investigated the suitability of a very large number of carbides, borides and silicides as redox electrodes for the ferrocyanide-ferricyanide system as judged by the potential compared with a graphite or platinum electrode in the same solution and the response time. They point out that nearly all the suitable materials possess simple face-centered cubic crystal structures but the significance of this observation is not known.

III. Properties of the Most Useful Electrode Systems

A. PREPARATION

The properties of the active material are obviously of critical importance to the functioning of the membrane electrode. The most important properties appear to be grain size, crystalline form, conditions of precipitation (which reagent in excess) and solubility product. Macdonald and Toth [27] approached this problem from the viewpoint that a good precipitate for gravimetric analysis will be a good active material for a membrane electrode. For barium sulfate and silver chloride electrodes, the precipitates were prepared with an excess of anion [32]. For lanthanum fluoride, the opposite is necessary [27]. For silver iodide, it does not appear to matter. The optimum grain size is in the region 1-15 μm. Precipitation in the presence of p-ethoxychrysoidine retards secondary nucleation. Optimum proportion of active material to binder is about 50 wt %; the essential feature to the successful functioning of the electrode being that the particles of the active material should be in contact in order to achieve conduction through the membrane. Whether this conduction is achieved **through** the particles or over their surface is a moot point.

Full details of the membrane preparation have not been published but the following may be typical [33]. The active material is dispersed in polysiloxane in a laboratory mixer. Homogenization is carried out in a small roller mill and, at this stage, the cross-linking agent (silane derivative) and catalyst are added. The degree of cross linking determines how well the particles remain embedded in the surface of the final membrane, which is now formed by calendering. The cured membrane is removed from the roller, and discs are cut from it. Discs about 0.3-0.5 mm thick are secured into the ends of glass tubes using silicone rubber adhesive. Buchanan and Seago [20] used simply a room temperature vulcanized silicone rubber (General Electric, "Clear Seal"), which was mixed with finely powdered active material and pressed between a heavy polyethylene plate and a PVC sheet to give a 0.5 mm thick sheet.

Subsequent conditioning of the membrane is important [20] and a few hours' soaking in an appropriate solution is suggested. An internal reference electrode is necessary, and the solution must contain one of the ions of the active material. Thus, for the iodide electrode, a conventional silver iodide electrode in potassium iodide solution is used or a silver wire in silver nitrate solution for the sulfide electrode.

B. SILVER HALIDE ELECTRODES

A few results obtained with the chloride electrode were presented by Pungor, Havas and Toth [12] and with the iodide electrode by Pungor, Toth and Havas [11]. More detailed results with the bromide and chloride electrodes were given by Havas, Papp and Pungor [32]. Independent appraisal of the commercial forms of these electrodes has been carried out by Rechnitz, Kresz and Zamochnick [34] (iodide) and by Rechnitz and Kresz [35] (chloride and bromide). Published information on the commercial forms is summarized in Table 2 and some applications given in Table 3. Pungor [36] has presented a general review of his work

Table 2. Characteristics of commercially available heterogeneous membrane (Pungor–type) electrodes.[a]

Electrode	Type no.	Measurement pIon range	Selectivity	Temperature range	Suggested pre–treatment
Iodide Selective	OP–I–711	1 – 7 pI 1 – 5 pAg 1 – 5 pCN (pH >11)	Concentration not to exceed: 10^{-1} M KCl 10^{-1} M KBr 1 M K_2SO_4 1 M KNO_3 2< pH < 12	5 – 50 °C	1 – 2 hours in 10^{-1} – 10^{-3} M KI
Bromide Selective	OP–Br–711	1 – 6 pBr	Concentration not to exceed: 10^{-1} M KCl 1 M K_2SO_4 1 M KNO_3 2< pH < 12	5 – 50 °C	1 – 2 hours in 10^{-1} – 10^{-3} M KBr
Chloride Selective	OP–Cl–711	1 – 5 pCl	Concentration not to exceed: 1 M K_2SO_4 1 M KNO_3 2< pH < 12	5 – 50 °C	1 – 2 hours in 10^{-1} – 10^{-3} M KCl
Sulfide Selective	OP–S–711	1 – 17 pS	No interference from: I^-, Br^-, Cl^-, NO_3^-, SO_3^{2-}, PO_4^{3-} or from CN^- if ten times less than S^{2-} concentration	5 – 50 °C	1 – 2 hours in 10^{-1} – 10^{-3} M $AgNO_3$
Carbon Voltammetric	OP–VM–711	1 – 5 pOx(Red)	–		
Carbon Potentiometric	OP–C–711	1 – 4 pOx(Red)	–	5 – 90 °C	1 hour in distilled water

[a] Information derived from the brochures of Radelkis Electrochemical Instruments, Budapest II, Hungary.

Table 3. Some applications of Pungor–type membrane electrodes.

Chloride Electrode   Determination of organic bases through their
                                        hydrochlorides;
                                    Chloride in urine and horse blood serum.

Iodide Electrode   Titration of mixed halides;
                                    Iodide content of Hungarian mineral waters;
                                    Sulfur dioxide determination by iodine–iodide;
                                    Cyanide content of amygdalin by hydrolysis;
                                    Cyanide content of sewage, brandies, peach
                                        leaves;
                                    Anodic corrosion of silver.

Sulfide Electrode   Titration of mixed halides;
                                    Sulfide content of waste liquor of sulfate
                                        paper pulp production;
                                    Sulfide content of brine liquors used for
                                        dehairing leather.

up to June 1967. In this paper, results are presented graphically for the calibration of the silver halide electrodes. Linear response is shown between pX 1-4 for chloride and bromide, and pX 1-5 for iodide with a slope of about 56 mV/pX (concentration). Rechnitz et al. [34,35] obtained the following results from the commercial forms: 56 ± 3 mV/pI (iodide, pI 1-6); 53.6 mV/pBr (bromide, pBr 1-3.5); 55 mV/pCl (chloride, pCl 1-3). The electrodes also respond to silver ion (57 mV/pAg;pAg 1-4; chloride electrode [36]). Overall reproducibility is about 1 mV. The only effect of cations on the calibration curve is through the different mean ionic activity coefficients. This was shown by Rechnitz, Kresz and Zamochnick [34] for the iodide electrode in the presence of potassium, barium and cerium iodides. As expected, the deviations at low pI are greatest for the cerium salt.

The lower limit of detection of the electrodes for halide ions will depend upon the solubility product of the precipitate. This problem is akin to that of the excessive solubility of material from electrodes of the second kind [37]. An additional potential term $(RT/F) \ln (1 + S/C)$ will arise where S is the solubility of the silver halide in the halide solution of concentration, C. When $S = C/10$, the additional term will be 2.4 mV, which is about detectable as a deviation from a linear calibration curve. Since the solubility product of the silver halide (K_{sp}) is given approximately by

$$K_{sp} = S(S + C)$$

then solving the quadratic gives $C = (9.1 \ K_{sp})^{1/2}$. Thus $C = 3 \times 10^{-8} M$ for silver iodide, $2.7 \times 10^{-6} M$ for silver bromide and $3.8 \times 10^{-5} M$ for silver chloride. This method is simpler and hence preferable to that of Pungor, Toth and Havas [38; see also 32,36].

Havas, Papp and Pungor [32] have studied the effect of another halide solution on the chloride and bromide electrodes, and Rechnitz et al. [34,35] have studied all three electrodes. Rechnitz [39] expresses the selectivity for one ion over another in terms of Equation (1)

$$E = \text{constant} + (RT/F) \ln (a_{Br} + K_{Br,Cl} a_{Cl}) \qquad (1)$$

written for chloride and bromide ions in terms of their activities, where $K_{Br, Cl}$ is the selectivity constant. This has the form of the original equation of Nicolsky based on his ion-exchange theory of the glass electrode [40], but it is sometimes called the simplified Eisenman equation [41]. If measurements are made in two solutions each containing one of the cations only, at say $0.1 M$, then

$$E_{(0.1M KCl)} - E_{(0.1M KBr)} = (RT/F) \ln \left[K_{Br, Cl} \left(\frac{a_{Cl}}{a_{Br}} \right) \right] \qquad (2)$$

hence the selectivity constant can be determined as $a_{Cl}/a_{Br} \approx 1$. From this equation, Rechnitz's definition [34,39] of selectivity arises as the ratio of the chloride ion concentration to the bromide ion concentration to yield the same emf under otherwise identical conditions. The above is also the method used by Eisenman [41] to determine selectivity constants for aluminosilicate glasses showing mixed sodium-hydrogen ion response. The same definition can, of course, be used for anion-selective electrodes. In this way, Rechnitz et al. [34,35] have derived selectivity ratios for the Pungor type silver halide electrodes as shown in Table 4.

Pungor et al. [32,36,42] have given a generalized equation, which for a bromide electrode in the presence of several anions, i, (including bromide) takes the form:

$$E = \text{constant} + (RT/F) \ln a_{Br} \sum_i K_{Br,i} \left(\frac{a_i}{a_{Br}} \right) \tag{3}$$

We have retained the same example as before for clarity. As for the glass electrode, the selectivity constant is interpreted in terms of the equilibrium constant for the exchange process:

$$AgBr\ (s) + Cl^- \rightleftharpoons AgCl\ (s) + Br^-$$

for which $K_{Br,Cl} = K_{sp}\ (AgBr)/K_{sp}\ (AgCl)$ in this special case.

But

$$K_{Br,\ Cl} = \frac{A_{Cl} a_{Br}}{A_{Br} a_{Cl}} \tag{4}$$

writing A_{Cl}, A_{Br} for the ionic activities in the solid.

If

$$E = \text{constant} + (RT/F)\ \ln \frac{a_{Br}}{A_{Br}} \tag{5}$$

represents the potential arising across the outer surface of the membrane by virtue of the equality of electrochemical potentials, then substitution may be made for A_{Br}. However, following Nicolsky's treatment [40] and writing concentrations for activities in the solid, then $C_{Cl} = C_0 - C_{Br}$, where C_0 is the total anion concentration (the concentration of exchangeable sites on the glass surface in Nicolsky's theory). Accordingly,

$$K_{Br,\ Cl} = \left(\frac{C_0 - C_{Br}}{C_{Br}} \right) \left(\frac{a_{Br}}{a_{Cl}} \right) \tag{6}$$

and by substituting Equation (6) into Equation (5), there results

$$E = \text{constant} + \frac{RT}{F} \ln\ (a_{Br} + K_{Br,\ Cl} a_{Cl}) - \frac{RT}{F} \ln C_0 \tag{7}$$

which is identical with Equation (1) except for the last term which can be included in the constant. Equation (7), is also identical with Equation (3) written for bromide and chloride ions. Thus Pungor's Equation (3) and the Nicolsky-Eisenman Equation (1) are essentially the same, and the selectivity constant K has the same interpretation.

There appears to be some confusion whether the selectivity constant is to be written in terms of the equilibrium constant for the exchange process or its reciprocal. Nicolsky [40] originally used the latter. However, it is clear that $K_{ij} = 1/K_{ji}$, and Equations (1) and (3) have symmetrically related forms.

In Table 4, we compare the selectivity constants as defined above (the first mentioned ion is that of the precipitate embedded in the electrode membrane) obtained by Rechnitz and by Pungor and their respective coworkers. Pungor et al. [42] obtained their selectivity constants from the ratio of the concentration of the interfering ion to that of the ion to which the electrode is primarily responsive evaluated at the break in the calibration curve. Differences are no doubt a result of the different experimental approaches. It may be mentioned that Bishop and Dhaneshwar [43] have carried out similar experimental studies of the behavior of conventional silver halide electrodes in mixed halide solutions with somewhat analogous results.

Table 4.   Selectivity constants[a].

		Calc.[b]	Pungor et al. [36 ,42][c]	Rechnitz et al. [34, 35][d]
Bromide Electrode	$K_{Br, Cl}$	4.9×10^{-3}	1.5×10^{-3}	1.0×10^{-2}
Iodide Electrode	$K_{I, Br}$	1.3×10^{-4}	2×10^{-4}	4.8×10^{-3}

[a] Values are for the equilibrium constant of the exchange process

$$AgX \text{ (in electrode)} + Y^- \rightleftarrows AgY \text{ (contaminating } + X^-$$
$$\text{the electrode)}$$

[b] From solubility product ratio.

[c] Determined from the break in the emf curve; values (25 °C) are reciprocals of selectivity constants given in [36, 42]

[d] Determined from measurements in pure potassium halides at $0.1 M$ and 30 °C; values here are the reciprocals of the selectivity ratios given in [34, 35] .

The effect of anions which complex with silver, *e.g.*, CN^- and $S_2O_3^=$ has been studied [42]. All three electrodes respond to cyanide (Fig. 1). Rechnitz *et al.* [34] studied interferences by ferrocyanide, phosphate, perchlorate and sulfate on the iodide electrode; the effect diminishing in the order given. They pointed out that interferences were not simply a function of the solubilities of the respective silver salts. However, this conclusion is doubtful and may be a result of the method of determining the selectivity ratios, through Equation (1).

The response times of the electrodes have been studied by Rechnitz *et al.* [34,35] who find that the half times for response to a twofold change in anion concentration ranged from 8 seconds for the silver iodide electrode to 20 seconds for the silver chloride electrode. The response time of the iodide electrode in cyanide solutions is similar [42]. The successive

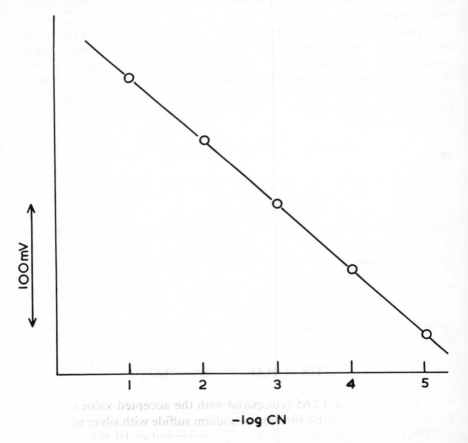

Figure 1.   Response of silver iodide electrode to cyanide ion (after [42]); Reference electrode: $KNO_3||KCl(sat)|Hg_2Cl_2$; Hg.

titration of chloride, bromide and iodide with the silver iodide electrode has been described [44]; the sulfide electrode is even more suitable for this purpose.

C. SULFATE AND PHOSPHATE ELECTRODES

The barium sulfate impregnated electrode was one of the first studied by Pungor and his collaborators [11-13]. The response, to changes in sulfate concentration in the range 10^{-1} - $10^{-6}M$, was encouraging (24-29 mV/pSO$_4$). However, some difficulties must be present, for this electrode has not yet appeared commercially, although Rechnitz, Lin and Zamochnick [45] have carried out appraisal studies of a prototype form. They found an approximately Nernstian response (31 mV/pSO$_4$) at concentrations of potassium sulfate above $10^{-4}M$. Chloride ions interfere when present above $10^{-3}M$.

A phosphate electrode consisting of bismuth phosphate as the active material [45] was similarly studied. The particular electrode used showed poor stability (drifting 1 mV/10 min even after extensive soaking). Even so, the titration curve of phosphoric acid with sodium hydroxide showed two inflections corresponding to the first and second dissociations of phosphoric acid. It seems likely that these two prototype electrodes were not representative.

D. SULFIDE ELECTRODE

The behavior of the sulfide electrode which consists of silver sulfide impregnated silicone rubber has been described by Pungor, Schmidt and Toth [46]. This electrode is probably one of the most important of the new ion-selective electrodes as the conventional silver-silver sulfide electrode does not appear to be well characterized [47] although at least one firm includes it in their catalogue of reference electrodes.

The sulfide membrane electrode gave a linear calibration curve (Fig. 2) in 0.5-$10^{-4}M$ sodium sulfide solutions containing $10^{-1}M$ sodium hydroxide. It also showed a linear response to silver ion in the range of pAg 1-5. Studies with $0.1M$ sodium sulfide solutions at different pH yielded a linear pH *versus* pS plot (Fig. 3) from which pK$_2$ for

$$HS^- + H_2O \;\rightleftharpoons\; S^= + H_3O^+$$

was evaluated to be 12.65 (compared with the accepted value of 12.92). From the potentiometric titration of sodium sulfide with silver nitrate, the solubility product of silver sulfide was estimated at $10^{-43.5}$. Hseu and Rechnitz [48], using the commercial solid-state electrode, found 1.5 $\times$ 10^{-51} for the solubility product. A detailed comparison of Hseu and

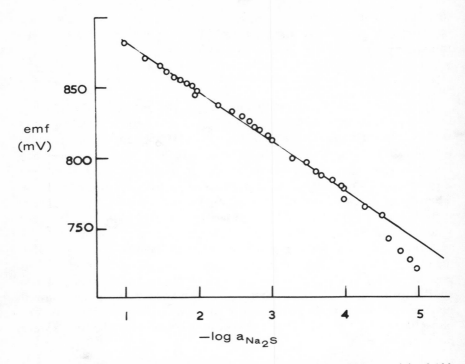

Figure 2. Calibration curve for silver sulfide electrode in sodium sulfide containing $0.1M$ NaOH (after [46]); Reference electrode: $KNO_3\|0.1M$ KCl|AgCl; Ag.

Rechnitz's appraisal [48] of the solid-state electrode and the above mentioned study of the heterogeneous membrane electrode is not possible from the results presented. However, Hseu and Rechnitz found a linear calibration curve down to pS = 7 for the solid-state electrode, whereas Pungor *et al.* [46] found that deviations commenced at pS = 4. This could be a liquid junction potential effect, since Hseu and Rechnitz added sodium nitrate to their sulfide solutions. A direct comparison of the two electrodes would be valuable, as indeed would be comparative studies of the solid-state halide electrodes with the corresponding heterogeneous membrane halide electrodes.

E. Fluoride Electrode

No commercial heterogeneous membrane fluoride selective electrode has yet appeared, but Macdonald and Toth [27] have published some developmental studies aimed in this direction which were commenced before the solid-state lanthanum fluoride electrode became available commercially.

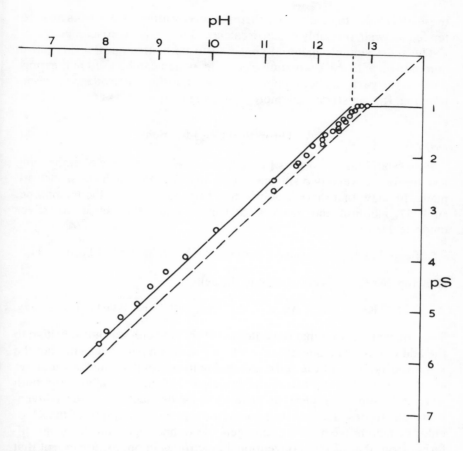

Figure 3. Relation between pH and sulfide concentration in sodium sulfide solutions (stoichiometric sulfide concentration $0.1M$) (after [46]); Reference electrode: $KNO_3||0.1M$ KCl|AgCl; Ag.

They selected thorium, calcium and the rare earth fluorides for study as being suitably insoluble. Detailed investigation of precipitation procedures was necessary since normal precipitates of these fluorides tend to be gelatinous. Electrodes prepared from lanthanum fluoride precipitated from sodium fluoride with a 30% excess of lanthanum acetate in the presence of p-ethoxychrysoidine gave reproducible and theoretical response over the range pF 2-4. Response times were rapid, but production success was unpredictable.

Calcium fluoride precipitates prepared under conditions of excess anion showed selective response to fluoride with 80% of the theoretical response over the range pF 2-4. Incorporating carbon with the precipitate extended the response to pF 5 and improved the response time. However, these electrodes tended to lose their sensitivity after a few weeks and also tended to swell, probably because calcium fluoride is hygroscopic.

The most suitable material appeared to be lanthanum fluoride but in comparison with the solid-state electrode, which can be used in the range pF 1-6, the performance of heterogeneous fluoride electrodes was disappointing. Recent studies are more promising [49].

IV. Theoretical Considerations

Pungor and his coworkers [11-12] have used the device of embedding a silver foil between two silicone rubber discs, from which electrodes are made, to show that there is no material transport through the membrane. In 1937, Kolthoff and Sanders [50] investigated the use of cast silver chloride discs in the cell:

Ag; AgCl | KCl | AgCl disc | AgNO$_3$ || KNO$_3$|| KCl(sat) | Hg$_2$Cl$_2$; Hg

showing that this was equivalent to the cells

Ag; AgCl | KCl | AgCl; Ag . . . . Ag; AgCl | KCl(sat) | Hg$_2$Cl$_2$; Hg.

They further showed that the potential of the first cell was not sensitive to the addition of oxidizing agents such as potassium permanganate, but the same was not true of the cell combination using conventional silver-silver chloride electrodes. This is the principal advantage claimed for both solid-state and heterogeneous membrane halide electrodes over conventional electrodes. The question then arises, is the functioning of the silver chloride membrane in either homogeneous or heterogeneous form any different from that of two conventional electrodes in opposition **except** that the silver wire is absent and conduction is provided within the silver chloride? One difference could lie in whether the silver halide coating on the electrode of the second kind is coherent or cracked and porous [51]. For adequate functioning of an electrode of the second kind, there need only be a saturated solution of the salt in contact with the metal.

Pungor et al. [36,42] discussed the mechanism of the formation of the membrane potential in terms of an exchange equilibrium and the distribution of ions across the inner and outer surfaces of the membrane as in Nicolsky's theory of the glass electrode (see Section III-B). Experiments with radiotracer iodide showed that the exchange was rapid. The silicone rubber matrix swells very slightly in water (0.1%), and this fact was interpreted in terms of the formation of a swollen layer on the membrane surface analogous to the silicic acid layer on the surface of the glass electrode. Such analogies are rather dangerous. That the correct form of Nernst-type equation, which expresses the experimental behavior of membrane electrodes, can be derived by purely thermodynamic means is no guarantee that any of the assumptions made about the processes responsible are valid. Different models may produce the same form of the equation. Further, the mechanisms involved with solid-state membranes, glass electrodes and ion exchange resin membranes may be different, while formally leading to the same **thermodynamic** equations.

Buck [52] has discussed the theory of solid-state membrane electrodes from the point of view of interface potentials and diffusion potentials in a way similar to what Eisenman has done for the glass electrode [53]. Diffusion potentials are zero under zero current conditions for pure crystalline membranes. Buck [52] also discusses the treatment of interferences and, in a second paper, the response under non-zero current conditions. The most important feedback from the successful application of theoretical principles to practical problems is the suggestion of new lines of investigation. A good example of this is the work of Eisenman on cation-responsive glass electrodes [53]. The successful explanation of already known facts is insufficient. At the present, however, the solution of problems associated with the production of heterogeneous membrane electrodes appears to require a better understanding of such properties of finely divided solid materials as conductivity, non-stoichiometry and defect structure and how these may be controlled by suitable preparative procedures, doping, *etc.* and which of them are critical for the production of successful electrodes.

V. Acknowledgment

I am grateful to Dr. A. M. G. Macdonald (Birmingham) and Dr. K. Toth (Veszprem) for reading and commenting on the manuscript.

VI. References

[1] Sollner, K., Ann. N. Y. Acad. Sci. **148**, 154 (1968).
[2] Hills, G. J., in Reference Electrodes, D. J. G. Ives and G. J. Janz, Eds., Academic Press, N. Y., 1961, pp. 411-432.
[3] Lakshminarayanaiah, N., Chem. Rev. **65**, 491 (1965).
[4] Ross, J. W., paper presented at the Symposium on Ion-Selective Electrodes, NBS, Jan. 30-31, 1969.
[5] Wyllie, M. R., and Patnode, H. W., J. Phys. Chem. **54**, 204 (1950).
[6] Bose, S. K., J. Indian Chem. Soc. **37**, 465 (1960).
[7] Basu, A. S., J. Indian Chem. Soc. **39**, 619 (1962); *ibid.* **35**, 451 (1958).
[8] Hale, D. K., and McCauley, D. J., Trans. Faraday Soc. **57**, 135 (1961).
[9] Joshi, K. M., and Suryanarayana, N. P., J. Indian Chem. Soc. **45**, 537 (1968).
[10] Parsons, J. S., Anal. Chem. **30**, 1262 (1958).
[11] Pungor, E., Toth, K., and Havas, J., Hung. Sci. Instr. **3**, 2 (1965).
[12] Pungor, E., Havas, J., and Toth, K., Acta Chim. Hung. **41**, 239 (1964).

[13] Pungor, E., and Havas, J., Acta Chim. Hung. 50, 77 (1966).
[14] Tendeloo, H. J. C., and Krips, A., Rec. Trav. Chim. 76, 703 (1957).
[15] Tendeloo, H. J. C., and Krips, A., Rec. Trav. Chim. 76, 946 (1957).
[16] Tendeloo, H. J. C., and Krips, A., Rec. Trav. Chim. 78, 177 (1959).
[17] Tendeloo, H. J. C., and van der Voort, F. H., Rec. Trav. Chim. 79, 639 (1960).
[18] Cloos, P., and Fripiat, J. J., Bull. Soc. Chim. Fr. 423 (1960).
[19] Shatkay, A., Anal. Chem. 39, 1056 (1967); Bloch, R., Shatkay, A., and Saroff, H. A., Biophys. J. 7, 865 (1967).
[20] Buchanan, E. B., and Seago, J. L., Anal. Chem. 40, 517 (1968).
[21] Fischer, R. B., and Babcock, R. F., Anal. Chem. 30, 1732 (1958).
[22] Hirsch-Ayalon, P., J. Polym. Sci. 23, 697 (1957); Rec. Trav. Chim. 79, 382 (1960).
[23] Geyer, R., and Syring, W., Z. Chem. 6, 92 (1966).
[24] Morazzani-Pelletier, S., and Baffier, M. A., J. Chim. Phys. 62, 429 (1965).
[25] Pungor, E., Havas, J., and Toth, K., Z. Chem. 5, 9(1965).
[26] Pungor, E., and Hollos-Rokosinyi, E., Acta Chim. Hung. 27, 63 (1961).
[27] Macdonald, A. M. G., and Toth, K., Anal. Chim. Acta 41, 99 (1968).
[28] Pungor, E., and Toth, K., Mikrochim. Acta, 565 (1964).
[29] Pungor, E., Szepesvary, E., and Havas, J., Anal. Lett. 1, 213 (1968); also Pungor, E., and Szepesvary, E., Anal. Chim. Acta 43, 289 (1968).
[30] Farsang, G., Hung. Sci. Instr. 12, 22 (1968).
[31] Weser, A., and Pungor, E., Proc. IMEKO Symposium on Electrochemical Sensors, Veszprem, Hungary, 1968, pp.99-110.
[32] Havas, J., Papp, E., and Pungor, E., Magy. Kem. Foly. 73, 292 (1967).
[33] Havas, J., and Pungor, E., Proc. IMEKO Symposium on Electrochemical Sensors, Veszprem, Hungary, 1968, pp. 79-88.
[34] Rechnitz, G. A., Kresz, M. R., and Zamochnick, S. B., Anal. Chem. 38, 973 (1966).
[35] Rechnitz, G. A., and Kresz, M. R., Anal. Chem. 38, 1787 (1966).
[36] Pungor, E., Anal. Chem. 39, 29A (1967).
[37] Covington, A. K., paper presented at the Symposium on Ion-Selective Electrodes, NBS, Jan. 30-31, 1969.
[38] Pungor, E., Toth, K., and Havas, J., Mikrochim. Acta, 689 (1966).
[39] Rechnitz, G. A., Chem. Eng. News 45, 146 (1967).
[40] Nicolsky, B. P., Acta Physicochim. USSR 7, 597 (1937); see also Isard, J. O., in Glass Electrodes for Hydrogen and Other Cations, G. Eisenman, Ed., Dekker, New York, p. 64.
[41] Eisenman, G., Rudin, D. O., and Casby, J. U., Science 126, 831 (1957).
[42] Toth, K., and Pungor, E., Proc. IMEKO Symposium on Electrochemical Sensors, Veszprem, Hungary, 1968, pp. 35-50.
[43] Bishop, E., and Dhaneshwar, R. G., Analyst (London) 88; 424; 432; 442 (1963).
[44] Csakvari, B., and Meszaros, K., Hung. Sci. Instr. 11, 9 (1968).
[45] Rechnitz, G. A., Lin, Z. F., and Zamochnick, S. B., Anal. Lett. 1, 29 (1967).
[46] Pungor, E., Schmidt, E., and Toth, K., Proc. IMEKO Symposium on Electrochemical Sensors, Veszprem, Hungary, 1968, pp. 121-134.
[47] Ives, D. J. G., in Reference Electrodes, D. J. G. Ives and G. J. Janz, Eds., Academic Press, New York, pp. 381-383.
[48] Hseu, T-M., and Rechnitz, G. A., Anal. Chem. 40, 1055 (1968).
[49] Macdonald, A. M. G., private communication, 1968.
[50] Kolthoff, I. M., and Sanders, H. L., J. Amer. Chem. Soc. 59, 416 (1937).
[51] Janz, G. J., and Ives, D. J. G., Ann. N. Y. Acad. Sci. 148, 210 (1968).
[52] Buck, R. P., Anal. Chem. 40, 1432; 1439 (1968).
[53] Eisenman, G., in Glass Electrodes for Hydrogen and Other Cations, G. Eisenman, Ed., Dekker, New York, 1967, Chapter 9.

CHAPTER 4

REFERENCE ELECTRODES

Arthur K. Covington

Department of Physical Chemistry
School of Chemistry
University of Newcastle
Newcastle upon Tyne, England

I. Introduction

A two electrode system is the *sine qua non* of all measurements on electrochemical cells, but usually interest is directed more toward one electrode than the other; this other is called the **reference** electrode, and it is mandatory that its function should be thoroughly understood.

To judge from reading the literature on ion-selective electrodes, too often the **only** reference electrode used is the saturated or $3.5M$ KCl calomel, perhaps with an additional salt bridge if chloride is incompatible with the test solution. It is assumed to be an electrode of invariant (fixed) potential with no variation of liquid junction potential when the test solution is varied or replaced by a standard or calibrating solution. For initial appraisal of a new electrode and many other purposes, this procedure may be adequate, but the reference electrode must not be considered unimportant in spite of temptation to do so. In fact, it is significant that in commercial practice, trouble shooting of pH problems reveals that it is the users' lack of attention to the reference electrode aspect of control processes which is the cause of much malfunctioning.

With most ion-selective electrodes, the effective operational range is restricted to four or five decades of concentration (~ 300 mV for a univalent ion), whereas in the familiar case of pH measurements about a dozen decades or some 720 mV are involved. With divalent ion responsive electrodes the millivolt range is further reduced by a factor of two. Invariably, with the new ion-selective electrodes, measurements are required with greater precision than for most pH measurements and reference electrode considerations cannot be disregarded.

As indicated above, a reference electrode will be defined as the electrode which is not of primary interest in the cell. A monograph with the title *Reference Electrodes* appeared in 1961 which provided a valuable critical compilation of the properties of many electrode systems [1]. The editors' definition of a reference electrode was somewhat broader than that adopted here, being effectively any electrode used in combination to obtain thermodynamic information. In this context, the properties of

107

348–381 O–69—9

nearly all known electrode systems apart from metal-metal ion and certain amalgam-metal ion electrodes were exhaustively reviewed [1]. Consequently, the discussion in this chapter will be restricted to points particularly pertinent to ion-selective electrodes. The essential features of the most important reference electrode systems will be outlined and work since 1961 reviewed in some detail. First, however, we shall discuss the methods of utilizing the available reference electrodes in cells of various designs. In the final section, the problems of liquid junction potentials and of temperature effects in non-isothermal cells will be discussed.

Janz and Ives [2] have given the three main requirements for satisfactory reference electrode systems: 1) reversibility, 2) reproducibility, and 3) stability, which are, as they state, interrelated quantities. The quantitative measure of the first of these is the exchange current; unless a reference electrode has a high exchange current, its potential will depart from its equilibrium value when current demands are made upon it. These will depend on the measuring circuit in potentiometric applications and may become important for miniature electrodes and at low concentrations of the potential-determining ion. Reproducibility covers two aspects: the ability of a particular electrode specimen to respond according to the Nernst equation without temperature- (or concentration-) change hysteresis, and the feasibility of establishing a standard method of electrode preparation, which will produce electrodes on one or many occasions that group acceptably about a mean potential, *i.e.*, show small bias potentials. The third requirement, stability, is self explanatory, referring also to the useful life of an electrode system. How closely it is necessary to satisfy these three basic requirements depends upon the use to which the reference electrode is put; which we will consider in the next section. For example, it may be possible to tolerate slow changes in the standard potential of electrodes (*e.g.*, aging of silver-silver chloride electrodes) if this process is slow compared with the time of measurements.

II.   Classification of Reference Electrodes and Their Usage

Most of the reference electrodes to be considered in this chapter are electrodes of the second kind, that is, anion reversible. Included in this category is the case where the metal is amalgamated. There are, apart from the hydrogen electrode and perhaps the quinhydrone electrode which is largely out of favor in the West, few cation-responsive reference electrodes. Such cation-response electrodes that are well behaved tend to be of specialized usefulness, *e.g.*, $Hg_2^{2+}|Hg$, $Ag^+|Ag$, $Pb^{2+}|Pb(Hg)$, and $Cd^{2+}|Cd(Hg)$. The alkali-metal amalgam electrodes would be of considerable use if it were not for their disadvantage of hydrogen evolution. However, these amalgam electrodes have received more attention recently [3,4]. Sodium- and potassium-responsive glass electrodes are a better proposition but only under limited circumstances could they be considered as reference electrodes.

Anion-reversible electrodes are more generally useful than cation-responsive reference electrodes, but even so the absence of nitrate and perchlorate reversible conventional systems makes the choice somewhat restricted. This is presumably one reason for the attractiveness of electrodes of fixed potential such as the saturated calomel, particularly in its commercial forms. The utility of this electrode for pH measurements should not, however, make it a universal choice for ion-selective electrode measurements, since the problem of the reference electrode to use is basically one of cell design. With particular relevance to ion-selective electrodes, we shall now consider six methods of reference electrode usage.

A. INTERNAL REFERENCE ELECTRODES FOR ION-SELECTIVE ELECTRODES

Ion-selective electrodes and the glass electrode in particular are actually electrode assemblies, in which a stable inner reference system is required. It seems to be essential that a well-defined potential determining process takes place at the inside surface of the ion-selective "membrane," but mercury has proved satisfactory in the case of the glass electrode [5,6] and a solid silver chloride coating has been described [7]. The silver-silver chloride electrode in hydrochloric acid or in a chloride-containing buffer solution is commonly used for hydrogen-responsive glass electrodes, and sodium-responsive electrodes function with an acid filling not containing sodium ions, because the glass shows some hydrogen ion function at low pH. The question of the solvent used for the inner reference solution of the glass electrode, when it is to be used in partially aqueous media, has received some attention recently by several French workers [8-10] and by Ritchie and his collaborators [11]. Bottom and Covington [6] have recently investigated this problem with the surprising findings that the potential difference on transferring a glass electrode between two partially aqueous solutions can depend on the solvent of the inner solution. This may have some implications for work on the newer ion-selective electrodes.

The silver-silver chloride electrode is used for some ion-selective electrodes. For example, in the lanthanum fluoride electrode [12], the internal system is

$$Ag; AgCl|NaCl, NaF|LaF_3$$

However, for some electrodes a cation-responsive internal reference is used, e.g.,

$$Ag \mid AgNO_3 \mid Ag_2S.$$

When there is an alternative between a possible cation or anion system, there may be a difference in behavior which could be significant of the mechanistic process involved at the "membrane."

B. Use of Reference Electrodes for Direct Comparison with an Ion-Selective Electrode Supposedly Reversible to the Same Ionic Species

The only unequivocal way of showing that a new electrode responds to a certain ion, that does not require knowledge of activity coefficients, is by a direct check against another electrode responsive to the same ion. This technique has been used with hydrogen-responsive glass electrodes (*e.g.,* [6,13]). The emf of the cell

$$glass \mid X \mid H_2; Pt$$

should be the same irrespective of X, provided it contains hydrogen ions, if the glass electrode is behaving solely as a hydrogen ion responsive electrode. If X contains sodium ions and at high pH the electrode shows some sodium function, then there will be some change in emf. A similar technique has been employed to determine the silver response of glass electrodes using the silver electrode [14], and the sodium response using a sodium amalgam electrode [15]. The deuterium gas electrode has been used [16] to check the deuterium ion function of hydrogen ion responsive glass electrodes. This technique has not been sufficiently explored with the new ion-selective electrodes, apart from the work of Alfenaar and Bates [17]. Of course, this technique is inapplicable if no conventional electrode system exists responsive to the ion in question, as is the case for the nitrate and perchlorate liquid ion exchanger electrodes.

C. Use of Reference Electrodes Reversible to Another Ion; Often That of an Added "Inert" Electrolyte

Few measurements are made on solutions containing a single electrolyte, and it may not be possible to choose an electrode reversible to its counter ion. Thus it may be necessary and sometimes advantageous to add an electrolyte to a solution of interest in order to make the determination possible. The most common example of this is the addition of sodium chloride to the Harned cell for the determination of the pK of a weak acid (the basis, in fact, of pH scale determinations) so that the silver-silver chloride reference electrode may be used, *e.g.,*

$$Pt; H_2 \mid HA, NaA, NaCl \mid AgCl; Ag$$

where A^- is the anion of a weak acid [18].

If it is advantageous to buffer a solution to facilitate the determination with an ion-selective electrode, then the hydrogen gas electrode could be used as reference electrode. The use of a glass electrode as an alternative to the hydrogen electrode is placed under Section II.D. below because of the need to standardize it, that is, to eliminate its "standard potential."

D. USE OF REFERENCE ELECTRODES AS "BRIDGING" ELECTRODES

All electrode determinations are concerned with emf differences and concentration differences, although this fact is obscured by referring the emf to a standard state, an unreal solution with an associated emf, $E°$. This can be exemplified for the Harned cell above, because the determination of the pK requires $E°$ to be obtained from the cell

$$Pt; H_2 \mid HCl \mid AgCl; Ag.$$

Hence, we are interested in a **difference** in emf between two cells. As discussed below, the standard potential of the silver-silver chloride electrode can vary by as much as 0.2 mV. Hence, it has been suggested [19] that it should be redetermined for each set of newly prepared electrodes by making measurements in the cell

$$Pt; H_2 \mid HCl(m = 0.0100) \mid AgCl; Ag$$

assuming a value for the activity coefficient of hydrochloric acid at $0.01m$. In a sense, the silver-silver chloride electrode here is being used as a "bridging" electrode.

The foregoing serves as an introduction to the technique of using a glass electrode and, indeed, any ion-selective electrode in this way. Zielen [20] made measurements on the cells

$$Pt; H_2 \mid HCl(m) \mid glass$$

$$Ag; AgCl \mid HCl(m) \mid glass$$

where the same glass electrode is transferred between the two solutions of HCl of the same molality. By this technique, dissolved silver chloride is prevented from reaching the hydrogen gas electrode and being reduced; it has no effect on the glass electrode. Zielen described his technique as being one for eliminating the effect of a liquid junction potential produced by dissolved silver chloride. This technique was also used by Covington, Dobson and Wynne-Jones [21] as a check on the effect of the more soluble mercurous sulfate in sulfuric acid solutions. If the second cell above were instead [20]:

$$Pt;\ H_2\ |\ HX\ |\ glass$$

then the method is basically the application of Section B above.

A similar technique has been used by Srinivasan [22] with sodium-responsive glass electrodes to determine the standard potential of the mercury-mercurous picrate electrode using the cells

$$glass\ (Na)\ |\ NaCl\ |\ AgCl;\ Ag$$

$$glass\ (Na)\ |\ NaPc\ |\ Hg_2Pc_2;\ Hg$$

where Pc^- is the picrate anion. The remaining two categories are concerned with cells with liquid junctions.

E. Use of Reference Electrodes of (Ideally) Invariant Potential

The use of the saturated calomel electrode has already been discussed in Section I. To be specific, we will take the example of the operational pH cell:

$$Pt;\ H_2\ |\ S\ ||\ KCl(sat)\ |\ Hg_2Cl_2;\ Hg$$

where S is a standard solution of assigned pH(S). The emf of the cell is given in terms of pH(S) by, [23]

$$(RT\ \ln 10/F)\text{pH(S)} = E - (E^{\circ\prime} + E_j) \qquad (1)$$

where E_j is the liquid junction potential and $E^{\circ\prime}$ includes, besides the E° of the cell, a term involving the single ion activity of chloride ion in the potassium chloride. The term $(E^{\circ\prime} + E_j)$ is often referred to as the "standard potential" of the calomel electrode. Clearly, since the liquid junction potential depends on the solution, S, the value of the standard potential will be somewhat dependent on the solution used to determine it. Values of $(E^{\circ\prime} + E_j)$ are tabulated but they are rarely required, since as in pH measurements, the measurement is comparative, and the cell effectively involved is:

$$Pt;\ H_2\ |\ X\ ||\ KCl(sat)\ ||\ S\ |\ H_2;\ Pt \qquad (E_X - E_S)$$

where X is a solution of unknown pH and

$$\text{pH(X)} = \text{pH(S)} + (E_X - E_S)\ F/RT\ \ln 10 \qquad (2)$$

Hence, if the residual liquid junction potential $\Delta E_j = E_{j(X)} - E_{j(S)}$ is zero, the standard potential cancels out. If ΔE_j is not zero, the error will be incorporated in pH(X). Similar considerations are applicable to an operational determination of pIon [24] using ion-selective electrodes. The question of liquid junction potential variation will be discussed in Section IV.

Besides the system KCl(sat)|Hg$_2$Cl$_2$; Hg, different potassium chloride concentrations, e.g., 3.8, 3.5, 1.0, and 0.1M are sometimes used, the last two being out of favor. Sodium chloride [25] and, for ethylene diamine media, saturated lithium chloride [26] have also been used. Some workers prefer the system KCl(sat), AgCl(sat) | AgCl; Ag, and the system K$_2$SO$_4$(sat) | Hg$_2$SO$_4$; Hg is available commercially for cases where chloride contamination cannot be tolerated. Otherwise, an intermediate salt bridge of ammonium nitrate is used with the saturated calomel electrode.

It is possible to conceive other potential invariant systems which might be more appropriately used with ion-selective electrodes but, as emphasized earlier, this is a problem of whole cell design, and we shall defer further discussion to the section dealing with liquid junction potentials, giving only an example here [27]:

$$\text{LaF}_3|\text{NaCl, NaF}||\text{NaCl, HCl}|\text{H}_2; \text{Pt}$$

F. Use of a Second Similar Ion-Selective Electrode as a Reference Electrode

This method is an extension of the well-known homo-ionic concentration cell with two similar electrodes, e.g.,

$$\text{Ag; AgCl}|\text{CaCl}_2(m_1)||\text{CaCl}_2(m_2)|\text{AgCl; Ag}$$

to ion-selective electrodes, e.g.,

$$\text{LaF}_3 \mid \text{KF}(m_1) \parallel \text{KF}(m_2) \mid \text{LaF}_3$$

and an intermediate salt bridge may be inserted.

Such cells may be adapted for potentiometric titration determinations. A good example of this is the work of Durst [28] using the cell:

$$\text{LaF}_3 \mid \text{F}_{x}^{-}, \text{KNO}_3(0.1M) \parallel \text{KNO}_3(0.1M) \parallel \text{KNO}_3(0.1M), \text{F}_{s}^{-} \mid \text{LaF}_3$$

where the left hand side of the cell is kept constant and comprises a micro-amount of fluoride-containing solution. The solution in the right hand side compartment is titrated, adjusting the fluoride ion concentration until the cell emf is zero. The technique is termed linear null-point potentiometry (LNPP). It is necessary to take into account any asymmetry potential difference, including differences in the internal reference systems of the two fluoride electrodes. This can be measured by directly comparing the two electrodes in a fluoride solution (bias potential determination). Since the new ion-selective electrodes tend to have much lower resistances than do glass electrodes, the problem of the measurement of potential with two high resistance electrodes and grounding difficulties are not so serious.

III. Preparation and Properties of Some Important Reference Electrodes

A. THE HYDROGEN GAS ELECTRODE

The hydrogen gas electrode is worthy of discussion first, not only because it is the electrode whose standard potential is conventionally set at zero at all temperatures in order to tabulate standard potentials of other electrodes, but because it is probably the most reproducible electrode which we have available. Bias potentials are always less than $10 \mu V$ for freshly prepared electrodes.

The hydrogen electrode consists of a platinum foil, the surface of which is able to catalyze the reaction

$$H^+ + e^- \rightarrow 1/2 \ H_2$$

which does not occur in the solution phase. Platinum black is the most useful catalyst. It is usually deposited from a 1-3% solution of chloroplatinic acid with the addition of a small quantity of lead acetate as suggested by Popoff, Kunz and Snow [29]. The additive is not essential as Hills and Ives [30] showed, but it is desirable, as electrodes prepared using it have a longer life and are less susceptible to poisoning. The electrode is poisoned by traces of sulfide and cyanide, but when this occurs, the potential is so far from the expected value for there to be no doubt about an electrode malfunction. Drifting potentials are observed when the chemical reduction of species such as benzoic acid, nitrophenols, *etc.*, can take place at the catalyst surface. This can be overcome, as in the case of measurements on the standard buffer substance potassium hydrogen phthalate, by using a palladium black deposit, which has a lower catalytic activity. If reduction of some solution species is suspected, two electrodes of different catalytic activity may be employed so that differences in potential and variations with time would confirm suspicions. This technique has been used for concentrated ($5M$) perchloric acid solutions [31], and contrary to reports in the literature, hydrogen gas electrodes can be used in these solutions.

The twin roles of the platinum black and the platinum substrate were nicely demonstrated by Hills and Ives [30] with their catalyst electrode. They showed that the potential of an electrode consisting of a bright platinum cone with platinum black dispersed in solution by the continuous bubbling of the hydrogen gas agreed to within 10 μV with the potential of a conventional hydrogen electrode.

The hydrogen electrode is not as difficult to use as might be imagined. A supply of pure hydrogen gas is required, and it may be noted that palladium diffusion purifiers are now commercially available. A means of saturating the solution with hydrogen gas without changing its composition is required, but a wash-bottle with a fritted disc bubbler and filled with the cell solution is perfectly adequate. Potential readings are corrected to the standard atmospheric partial pressure of hydrogen gas from knowledge of the vapor pressure of the solutions and the prevailing barometric pressure. The bubbler depth correction noticed by Hills and Ives [30] can ordinarily be ignored as insignificant. Further details can be found in Ives and Janz's monograph [1] or that of Bates [32].

B. Silver-Silver Halide Electrodes

Next to the hydrogen electrode, the silver-silver chloride electrode is probably the most reproducible and certainly the most reliable and convenient reference electrode. It has been the subject of many reviews [33-35], the most recent being that of Janz and Ives [2].

The electrode reaction is

$$AgCl + e^- \rightarrow Ag + Cl^-.$$

The solubility of silver chloride in water is about 10^{-5} mol liter^{-1} at 25 °C which sets a lower limit on the use of the electrode for determining low chloride concentrations. The solubility in saturated potassium chloride solution is such (about 6×10^{-3} mol liter^{-1} at 25 °C) that it is necessary to presaturate the solution with silver chloride, otherwise the electrode becomes stripped of its coating.

Of the several methods of preparing silver-silver chloride electrodes only three need concern us here:

1. A silver wire is coated with silver chloride by making it the anode in a suitable chloride solution, usually 0.1M hydrochloric acid or potassium chloride. Electrodes prepared in this way are suitable for potentiometric titrations or as inner reference electrodes for membrane electrodes. Strains and probably impurities introduced in the drawing process cause the bias potentials of such electrodes to be fairly high ($\pm$ 5 mV), but this is of no consequence in the applications mentioned.

2.   Silver is plated on a platinum substrate from a cyanide bath, and the silver chloride coating is formed as described above. These electrodes are free of the objections raised above. Their response times are short so, when this is important, for example, in potentiometric titrations, they are preferable to the thermal-electrolytic type (*vide infra*).

3.   In the thermal-electrolytic type, silver is formed by heating a paste of silver oxide on a platinum substrate, usually wound in the form of a spiral. Part of the spongy silver mass is converted to chloride by the electrolysis process described above. Because the silver is porous, the electrodes tend to be rather sluggish and show concentration polarization effects due to the occlusion in the pores of electrolyte from the chloridizing process. They can, however, be prepared with a very small range of bias potentials ($\pm 20\,\mu V$), provided that the silver oxide, prepared from the addition of sodium hydroxide to silver nitrate solution, is washed very well. Electrodes with higher bias potentials can sometimes be brought into line by heating them for two hours in distilled water at 50-60 °C [36].

In acid solutions, the silver-silver chloride electrode is sensitive to traces of oxygen, which is attributed to the reaction:

$$2Ag + 2H^+ + 2Cl^- + 1/2\ O_2 \rightarrow 2AgCl + H_2O$$

which causes a decrease in the chloride ion concentration. In high precision work, nitrogen is bubbled through the cell solutions before and during measurements. This procedure is not necessary when work of a precision of less than 0.3 mV is required or for neutral solutions, although Manov *et al.* [37] state that the potential is raised 1.5 mV when a saturated potassium chloride solution is saturated with air.

The electrode is very sensitive to traces of bromide impurity. The effect has been studied by Pinching and Bates [38], who found that 0.064 mole percent of potassium bromide affected the bias potential of an electrode (relative to an electrode in a Br^--free solution) by about 1 mV. This large effect is attributed to the fact that silver chloride and silver bromide form solid solutions. The effect of iodide is much less, probably because the iodide and chloride of silver do not form solid solutions. The effect of bromide impurity is to change the standard potential of the electrode. This conclusion is a by-product of the painstaking work of Güntelberg, who repeated [39] most of his earlier work [40] on the variation of the activity coefficient of hydrochloric acid in the presence of alkali metal chlorides at constant molality ($0.1\,m$) when he discovered that his chlorides were contaminated with bromide. Pinching and Bates [38] have described a method of preparing chlorides free from bromide impurities and a sensitive colorimetric test for detection of small traces of bromides.

In spite of using apparently identical preparative procedures, it has been repeatedly found that thermal-electrolytic electrodes prepared in different, and from time to time in the same, laboratories differ slightly in standard potential. It is usual to prepare batches of electrodes, discarding electrodes that show wide divergences from the mean. The mean potentials of separate batches may differ by up to 0.2 mV [41,42]. For this reason, it has been suggested by a group of eminent physical chemists [19] that the standard potential of the electrode be redetermined for all new precise investigations by making a single measurement at 25 °C in 0.0100 molal hydrochloric acid against a hydrogen gas electrode. The activity coefficient of hydrochloric acid to be assumed is 0.904. For other temperatures, this principle can be extended by using the values given in Table 1, which have been calculated from the best values for the activity coefficients of 0.0100 molal hydrochloric acid [43], by noting that Guggenheim's specific interaction coefficient [44] is almost independent of temperature in the range 0-55 °C. If this suggestion of redetermining the standard potential each time is adopted, it may not be necessary to avoid traces of bromide except in work of the highest precision.

For convenience, standard potentials for 0-95 °C are given in Table 2. The standard potential $(E^{o\prime} + E_j)$ for the electrode system KCl(sat), AgCl(sat) | AgCl; Ag was found to be 198.1 mV at 25 °C by Manov, DeLollis and Acree [37]. Measurements at other temperatures are not available apart from a single measurement at 60 °C [45] of 165.7 mV.

Lastly, we may mention that the silver-silver bromide and silver-silver iodide electrodes may be used with care and comparable precision, but the effects of oxygen are much more serious. Standard potentials have been determined recently at the NBS [46,47] and are given in Table 2. Variations of standard potential between preparations can occur, and activity coefficient values for 0.01 molal acids are given in Table 1, thus permitting checks to be made.

Table 1. Activity coefficients of HCl, HBr and HI at 0.01 mol kg^{-1} (required for the determination of the standard potentials of silver–silver halide electrodes).

°C	γ_{HCl}	γ_{HBr}	γ_{HI}
0	0.907	0.910	–
10	0.906	–	0.909
25	0.904	0.906	0.907
40	0.901	–	0.904
50	0.899	0.902	–

C. The Mercury-Mercurous Chloride (Calomel) Electrode

The calomel electrode as a chloride-reversible electrode was extensively used before 1930, but later it was abandoned in favor of the more reliable silver-silver chloride for all precise work. The ideally potential-invariant saturated or $3.5M$ calomel electrode has always ubiquitously enjoyed popularity. Prepared by grinding calomel, mercury and a little potassium chloride solution together and placing the resultant slurry in a layer about 1 cm thick on the surface of mercury, this electrode will be called the classical electrode. Hills and Ives [48] argued that this thick paste was unnecessary and probably detrimental, and motivated by the idea that a liquid metal substrate for an electrode of the second kind should be better than a solid metal, reinvestigated the calomel electrode. They devised a new method of preparation in which calomel and mercury were shaken together in the dry state and a small quantity introduced on to a mercury surface where it immediately spread. Solution was then added carefully to this "skin" electrode. Hills and Ives' [48] results with the hydrogen-hydrochloric acid-calomel cell were of outstanding precision. The electrode is very sensitive to traces of oxygen, which cannot be explained entirely by the reaction:

$$2Hg + 2HCl + 1/2\ O_2 \rightleftarrows Hg_2Cl_2 + H_2O$$

because at small concentrations of gas, the effect is reversible. A second important experimental point was the prevention of the formation of annular solution films between mercury and the glass and, thus out of equilibrium with the bulk of the solution, by the expedient of silicone treatment of the glass.

Hills and Ives' standard emf at 25 °C was reproduced by Schwabe and Ziegenbalg [49] but Grzybowski [50] found a value 0.2 mV higher. Additional indications that the electrode was not as good as at first thought came from the failure to use it at other temperatures because of marked temperature hysteresis. In a further series of investigations, which have been summarized [51], Ives and his coworkers traced the cause of the troubles to the disproportionation of calomel:

$$Hg_2Cl_2 \rightarrow Hg + HgCl_2$$

and the resultant formation of mercuric complexes in solution. This reaction is slow and over two days leads to a rise in potential of about 0.2 mV. Hills and Ives' readings were taken after about 6 hours whereas Grzybowski's were "next-day" values. This led to the concept of "first" and "second day" calomel potentials. Temperature hysteresis effects arise from the solution still containing dissolved mercuric species formed at higher temperatures when the electrode is returned to lower temperatures.

Covington, Dobson and Wynne-Jones [43] essentially supported Ives' findings and demonstrated spectrophotometrically the gradual accumulation of mercuric species in solution (Fig. 1). Using much smaller ratios of surface area of mercury to volume of solution than Hills and Ives [48] (as had also Grzybowski [50]), Covington et al. used two to three times more of the dry calomel-mercury mixture for the smooth skin electrode of Hills and Ives [48]. This has a definite advantage at higher temperatures. By comparison of all available data for the hydrogen-calomel and hydrogen-silver chloride cells, Covington et al. concluded that Grzybowski's data at temperatures other than 25 °C, which on reanalysis were in good agreement with their own less extensive data, were probably the most reliable. For convenience, these values are given in Table 2; it is considered that restricting the accuracy of the stated values to 0.1 mV is justified in view of the difficulties associated with using this electrode.

There have been numerous electrode kinetic studies of the calomel electrode. Armstrong, Fleischmann and Thirsk [52], who give references to earlier work, conclude that two competing processes occur in the

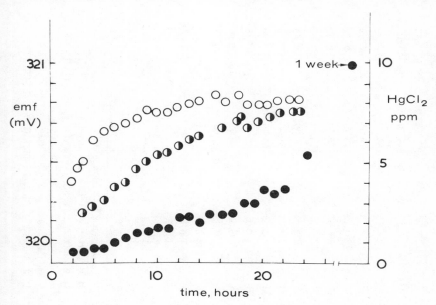

Figure 1. Variation of the calomel electrode potential with time (○ Covington et al. [43] type of electrode with thicker calomel layer; ◑ Hills and Ives' type electrode) compared with the increase in mercuric species in solution with time, ●, measured spectrophotometrically at 230 nm by calibration using stock solutions of mercuric chloride in 0.5 m HCl (after Covington, Dobson and Wynne-Jones [43]).

Table 2. Standard potentials of some reference electrode systems.

°C	$E°$ (mV) H_2 – AgCl; Ag[a]	$E°$ (mV) H_2 – AgBr; Ag[b]	$E°$ (mV) H_2 – AgI; Ag[c]	$E°$ (mV) H_2 – Hg_2Cl_2; Hg[d]	$E°' + E_j$ (mV) H_2 – KCl(sat) | Hg_2Cl_2; Hg[e]
0	236.55	81.28	−146.37	274.0	259.18
5	234.13	79.61	−147.19	273.1	–
10	231.42	77.73	−148.22	–	253.87
15	228.57	75.72	−149.42	270.9	–
20	225.57	73.49	−150.81	–	247.75
25	222.34	71.06	−152.44	268.0	244.53
30	219.04	68.56	−154.05	–	241.18
35	215.65	65.85	−155.90	265.0	–
40	212.08	63.10	−157.88	–	234.49
45	208.35	60.12	−159.98	260.5	–
50	204.49	57.04	−162.19	–	227.37
55	200.56	–	–	256.1	–
60	196.49	–	–	–	–
70	187.82	–	–	–	–
80	178.7	–	–	–	–
90	169.5	–	–	–	–
95	165.1	–	–	–	–

[a] R. G. Bates and V. E. Bower [42]

[b] H. B. Hetzer, R. A. Robinson and R. G. Bates [46]

[c] H. B. Hetzer, R. A. Robinson and R. G. Bates [47]

[d] Based on the analysis by A. K. Covington, J. V. Dobson and Lord Wynne–Jones [43] of Grzybowski's results, [50] and their own.

[e] D. J. Alner, J. J. Greczek and A. G. Smeeth [45]. The value at 0 °C appears to be a misprint; the value from [55] is used.

anodic polarization of mercury in chloride solutions, the dissolution of mercury as $HgCl_4^{2-}$ and the formation of calomel. The complex ion species is identified as $HgCl_4^{2-}$ at concentrations greater than 1 mol liter^{-1} on the basis of Dry and Gledhill's studies by conductance [53], other species being present in much too low concentration to account for the observed kinetics. Armstrong et al. [52] consider that the time dependent effects of the "equilibrium" calomel potential are due to a mixed potential, the two competing processes being:

$$2Hg + 2Cl^- \rightleftarrows Hg_2 Cl_2 + 2e^-$$

$$Hg + 4Cl^- \rightleftarrows HgCl_4^{2-} + 2e^-$$

It is not clear, however, why the electrode should take so long to come to equilibrium with mercuric species in solution if the process responsible is purely diffusional. Figure 1 shows that the concentration of mercuric species continues to rise after the electrode has reached a steady potential, and these results suggest that other factors may be involved such as recrystallization of the calomel.

It is also not clear whether the above outlined difficulties associated with the calomel electrode in acid solution are relevant to its functioning in neutral potassium chloride solution. Armstrong et al. [52] noted a similar kinetic behavior in KCl solutions. Covington et al. [43] found some differences between the potentials of the calomel-silver chloride cell when different chlorides were used, and it is conceivable that the presence of different cations will affect the stabilities of the various mercuric chloride complexes present. It must be emphasized, however, that in these studies one is concerned with small differences of the order of 0.2 mV only, and other effects notably that of oxygen can easily swamp these. There is no reason to believe that the classical calomel electrode will not be in equilibrium with mercuric species, but the process of grinding calomel and mercury together wet will aid any process involving atmospheric oxygen. Alner, Greczek and Smeeth [45] have used the improved calomel electrode in a study of the operational pH cell and a variety of buffer solutions. They reported that the behavior of the calomel electrodes was satisfactory and calculated values for the standard potential ($E^{o'} + E_j$) of the saturated calomel electrode using the NBS values for the pH of potassium hydrogen phthalate standard buffer from 0-50 °C [54]. They believe that these values (given in Table 2) are equilibrium values, but "the measurement of these potentials was only a small part of the present work and the calomel electrodes were discarded as soon as their potential values began to drift." The electrodes "remained stable to within $\pm 10\ \mu V$ for at least ten days and much longer at the lower temperatures." This is remarkably good for a cell involving a liquid junction.

Although not stated in the paper [45] where it is said that the calomel electrodes were prepared "according to the recommendations of Ives and his coworkers," it is significant that Greczek states [55] that a 5 mm layer of calomel was used instead of 0.5 mm. This procedure was stated not to affect the equilibrium potential nor the time taken to achieve it but did greatly improve the stability of the electrode at 40 and 50 °C. It will be recalled that a similar thicker layer was preferred by Covington *et al.* [43].

According to Shams El Din and Kamel [56], another source of time variation of calomel electrodes is impurities such as zinc, cadmium, tin, lead or copper in the mercury. They conclude that time must be allowed for impurities to diffuse to the mercury surface and dissolve in the solution phase. This effect is unlikely to be present in the precision studies mentioned above but could be a factor with commercial electrodes. In the author's experience, commercial electrodes can show large bias potentials when intercompared as well as fluctuations from day to day. Sibbald and Matsuyama [57] report a standard deviation of ± 0.25 mV over 12 days with a commercial electrode. Normally for pH measurements such variations do not matter if standardization is carried out frequently. It must not be assumed, however, that the glass electrode is always to blame for variations.

The calomel electrode cannot be recommended as a reference electrode responsive to chloride ions. The silver-silver chloride electrode is far more reliable and convenient to prepare. Even as a potential-invariant electrode, the calomel electrode has distinct limitations, principally due to temperature hysteresis effects (see Fig. 3). It is to be hoped that it will gradually be replaced by more reliable alternatives such as the thallium amalgam-thallous chloride electrode (Section III.F.).

D. MERCURY-MERCUROUS SULFATE ELECTRODE

Some commercial suppliers include the mercury-mercurous sulfate electrode in saturated potassium sulfate in their catalogs of reference electrodes. Mattock [58] gives the standard potential $(E^{\circ\prime} + E_j)$ of this electrode system as 658 mV at 22 °C, but no measurements seem to be available at other temperatures.

Ives and Smith [59] comment that in spite of the tendency to hydrolyze and its rather high solubility, the mercury-mercurous sulfate electrode is "alongside the hydrogen electrode in being capable of outstanding reproducibility." It is of course one of the electrodes of the Weston standard cell. In contrast to the calomel electrode, it needs no special preparative procedure, except for the preparation of the sulfate electrolytically [60].

In an investigation of the hydrogen-sulfuric acid-mercurous sulfate cell at molalities of 0.1-8.0, Beck, Dobson and Wynne-Jones [61] elegantly demonstrated that their data were consistent with vapor pressure data at 25 °C giving a standard emf of 615.81 mV, that is, 0.45 mV higher than Harned and Hamer's value [62]. (Note that the values given in Ref. [59] are incorrect.) Unfortunately, vapor pressure data of sufficient accuracy are not available at other temperatures so that standard emf's at temperatures other than 25 °C cannot be obtained. Published values are those of Harned and Hamer [62], which are incorrect at 25 °C and probably also at other temperatures.

Harned and Hamer [62] had stated that the cell could not be used at molalities below 0.05 because of the enhanced solubility of mercurous sulfate giving rise to the possibility of an appreciable liquid junction potential. No experimental measurements were given in support of this assertion, and the point was reinvestigated by Covington, Dobson and Wynne-Jones [21]. The mercurous sulfate electrode was compared with two other sulfate-reversible electrodes and simultaneously with the hydrogen electrode – a good example of the power of such an approach. It was concluded that the mercurous sulfate electrode functioned down to 0.01 mol kg^{-1}, and that it was possible to determine the standard potential of the electrode by extrapolation, provided the second dissociation constant of sulfuric acid was known and the Debye-Hückel equation used for the ionic activity coefficients. Each of these introduces an uncertainty, for the former depends also on the value taken for the distance of closest approach parameter in the Debye-Hückel equation [63]. The standard potential at 25 °C was stated to be 612.5 mV with an uncertainty of at least ±0.3 mV. Clearly, the evaluation of the standard potential from the data at higher concentrations would be free of such uncertainty, but this must await accurate vapor pressure data in the range 0-55 °C. Until this is available, stoichiometric activity coefficients for sulfuric acid remain unknown at temperatures other than 25 °C.

E. MERCURY-MERCUROUS CARBOXYLATE ELECTRODES

Interest in these electrodes has been revived recently and some of them show considerable potentiality as reference electrodes, particularly in buffered solutions. Larson and his coworkers [64-67] studied the acetate and oxalate electrodes in solutions of the corresponding acids. Covington, Talukdar and Thirsk [68] reexamined the acetate electrode in buffer solutions and found $E_m^\circ = 511.3$ mV at 25 °C (where subscript m refers to molality) with only small discrepancies with Larson's early work [65] and a later supplement [66]. Almost simultaneously, Gryzin [69] compared the electrode in sodium acetate solutions against the saturated calomel electrode, but his result at 25 °C is discrepant ($E_m^\circ = 498.4$ mV), while Chauchard and Gauthier's [70] recent value by the same method is intermediate ($E_c^\circ = 502$ mV), where subscript c refers to molarity. Schwabe and Glockner [71] had earlier used the electrode successfully as an internal reference electrode for glass electrodes. From a determination *versus* the hydrogen electrode in Michaelis buffer (0.1 equimolar acetic acid + sodium acetate), one can calculate $E_m^\circ = 511$ mV [68] in support of the value first mentioned above. Schwabe [72] has also used the electrode successfully in methanol and isopropanol solutions.

The propionate electrode has been studied by Aditya *et al.* [73], who find $E^\circ = 500$ mV at 30 °C in good agreement with the French workers [70], mentioned above, who also studied the formate electrode ($E_c^\circ = 567$ mV) at 25 °C.

Larson and Tomsicek [67] investigated the oxalate electrode, and this work has been repeated by Srinivasan [22], whose value in oxalic acid solutions ($E_m^\circ = 417.3$ mV at 25 °C) differs by 1 mV from the earlier one when recalculated with more recent values for the dissociation constants for oxalic acid. The electrode did not function as well in buffered solutions for reasons not readily ascertained.

Bertram and Bone [74] determined the standard potential of the benzoate electrode in water (solubility 0.02 mol kg^{-1}) and in 20% methanol-water solution (0.06 mol kg^{-1}). In water $E_m^\circ = 426.3$ mV at 25 °C whereas Chauchard and Gauthier's value [70] is 10 mV higher. (Note: $E_m^\circ - E_c^\circ = 0.15$ mV for all these electrodes in water at 25 °C.)

The electrodes were prepared by introducing a slurry of the mercurous salt solution and mercury onto the mercury surface in the manner of the classical calomel electrode. While the reproducibility of the electrodes is not high (± 0.1 mV), and there are some unexplained discrepancies, these electrodes are worthy of further consideration as reference electrode systems. Some care needs to be exercised in using them in solutions that are dilute, because of possible hydrolysis of mercury ions and of liquid junction potentials resulting from enhanced solubility (but see Section IV). Some electrode forms suitable for use with mercury-mercurous salt electrodes are shown in Figure 2.

F. Thallium Amalgam-Thallous Chloride Electrode

The reference electrode system:

$$KCl(sat), TlCl(sat) \mid TlCl(s); Tl(Hg)$$

was suggested by Fricke [75-77] and is commercially available ("Thalamid" electrode). It is claimed to be reproducible, usable to higher

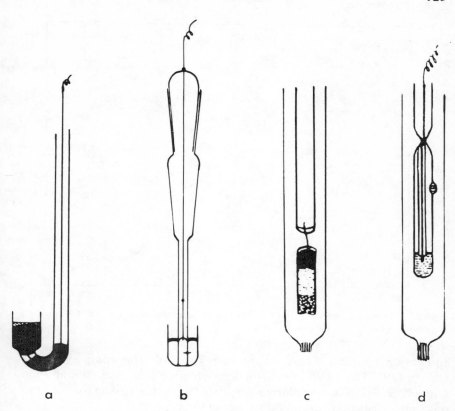

Figure 2. Some useful electrode forms for mercury-mercurous salt electrodes: a. cup-type [45], b. dip type [21,43,68], c. encapsulated type, d. Thalamid [77].

temperatures (135 °C) than calomel, and moreover to be free of temperature hysteresis, which even the silver-silver chloride system is not (Fig. 3). The principal advantage claimed is for its use in symmetrical glass electrode cells (*i.e.*, as internal and external reference electrodes) when a well-defined "isothermenschnittpunkt" [76] is found close to the "nullpunkt" of the system (these terms will be discussed in Section V).

The thallium-mercury system contains an intermetallic compound Tl_2Hg_5, which disappears above about 14.5 °C [78], so above this temperature the electrode is not the usual form of the two-phase amalgam system, liquid + intermetallic compound. An amalgam of 40 wt percent is suggested for the reference electrode.

The solubility of thallous chloride in saturated potassium chloride is fairly high (3×10^{-5} mol liter^{-1} at 25 °C [79]), but it is less in ammonium chloride, which perhaps is why this is suggested as an alternative medium [75]. Above 3.5 mol liter^{-1} potassium chloride, the solid phase in

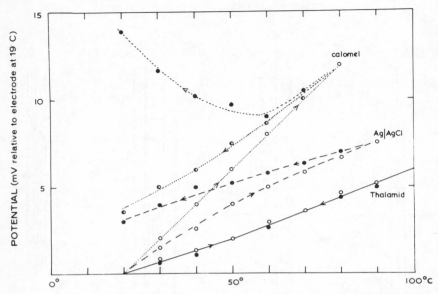

Figure 3.   Temperature hysteresis of calomel, silver-silver chloride and thallium amalgam-thallous chloride reference electrodes (after Fricke [75]): ● 3 min after drop in temperature: ○ 5 min after drop in temperature.

equilibrium contains potassium chloride (7%) indicating complex salt formation [79]. The solubility of thallous chloride is a minimum at about 1 mol liter^{-1} potassium chloride [79], which was the reason for selecting this as the electrolyte in careful studies of the cell

$$Tl(Hg); TlCl \,|\, KCl \,|\, AgCl; \; Ag$$

carried out by Mussini and Longhi [80]. Standard potentials for various amalgam concentrations in the range 0.2-39.5 mole percent and 0-80 °C were calculated. Thallium amalgams react with air, which is one disadvantage of the system. Studies of the cell

$$Tl(Hg) \,|\, TlCl \,|\, AgCl; \; Ag$$

were made by Cowperthwaite, La Mer and Barksdale [81] at thallous chloride concentrations below saturation (< 0.01 mol kg^{-1}) in water. Thallous chloride is too soluble for the electrode system to be useful as an electrode of the second kind responding to variations in chloride ion concentration.

Standard potentials ($E^{o\prime} + E_j$) for the 40 wt percent saturated potassium chloride electrode have not been published. If required, they could be obtained by the method used for the saturated calomel electrode [45]. The potential relative to the saturated calomel electrode at 20 °C is 816.0 mV [77].

IV. Liquid Junction Potentials

A welcome renewal of interest in the problems associated with liquid junction potentials can be discerned during the past few years. It bears repeating, however, that the potential across liquid junctions is indeterminate practically, being dependent on single ion activities, themselves indeterminate. A nomenclature preferable to the E_j used earlier is that of Guggenheim [82]. The cell emf, E, is split into the thermodynamically exact formula:

$$E = E_{el} + E_d + E_s$$

where E_{el} is the electrode potential given by the Nernst equation for the cell in terms of **concentrations**, and for dissimilar electrodes includes the standard emf of the cell. The diffusion potential, E_d, is given by:

$$E_d = (RT/F) \int_I^{II} \sum_i (t_i/z_i) \, d \ln m_i \qquad (3)$$

in which t_i, z_i, and m_i are the transference number, charge, and molality, respectively, of the ion i, and I and II refer to the junction terminal solutions. E_s is the salt effect potential comprising both the single ion activity coefficients (γ_i) from the Nernst expression and from the liquid junction potential (E_j) where:

$$E_j = -(RT/F) \int_I^{II} \sum_i (t_i/z_i) \, d \ln (m_i \gamma_i). \qquad (4)$$

The most important feature of this division is that E_s is a function of **mean** ionic activity coefficients and is therefore in principle experimentally determinable. Thus E_{el}, E_d, E_s and hence E are separately calculable provided certain assumptions are made about the composition variation across the boundary and the constancy of mobilities independent of environment, and the necessary experimental information is available. E_j is not calculable unless some convention is adopted for single ion activities. The so-called calculation of liquid junction potentials by the Henderson, Planck, or Lewis and Sargent equations is, in this nomenclature, a calculation of E_d.

The emf of a cell involving a liquid junction is, except for homo-ionic junctions (those between two concentrations of the same solute electrolyte), known to depend on the method of forming the junction and the subsequent interdiffusion of the two solutions. For those cells which have been studied, the variations are not large, being of the order of a few millivolts. Unfortunately, our knowledge is very meager and almost entirely restricted to junctions between HCl and the alkali metal chlorides [83-86].

Guggenheim has distinguished a number of types of junction [82] including:

a. continuous mixture, important not from the practical standpoint but because a linear mixing form $xI + (1-x)II$ is assumed in the Henderson integration for E_d;

b. free diffusion formed by the natural interdiffusion of the two solutions;

c. restrained diffusion, where the length of the diffusion zone is kept constant, and is important only because it forms the basis of the assumption made by Planck in his integration for E_d; and

d. flowing junctions.

Unfortunately, the type of junction most often used and associated with commercial reference electrodes of "fixed" potential falls into none of these groups. Guggenheim has referred to these as "sharp junctions of indefinite type" [82]. Invariably, the basic requirement for stability, that of denser solution below, is not observed, and there is a flow of electrolyte, *e.g.*, potassium chloride, radially outward from the restraining diaphragm. These restrained flow junctions can take several forms [87], including a porous frit, a fiber wick, a ground glass sleeve, porous glass [88], a palladium annulus (a leaky glass-metal seal) and a cellophane membrane [89] to mention only the commonest (Fig. 4). Although the diffusion is free, the second essential criterion for stability, that of cylindrical symmetry [82], is not observed and there may be irregular fluctuations of several millivolts. Although there have been a few published accounts [57, 90] of investigations of commercial calomel reference elements, and no doubt some more information is held by the manufacturers, it seems that there is a need for a detailed investigation and comparison with properly formed free diffusion junctions [45,82,91]. The finite small leak rate developed by a head of potassium chloride solution seems to be essential to obtain stable pH readings in some dilute, poorly buffered solutions, but are the factors involved, as far as the junction is concerned, understood? It is possible that the wide variations of residual liquid junction potential observed by Kater, Leonard and Matsuyama [89] are not entirely due to the colloidal properties of blood.

Recent determinations involving carefully formed free diffusion junctions with the necessary requirement of cylindrical symmetry have been concerned with pH studies [45,91]. Paabo and Bates [91] have used a cell designed by Bates, Pinching and Smith [92] to investigate the internal consistency of the multistandard NBS pH scale. Alner, Greczek and Smeeth [45] formed their junctions in a 1 mm precision-bore capillary tube, 5 cm long, by removing the air trapped between the two solutions

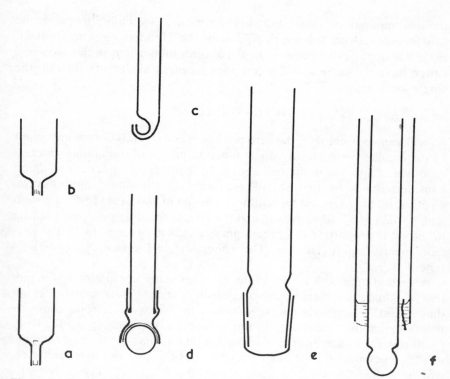

Figure 4. Some common forms of restrained-flow junctions: a. palladium annulus, b. ceramic plug, c. J-type [100] to overcome inverse density gradient, d. cellophane membrane [89], e. ground glass sleeve, f. fiber wick in silicone rubber grommet for combination electrode.

with a syringe. This size capillary gave the best results (stability to 0.04 mV over several hours); tubes of larger bore gave much poorer stability whereas narrow tubes increased the resistance of the cell and the sensitivity of the measurement system suffered.

It is worthwhile summarizing here the evidence on which the use of a saturated or $3.5M$ potassium salt bridge for reducing liquid junction potentials is based. The first is the experimental evidence of Guggenheim [82] from measurements on the cell

$$Hg; Hg_2Cl_2|0.1M\ HCl||xM\ KCl||0.1M\ KCl|Hg_2Cl_2;\ Hg$$

that, as x is increased, the **whole** cell emf falls. Since E_{el} is zero for this cell, then $E_d + E_s$ is reduced by increasing the concentration of the salt bridge. Guggenheim [82] used both free diffusion and continuous mixture junctions and found for this cell that the difference in emf was not more than 0.15 mV. On this evidence rests the justification for carrying out Henderson equation calculations (based on the assumption of continuous mixing) on free diffusion junctions. Secondly, there is the evidence based on the consideration of the Henderson equation itself [93], that for a salt bridge at high concentration when both anion and cation have the same mobility (the ions are equitransferent), then for the single junction, *e.g.*,

$$HCl(0.1M) \| KCl \,(sat)$$

E_d will vanish because of the zero pre-logarithm term. It is very important to distinguish between this **single** junction case and the **double** junction case which appears in the cell above. In the latter, Henderson equation considerations show that E_d will be a function of the dilute solutions principally, and not of the bridge solution. This point was made by Finkelstein and Verdier [94] who investigated the effect of adding potassium nitrate in different proportions to potassium chloride in order to make the ions more nearly equitransferent. The effect was to **increase** the whole cell potential.

A second approach to the problem of reducing liquid junction potentials, originated by Nernst, and one which is very popular, consists of adding "inert" electrolyte to the solutions in the two electrode compartments so that the potential determining ions are then present in effectively small relative concentration. The two solutions may be allowed to come directly in contact (single junction) or a salt bridge of the same inert electrolyte at the same concentration is used (double junction cell). A bonus is often additionally assumed, that if any variation in concentration of potential determining species is made, then their activity coefficients remain constant by the ionic strength principle. Prue and Read [95] have recently shown from measurements on the cell

$$Pt; H_2 \mid HCl \,(m_1),\, NaClO_4 \,(m_2) \mid AgCl;\, Ag$$

that changes in the activity coefficient of hydrochloric acid in the presence of the inert electrolyte, sodium perchlorate, are not negligible (Fig. 5), but can be predicted from consideration of the properties of the electrolyte mixture in terms of parameters relating to the single electrolytes. It is certainly true that as the concentration of potential-determining species tends to zero, then E_d approaches zero, and this method reaches its culmination in cells of the type introduced by Owen [96], *e.g.*,

$$Ag;\, AgCl \left| \begin{array}{c} KCl,\, xm \\ KNO_3 \,(1-x)m \end{array} \right\| KNO_3,\, m \left\| \begin{array}{c} AgNO_3, xm \\ KNO_3,\, (1-x)m \end{array} \right| Ag$$

Measurements are made at various values of x, and the emf is extrapolated to $x = 0$, where upon $E_d = 0$ and $E_s = (2RT/F) \ln \gamma_{AgCl(KNO_3)}$, where

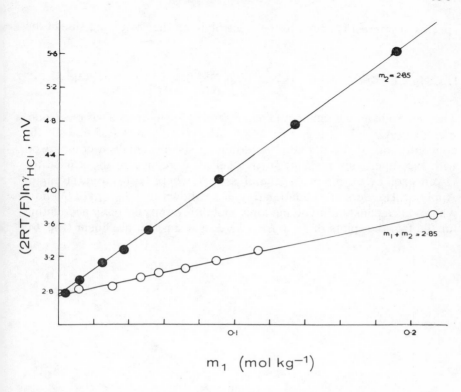

Figure 5. Variation of $\gamma_{HCl(NaClO_4)}$ as a function of acid molality (m_1) in sodium perchlorate solutions (m_2) (after Prue and Read [95]): O at constant ionic strength; ● at constant added salt molality. (If the ionic strength principle were correct, the lower line would have zero slope and the upper line a negative slope if a Debye-Hückel expression is assumed.)

$\gamma_{AgCl(KNO_3)}$ is the activity coefficient of silver chloride present in trace amount in a potassium nitrate solution. Such extrapolations are linear, and Spiro [97] and Covington [98] have shown that for the various possible types of such cells, where the ionic strength is constant throughout, this is to be expected on the basis of the known properties of mixtures of electrolytes embodied in Harned's rule and related expressions [99]. Covington [98] pointed out that in some double liquid junction cells, which are reasonably symmetrical, the two diffusion potentials (E_d) are not equal and opposite and hence $\Delta E_d \neq 0$ as is often assumed. Clearly, more experimental and theoretical work on the design of cells with liquid junctions is desirable.

Related to Owen's method and suitable for less precise determinations, such as the study of ionic equilibria by potentiometric techniques, is the method employed by Biedermann and Sillén [100], in which the solution species of interest is added to the electrolyte on the right hand side of the cell:

$$\text{Hg; Hg}_2\text{Cl}_2 \mid 4M \text{ NaCl} \parallel 3M \text{ NaClO}_4 \left\|\begin{array}{l}(3-0.001 \text{ h}) \ M \text{ NaClO}_4 \\ 0.001 \text{ h } M \text{ HClO}_4\end{array}\right| \text{H}_2\text{; Pt.}$$

The electrode on the right could be, instead of the hydrogen gas electrode, e.g., $Ag^+|Ag$; Hg_2^{2+} | Hg; Fe^{2+}, Fe^{3+} | Pt; or Cl^- | AgCl; Ag, with the concentration of the potential determining species small in comparison with the other ions present. In this cell, h is related to the x used for Owen's cell by $x = h/3$ or, in general, $x = h/I$, where I is the ionic strength. Applying Henderson's equation, it can be shown that $E_d = (RT/F) \ hd/I$ where d is a constant involving ionic mobilities, thus partially accounting for the fact that plots of $E_d + E_s(= E - E_{el})$ against h/I are linear (Fig. 6).

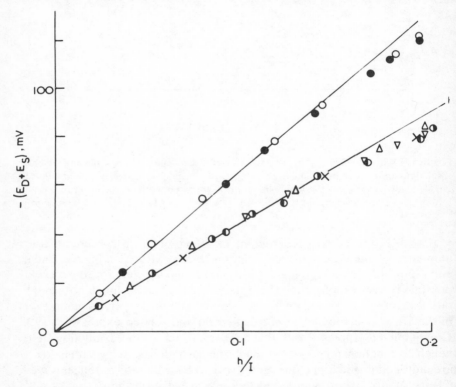

Figure 6.   Variation of emf with h/l for the Biedermann-Sillén cell [100]. Upper line: O Cl^-|AgCl; Ag; ● Br^-|AgBr; Ag. Lower line: ◑H^+|H_2; Pt; ◐ Ag^+|Ag; ▽Fe^{2+}, Fe^{3+}| Pt; X Cu^{2+}|Cu.

Spiro [97], taking into account the variation of E_s, has shown that the slope of the plots is in more reasonable accord with experiment. The experimental value of d can be used to make "liquid junction potential corrections" to titration results when h is not varied. Extensions of this work, including attempts to take into account activity coefficient variations, have been attempted by Sullivan and Zielen [101] and Rossotti and Rossotti [102].

Biedermann and Sillén [100] found that the slope of the $(E - E_{el})$ against h/I plots was different, depending on whether a cation or anion responsive electrode was used on the right hand side of the cell above (Fig. 6). This can be shown [103] to be a consequence of the particular combination of **mean** ionic activity coefficients involved in E_s for the anion-anion electrode cell and the unsymmetrical anion-cation electrode cell.

Most of our remaining knowledge of liquid junction potentials comes from studies of cells with junctions such as [84-86]:

$$HCl(0.1M) \| KCl (0.1 M).$$

For this and similar cells with other alkali metal chlorides, data are available from which E_s can be evaluated, making the assumptions of a continuous mixture junction [84, 97]. E_s is found to be small, 0.7 mV for $HCl \| KCl$, but it does not follow that this will always be so. Hafemann [104] has used a computer simulation method to calculate the potential and its rise time for these simple junctions. His results are in agreement with calculations by the Planck and Henderson equations and with experiment, if the results of Grahame and Cummings [86] are used and not those of MacInnes and Yeh [85], whose values, in which potassium chloride was one of the electrolytes, are incorrect. It is worth drawing attention to the fact that Bass [105] has reexamined and elaborated Planck's kinetic treatment of liquid junction potentials with particular reference to the inconsistent assumption of electroneutrality throughout the junction, and Picknett [106] has suggested a novel method of calculating E_j which apparently does not depend on the structure of the junction.

The problem of liquid junction potentials between aqueous and partially aqueous or non-aqueous solvents is an even more difficult one. Bates, Paabo and Robinson [107] have obtained data which suggest that the liquid junction potential is constant and reproducible between aqueous saturated potassium chloride and a given solvent mixture irrespective of the solute buffer system, provided it is not too acid or too alkaline. It is therefore unnecessary in operational pH measurements to replace the aqueous salt bridge by a partially aqueous one. Their δ values [107] can be used to correct operational pH measurements obtained with aqueous pH standards to the appropriate pH scale for the particular solvent mixture. Gutbezahl and Grunwald [108] have calculated E_j for ethanol-water saturated potassium chloride junctions and various buffer solute systems in low concentration so that the Debye-Hückel limiting equation could be used for the single ion activity coefficients. They concluded that E_j could be well over 100 mV for 100% ethanol. Schwabe and Geisler [109] have recently presented results from which they claim that E_j for such junctions is small and of the order of magnitude of aqueous diffusion potentials. They studied, essentially, cells involving single and double junctions of the forms:

$$Hg; Hg_2Ac_2|NaAc(sat), CH_3OH (98\%)\|KCl(sat), H_2O|Hg_2Cl_2; Hg \quad (I)$$

$$Hg; Hg_2Ac_2|NaAc(sat), CH_3OH (98\%)\|xX + (1\text{-}x) Y\|KCl(sat),$$
$$H_2O|Hg_2Cl_2; Hg \quad\quad\quad (II)$$

where various proportions x of the two solvents X and Y were used in the bridge solution which contained an acetate buffer. X and Y were water, methanol, isopropanol, dioxane, *etc.*, in various combinations. The measurements on cell (II) were made in two cells with hydrogen or glass electrodes as "bridging" electrodes (Section I.D.). The results should be the same, and the scatter obtained (± 2 mV) gives an indication of the precision of the determinations, a point not made clear in the paper [109]. They found that $E_{II} - E_I \not> 20$ mV for the solvent combinations in cell (II) mentioned, even when Y was phenol or toluene, substances which are immiscible with water, so that there is a sharp phase boundary at the right hand junction in cell (II). This latter result is particularly surprising, but Schwabe and Geisler's [109] conclusion, that the results demonstrate that E_j in cell (I) is small, is questionable. It has been pointed out above that in some cases [98] the residual diffusion potential in a double junction cell is the same as that in an otherwise identical single junction cell. The results are, however, extremely interesting and similar, though simpler, experiments along these lines would be valuable.

Lastly in this section, we will turn to the problem of the possibility of a liquid junction potential caused by excessive solubility from an electrode of the second kind in a cell without transference. Access of this dissolved material to the other electrode must often be prevented by a closed tap or similar means, and hence a liquid junction potential could arise. This problem has been considered recently by Smyrl and Tobias [110] for the cell

$$Li|LiCl, DMSO|TlCl(s); Tl(Hg)$$

in connection with their suggested use [111] of the thallium amalgam-thallous chloride electrode (Section III.F.) as a reference electrode in dimethylsulfoxide (DMSO). While their explanation of the divergence of their emf results from the expected values at low concentrations of lithium chloride is correct, their arguments are erroneous. The junction concerned is:

$$LiCl(m_1)\|LiCl(m_1), TlCl(m_2).$$

Because of the absence of mobility data in DMSO, they assumed that the three ions have equal ionic mobilities, without realizing that, if this were so, there would be no diffusion potential (E_d), the junction then being effectively homo-ionic:

$$LiCl(m_1)\|LiCl(m_1 + m_2).$$

Secondly, they failed to take into account that E_{el} will be affected by the additional chloride molality at the right hand electrode.

A correct treatment of the problem for this cell is as follows:

The emf is

$$E = E° - (RT/F) \ln (a_{Li^+} a_{Cl^-}) + E_d \tag{5}$$

$$= E° - (RT/F) \ln [m_1 (m_1 + m_2) \gamma_\pm^2] + E_d \tag{6}$$

$$= E° - (RT/F) \ln (m_1^2 \gamma_\pm^2) - (RT/F) \ln (1 + m_2/m_1) + E_d \tag{7}$$

if only the ideal part of E_j is considered. The symbol $\gamma_\pm$ is, with sufficient accuracy, the mean ionic activity coefficient of lithium chloride. The term $\ln (1 + m_2/m_1)$ takes into account the effect of the dissolved thallous chloride on E_{el}.

Using Henderson's equation, where the λ's are ionic conductances:

$$E_d = - (RT/F) \left(\frac{\lambda_{Tl} - \lambda_{Cl}}{\lambda_{Tl} + \lambda_{Cl}}\right) \ln \left[1 + \frac{m_2(\lambda_{Tl} + \lambda_{Cl})}{m_1(\lambda_{Li} + \lambda_{Cl})} \right] \tag{8}$$

and since $m_2 < m_1$ the logarithm can be expanded [98],

$$E_d = - (RT/F) \left[\frac{m_2(\lambda_{Tl} - \lambda_{Cl})}{m_1(\lambda_{Li} + \lambda_{Cl})} \right] \tag{9}$$

This can be combined with the solubility correction term to give for the cell emf

$$E = E° - (RT/F) \ln m_1^2 \gamma_\pm^2 - (RT/F) \left[\frac{m_2(\lambda_{Li} + \lambda_{Tl})}{m_1(\lambda_{Li} + \lambda_{Cl})} \right] \tag{10}$$

where the last term is the correction term which Smyrl and Tobias [110] attempted to calculate. If, in the absence of experimental results, we assume all the mobilities are equal, then only the solubility term remains as expected. Alternatively, if as for water [112] $\lambda_{Cl} \simeq \lambda_{Tl}$ then the mobility term is again unity and $E_d = 0$, but even so the mobility term is unlikely to be very different from unity.

The values of the correction term based on the solubility correction alone are very similar to Smyrl and Tobias' values [110], e.g., for $m_1 = 10^{-3}$ mol kg^{-1} the correction is about 8 mV and for $m_1 = 5 \times 10^{-4}$ mol kg^{-1} the correction is about 25 mV, which agrees well with 21 mV for the experimental value at this molality.

V. Temperature Effects

In all precise work it is essential that a constant temperature be maintained during a series of measurements, and precautions should be taken to see that this is so. In on-line pH measurements with glass electrodes, it does occur, however, that the temperature of the solution of interest may vary or differ from that of the standard buffer solution. Slope factor compensation is necessary on pH meters and "specific ion" meters in order that the pH or pIon may be read directly from the meter. This is only one factor in temperature compensation, however.

It is not certain, whether ideas developed for glass electrodes and pH meters can be applied to specific ion measurements, as this has not been tested, but there seems to be no reason why they should not be applicable apart from the proviso, mentioned in Section I, of the much smaller millivolt scale range involved. The use of the so-called "isopotential control" [113,114] will be discussed in relation to pH measurements and its possible application to pIon measurements follows directly.

Two distinct cases arise:

a. Both electrodes reach temperature equilibrium in the test and standard buffers. Thus there are two cells involved, each at a different temperature.

b. The glass electrode reaches temperature equilibrium in both solutions but the reference electrode is remote and remains at a constant temperature. Thus there is a temperature gradient in the potassium chloride solution.

For the operational pH cell, we have as in Section II.E. for a test solution X:

$$E_X = (E^{\circ\prime} + E_j + E_i) + (RT \ln 10 / F) \mathrm{pH_x} \tag{11}$$

except that there is an additional term, E_i, which is the emf of the glass electrode inner reference system, regarding the inner surface of the glass electrode as a hydrogen electrode, viz.

$$\mathrm{Ag; AgCl | HCl | H_2}$$

The difference of temperature in the measurements causes a change in the "standard potential" term $(E^{\circ\prime} + E_j + E_i)$ known as a "zero shift". In general, its variation with temperature can be expressed as a power series in temperature. However, over a limited range of temperature (20 °C) a simple linear variation is adequate, hence,

$$E_X = a + bT + (RT \ln 10/F) \, pH_X \qquad (12)$$

E will not be a function of temperature when

$$bT = (RT \ln 10/F) \, pH \qquad (13)$$

or when

$$pH_i = \frac{-b}{RT \ln 10/F} = \frac{F}{R \ln 10} \cdot \frac{dE_x}{dT} \qquad (14)$$

Here, pH_i is termed the isopotential [113] or the isothermenschnittpunkt (the isothermal intersection point), since it is the pH where the lines representing the variation of E_X with pH cross. The pH at which $E = 0$ is called the zero point or nullpunkt.

The zero shift error in terms of pH_i is [114]:

$$(R \ln 10/F) \, pH_i \, (T_X - T_S)$$

where T_X and T_S are the temperatures of the test and standard buffers respectively, or as an error in pH_X:

$$\Delta pH_X = \frac{T_X - T_S}{T_X} \, pH_i. \qquad (15)$$

In a pH meter with variable isopotential control, a bias potential equal to $(RT \ln 10/F) \, pH_i$ is derived automatically to correct for zero shift. Values of pH_i required for this can be derived from the temperature coefficients of the cell system, *e.g.*,

$$\text{Ag; AgCl} | \text{HCl} | \text{H}_2 \text{----} \text{H}_2 | \text{X} \| \text{KCl(sat)} | \text{Hg}_2\text{Cl}_2; \text{Hg}$$

Case (b), where the reference electrode is at a constant temperature, can be treated in a similar way to obtain **different** pH_i values, by combining with the cell system above the thermo-cell:

$$\text{Hg; Hg}_2\text{Cl}_2 | \text{KCl(sat)} \| \text{KCl(sat)} | \text{Hg}_2\text{Cl}_2; \text{Hg}$$
$$\text{(variable } T) \qquad \qquad \text{(fixed } T)$$

In this case, the pH_i values are independent of the reference electrode used. The pH_i value can be varied by suitable choice of the inner reference system for the glass electrode, and symmetrical cells have special advantages [76,77,115].

When the data necessary to calculate pH_i are not available (and this will certainly be so for ion-selective electrodes such as the fluoride electrode), then pH_i may be determined experimentally [114] using a buffer solution whose pH values at two temperatures about 20 °C apart are known. The pH meter is calibrated with the buffer at the lower temperature T_1 and then the pH read at T_2 after enough time for the electrode(s) to temperature equilibrate, using manual or automatic slope factor compensation. The pH value read from the meter at the second temperature T_2 will differ from the true known value by

$$\Delta pH = \left(\frac{T_2 - T_1}{T_2}\right) pH_i. \tag{16}$$

To my knowledge isopotential considerations have been applied only to pH measurements and not even to sodium ion determinations with glass electrodes. Even if such considerations are impractical in application to ion-selective electrodes, they do indicate the factors by which the effect of temperature differences can be reduced. The growing tendency among manufacturers to market their electrodes in kit form **dry** is greatly to be welcomed as it gives the user much greater degree of freedom in the design of his measuring system.

VI. References

[1] Ives, D. J. G., and Janz, G. J., Eds., Reference Electrodes, Academic Press, New York, 1961.

[2] Janz, G. J., and Ives, D. J. G., Ann. N. Y. Acad. Sci. **148**, 210 (1968).

[3] Butler, J. N., et al., J. Phys. Chem. **71**, 910; 3294; 4479 (1967).

[4] Feakins, D., in Hydrogen-Bonded Solvent Systems, A. K. Covington and P. Jones, Eds., Taylor and Francis, London, 1968, p. 236.

[5] Thompson, M. R., J. Res. Nat. Bur. Stand. **9**, 833 (1932).

[6] Bottom, A. E., and Covington, A. K., Paper presented at the International Measurement Confederation (IMEKO) Symposium on Electrochemical Sensors, Veszprem, Hungary, October 1968.

[7] Riseman, J. H., and Wall, R. A., U. S. Patent 3306837 (1967).

[8] Douheret, G., Bull. Soc. Chim. Fr. 3341 (1966).

[9] Martin, J. A., and Duperis, J., Bull. Soc. Chim. Fr. 138 (1968).

[10] Badoz-Lambling, J., Desbarres, J., and Tacussel, J., Bull. Soc. Chim. Fr. 53 (1962).

[11] Ritchie, C. D., et al., J. Amer. Chem. Soc. **89**, 1447; 1721 (1967).

[12] Frant, M. S., and Ross, J. W., Science **154**, 1553 (1966).

[13] Beck, W. H., Bottom, A. E., and Covington, A. K., Anal. Chem. **40**, 501 (1968).

[14] Covington, A. K., and Lilley, T. H., Phys. Chem. Glasses **8**, 88 (1967).

[15] Shultz, M. M., Uch. Zap. Leningrad Univ., No. 169 **13**, 80 (1953).

[16] Covington, A. K., Paabo, M., Robinson, R. A., and Bates, R. G., Anal. Chem. **40**, 700 (1968).

[17] Bates, R. G., and Alfenaar, M., NBS Technical Note, No. 453 (1968).

[18] Harned, H. S., and Ehlers, R. W., J. Amer. Chem. Soc. **54**, 1350 (1932).

[19] Bates, R. G., Guggenheim, E. A., Harned, H. S., Ives, D. J. G., Janz, G. J., Monk, C. B., Prue, J. E., Robinson, R. A., Stokes, R. H., and Wynne-Jones, W. F. K., J. Chem. Phys. 25, 361 (1956).

[20] Zielen, A. J., J. Phys. Chem. 67, 1474 (1963).

[21] Covington, A. K., Dobson, J. V., and Lord Wynne-Jones, Trans. Faraday Soc. 61, 2050 (1965).

[22] Srinivasan, K. V., Ph.D. Thesis, University of Newcastle upon Tyne, 1968.

[23] Bates, R. G., Determination of pH, Wiley, New York, 1964, pp. 24-25.

[24] Bates, R. G., Chapter 6, this publication.

[25] Lauchlin, A. D. E., and Page, J. E., Nature 151, 84 (1943).

[26] Gran, G., and Althin, B., Acta Chem. Scand. 4, 967 (1950).

[27] Mesmer, R. E., Anal. Chem. 40, 443 (1968).

[28] Durst, R. A., Anal. Chem. 40, 931 (1968).

[29] Popoff, S., Kunz, A. H., and Snow, R. D., J. Phys. Chem. 32, 1056 (1928).

[30] Hills, G. J., and Ives, D. J. G., J. Chem. Soc. 305 (1951).

[31] Caudle, J., Ph. D. Thesis, University of Durham, 1964.

[32] Bates, R. G., Determination of pH, Wiley, New York, 1964, pp.230-245.

[33] Bates, R. G., ibid., pp. 279-286.

[34] Janz, G. J., and Taniguchi, H., Chem. Rev. 53, 397 (1953).

[35] Janz, G. J., in Reference Electrodes, D. J. G. Ives and G. J. Janz, Eds., Academic Press, New York, pp. 179-230.

[36] Ashby, J. H., Crook, E. M., and Datta, S. P., Biochem. J. 56, 190 (1954).

[37] Manov, G. G., DeLollis, N. J., and Acree, S. F., J. Res. Nat. Bur. Stand. 34, 115 (1945).

[38] Pinching, G. D., and Bates, R. G., J. Res. Nat. Bur. Stand. 37, 311 (1946).

[39] Güntelberg, E., Studier over Electrolyt-Activiteter, G. E. C. Gads Forlag, Copenhagen, 1938.

[40] Güntelberg, E., Z. physik. Chem. 123, 199 (1926).

[41] Harned, H. S., and Ehlers, R. W., J. Amer. Chem. Soc. 55, 2179 (1933).

[42] Bates, R. G., and Bower, V. E., J. Res. Nat. Bur. Stand. 53, 283 (1954).

[43] Covington, A. K., Dobson, J. V., and Lord Wynne-Jones, Electrochim. Acta 12, 525 (1967).

[44] Guggenheim, E. A., and Turgeon, J. C., Trans. Faraday Soc. 51, 747 (1955).

[45] Alner, D. J., Greczek, J. J., and Smeeth, A. G., J. Chem. Soc. , 1205 (1967).

[46] Hetzer, H. B., Robinson, R. A., and Bates, R. G., J. Phys. Chem. 66, 1423 (1962).

[47] Hetzer, H. B., Robinson, R. A., and Bates, R. G., J. Phys. Chem. 68, 1929 (1964).

[48] Hills, G. J., and Ives, D. J. G., J. Chem. Soc. 311 (1951).

[49] Schwabe, K., and Ziegenbalg, S., Z. Elektrochem. 62, 172 (1958).

[50] Grzybowski, A. K., J. Phys. Chem. 52, 550 (1958).

[51] Hills, G. J., and Ives, D. J. G., in Reference Electrodes, D. J. G. Ives and G. J. Janz, Eds., Academic Press, New York, 1961, pp.127-162.

[52] Armstrong, R. D., Fleischmann, M., and Thirsk, H. R., Trans. Faraday Soc. 61, 2238 (1965); see also Behr, B., and Taraskewska, J., J. Electroanal. Chem. 19, 373 (1968).

[53] Dry, M. E., and Gledhill, J. A., Trans. Faraday Soc. 51, 1119 (1955).

[54] Hamer, W. J., and Acree, S. F., J. Res. Nat. Bur. Stand. 32, 215 (1944); Hamer, W. J., Pinching, G. D., and Acree, S. F., ibid., 35, 539 (1945); ibid. 36, 47 (1946).

[55] Greczek, J. J., Thesis, University of London, 1964.

[56] Shams El Din, A. M., and Kamel, L. A., J. Electroanal. Chem. 11, 111 (1966).

[57] Sibbald, P. G., and Matsuyama, G., Anal. Chem. 35, 1718 (1963).

[58] Mattock, G., pH Measurement and Titration, Heywood, London, 1961, p. 153.

[59] Ives, D. J. G., and Smith, F. R., in Reference Electrodes, D. J. G. Ives and G. J. Janz, Eds., Academic Press, New York, p. 403.

[60] Hulett, G. A., Phys. Rev. 32, 257 (1911).

[61] Beck, W. H., Dobson, J. V., and Wynne-Jones, W. F. K., Trans. Faraday Soc. 56, 1172 (1960).

[62] Hamer, W. J., and Harned, H. S., J. Amer. Chem. Soc. 57, 27 (1935).

[63] Covington, A. K., Dobson, J. V., and Lord Wynne-Jones, Trans. Faraday Soc. 61, 2057 (1965).

[64] Larson, W. D., and MacDougall, F. H., J. Phys. Chem. 41, 493 (1937).

[65] Larson, W. D., and Tomsicek, W. J., J. Amer. Chem. Soc. 61, 65 (1939).

[66] Larson, W. D., J. Phys. Chem. 67, 937 (1963).

[67] Larson, W. D., and Tomsicek, W. J., J. Amer. Chem. Soc. 63, 3329 (1941).

[68] Covington, A. K., Talukdar, P. K., and Thirsk, H. R., Trans. Faraday Soc. 60, 412 (1964).

[69] Gryzin, Yu. I., Zhur. fiz. Khim. 38, 2834 (1964).

[70] Chauchard, J., and Gauthier, J., Bull. Soc. chim. Fr. 2635 (1966).

[71] Schwabe, K., and Glockner, G., Z. physik. Chem. 59, 504 (1955).

[72] Schwabe, K., Naturwissenschaften 44, 350 (1957).

[73] Aditya, S., Aditya, S., and Mukherjee, S. K., J. Ind. Chem. Soc. 42, 252 (1965).

[74] Bertram, J., and Bone, S. J., Trans. Faraday Soc. 63, 415 (1967).

[75] Jena Glaswerk Schott und Gen., Mainz, British Patent 894249(1962).

[76] Fricke, H. K., Zucker 14, No. 7 (1961).

[77] Fricke, H. K., in Beitrage zur angewandte Glasforschung, E. Schott, Ed., Wiss. Verlags mbH., Stuttgart, 1960, pp. 175-198.

[78] Hansen, M., and Anderko, K., Constitution of Binary Alloys, 2nd ed., McGraw Hill, New York, 1958.

[79] Hu, K-H, and Scott, A. B., J. Amer. Chem. Soc. 77, 1380 (1955).

[80] Mussini, T., and Longhi, P., Ric. Sci. Rend. A 8, 1352 (1965).

[81] Cowperthwaite, I. A., La Mer, V. K., and Barksdale, J., J. Amer. Chem. Soc. 56, 544 (1934).

[82] Guggenheim, E. A., J. Amer. Chem. Soc. 52, 1315 (1930); J. Phys. Chem. 36, 1758 (1930).

[83] Unmack, A., and Guggenheim, E. A., Kgl. Danske Videnskab. Selskab. Mat. Fys. Med., No. 8, 10 (1930).

[84] Guggenheim, E. A., and Unmack, A., ibid., No. 14, 10 (1931).

[85] MacInnes, D. A., and Yeh, Y. L., J. Amer. Chem. Soc. 43, 2563 (1921).

[86] Grahame, D. C., and Cummings, J. I., ONR Techn. Rep. No. 5 (1950).

[87] Perley, G. A., Trans. Electrochem. Soc. 92, 497 (1947).

[88] Carson, W. M., Michelson, C. E., and Koyama, K., Anal. Chem. 27, 472 (1955).

[89] Kater, J. A. R., Leonard, J. E., and Matsuyama, G., Ann. N. Y. Acad. Sci. 148, 54 (1968); British Patent 1134140 (1968).

[90] Mattock, G., pH Measurement and Titration, Heywood, London, 1961, pp. 179-182.

[91] Bates, R. G., and Paabo, M., unpublished work quoted in Bates, R. G., Determination of pH, Wiley, New York, 1964, p. 87.

[92] Bates, R. G., Pinching, G. D., and Smith, E. R., J. Res. Nat. Bur. Stand. 45, 418 (1950).

[93] MacInnes, D. A., Principles of Electrochemistry, Dover, New York, 1961, p. 244.

[94] Finkelstein, N. P., and Verdier, E. T., Trans. Faraday Soc. 53, 1618 (1957).

[95] Prue, J. E., and Read, A. J., J. Chem. Soc. A, 1812 (1966).

[96] Owen, B. B., J. Amer. Chem. Soc. 60, 2229 (1938).

[97] Spiro, M., Electrochim. Acta 11, 569 (1966).

[98] Covington, A. K., Electrochim. Acta **11**, 959 (1966).

[99] Harned, H. S., and Robinson, R. A., Multicomponent Electrolyte Solutions, Pergamon, Oxford, 1968.

[100] Biedermann, G., and Sillén, L. G., Arkiv Kemi **5**, 425 (1953).

[101] Sullivan, J. C., and Zielen, A. J., J. Phys. Chem. **66**, 1065 (1962).

[102] Rossotti, F. J. C., and Rossotti, H., J. Phys. Chem. **68**, 3773 (1964).

[103] Covington, A. K., unpublished data.

[104] Hafemann, D. R., J. Phys. Chem. **69**, 4226 (1965).

[105] Bass, L., Trans. Faraday Soc. **60**, 1914 (1964); see also Guggenheim, E. A., Proc. Phys. Soc. **85**, 393 (1965).

[106] Picknett, R. G., Trans. Faraday Soc. **64**, 1059 (1968).

[107] Bates, R. G., Paabo, M., and Robinson, R. A., J. Phys. Chem. **67**, 1833(1963).

[108] Gutbezahl, B., and Grunwald, E., J. Amer. Chem. Soc. **75**, 565 (1953).

[109] Schwabe, K., and Geisler, H., Electrochim. Acta **12**, 147 (1967).

[110] Smyrl, W. H., and Tobias, C. W., Electrochim. Acta **13**, 1581 (1968).

[111] Smyrl, W. H., and Tobias, C. W., J. Electrochem. Soc. **113**, 754 (1966).

[112] Robinson, R. A., and Stokes, R. H., Electrolyte Solutions, Butterworth, London, 2nd ed., 1959, p. 463.

[113] Jackson, J., Chem. Ind. (London) **67**, 7 (1948).

[114] Mattock, G., pH Measurement and Titration, Heywood, London, 1961, pp. 190-197.

[115] Bates, R. G., Determination of pH, Wiley, New York, 1964, pp. 327-330.

CHAPTER 5

THERMODYNAMIC STUDIES

James N. Butler

Tyco Laboratories, Inc.
Waltham, Massachusetts 01254

I. Introduction

In this volume, we are concerned with the impact of a new technology on various aspects of chemistry. This chapter in particular is concerned with how solid-state and liquid ion exchange membrane electrodes can be used in studies of the thermodynamics of solutions. As is well known, the potential of an electrochemical cell usually depends on the composition of the electrolyte, and by a proper choice of electrodes, a cell can be made to yield the activity of a particular component over a wide range of composition. Studies of this kind have been well documented, and range from measurements of activity coefficients [1,2] (where the emphasis is on relatively small deviations from the ideal behavior of a completely dissociated electrolyte) to studies of multiple equilibria in a constant ionic medium [3] (where the emphasis is on strong chemical interactions and the identification of solution species). The measurement of standard potentials and oxidation-reduction equilibria [3,4,5], an important part of electrochemical thermodynamics, concerns us only peripherally in this chapter because we have limited ourselves to electrode systems of the membrane type, which make use of ion-exchange (rather than oxidation-reduction) equilibria.

To be somewhat general, for the moment, consider a cell of the type

"M-electrode" | M^+, X^-, solvent, *etc.* | "X-electrode"

where the left hand electrode is reversible to the cation M^+ and the right hand electrode is reversible to the anion X^-. Either or both of these ions could be polyvalent, and the *"etc."* which I have indicated in the electrolyte could include any number of other ions so long as the electrodes do not respond to them. For such a cell, the potential is given by

$$E = E° - \frac{RT}{nF} \ln \{ [M^+] [X^-] \gamma_\pm^2 \} \tag{1}$$

where R is the gas constant, T is the absolute temperature, F is the Faraday constant, $[M^+]$ is the concentration of the cation, $[X^-]$ is the concentration of the anion, $\gamma_\pm$ is the mean activity coefficient of the salt

MX in this particular electrolyte, and n is the number of electrons transferred (in this case, $n = 1$, but for polyvalent ions, n could be greater than unity). The concentration scale is usually taken to be moles per kilogram of solvent, but this is quite arbitrary, and might also be moles per liter of solution or mole fraction. The standard potential $E°$ is obtained by calibration of the cell with an MX solution of known activity, and this may be either a relatively concentrated solution for which the activity coefficients are known from other experiments, or may involve extrapolation of measurements with this particular cell to infinite dilution, where $\gamma_{\pm}$ can be taken equal to unity.

In the above discussion, we have made a tacit assumption which is not at all trivial; somehow we know that the electrodes are reversible to the cation or anion specified, and to no other. How is it possible to arrive at this conclusion? In dilute solutions, one can determine the reversibility of the "M-electrode," for example, by keeping the concentration of X^- constant and varying the concentration of M^+ over a wide range. If Equation (1) is obeyed within the accuracy that one can calculate $\gamma_{\pm}$ from the Debye-Hückel theory or from other measurements (such as isopiestic vapor pressure studies), then one can say with reasonable confidence that the "M-electrode" is reversible to the cation M^+.

Of course, the restriction of electrical neutrality in the solution requires that a second cation A^+ be present to balance the charge on the anions X^-, which are not necessarily equal in concentration to M^+, and this introduces the question of whether the "M-electrode" is **specific** for M^+ or whether it possibly is affected by A^+ also.

In the usual context, "interference" implies that the cell potential varies as if some fraction of A^+ behaved as if it were M^+:

$$E = E° - \frac{RT}{F} \ln \{[M^+] + k_s[A^+]\} - \frac{RT}{F} \ln \{[X^-]\gamma_{\pm}^2\} \qquad (2)$$

where k_s is called the selectivity ratio. In solutions where $[A^+] >> [M^+]$ and $[X^-]$ is constant, one expects to see a constant value of E. Such behavior is typical of cation-sensitive glass electrodes, and k_s is relatively insensitive to solution composition [12]. However, k_s may vary with both solution composition and electrode type.

Another type of effect which may occur is that A^+ forms some sort of complexes with X^-, thereby diminishing the concentration of free X^-. This is best treated within the framework of solution equilibria. An example is the effect of hydrogen ion on the fluoride-sensitive LaF_3 membrane electrode, discussed in the next section. If A^+ is in large excess, pseudo-Nernstian behavior with variations in $[M^+]$ may be observed, but deviations will be observable in the range where $[M^+]/[A^+]$ is between 0.1 and 10. If Equation (1) is obeyed in this range, then the specificity of the electrode for M^+ is confirmed. Unfortunately, the presence of a second cation affects to some extent the activity coefficient $\gamma_{\pm}$ of the salt MX, and so unless this activity coefficient is known from some independent experiment, a test of this type, particularly in solutions of concentration greater than 1 molal, may be somewhat ambiguous.

With membrane electrodes and electrodes of the second kind, interference phenomena may be kinetically limited and may be quite complex in form [10].

From a discussion such as this, it becomes quite apparent that measurements of activity coefficients with ion-selective electrodes are intimately bound up with the question of the reversibility of the electrodes themselves and their specificity for a particular ion. Only by amassing a considerable amount of evidence that ion-selective electrodes give the same thermodynamic data as completely unrelated methods, can we gain confidence in measurements on new systems where there are no other data with which to compare.

Thus there are no new **principles** involved in studies of solution thermodynamics using membrane-type electrodes, but there **is** a new collection of tools which have yet to be tested in detail to see how accurately they can determine the quantities we desire—activity coefficients and equilibrium constants. Before we proceed to a review of the few thermodynamic studies which have been made with these electrodes during their short history, let us take a somewhat broader view of the field and see how the electrodes discussed in this volume form a logical extension of classical measurements, and consider a number of new directions from which to approach systems which cannot be studied by the classical methods.

From the thermodynamic viewpoint, the most thoroughly studied electrochemical cell [1] is

$$\text{Pt}; \text{H}_2 \mid \text{H}^+, \text{Cl}^-, \text{solvent}, etc. \mid \text{AgCl}; \text{Ag}$$

which yields the mean activity coefficient of hydrochloric acid. Measurements can be made with this cell in aqueous solutions and many non-aqueous solutions with extraordinarily high accuracy [6,7]. Quite a wide variety of other ions can be added to the solution without interfering with the reversibility of the electrodes to hydrogen ion and chloride ion. Examples are: alkali metal, alkaline earth, and other cations with reduction potentials more negative than hydrogen ion; sulfate, fluoride, carbonate, acetate, and many other organic anions which are not easily reducible or oxidizable, and which do not form strong silver complexes or highly insoluble silver salts.

The hydrogen-silver chloride cell is usually called a "cell without liquid junction", but this is possible only because of the small amount of interference between the soluble species which inevitably result from each electrode. More rigorously, we might write the cell as

$$Pt;H(ads) \mid H_2, H^+, Cl^-, etc. \mid H^+, Cl^-, Ag^+, AgCl, AgCl_2^-, etc. \mid AgCl;Ag$$

a more complex notation which reflects the mechanism of the two electrodes as well as the materials which are dissolved in the electrolyte in contact with each electrode [5]. Only because the solubility of H_2 and AgCl in water is quite small, compared to the concentrations of HCl normally studied, can the liquid junction between the two solutions be neglected. In some non-aqueous media [7,8], the complexes of AgCl (or analogous electrodes) are much more stable than in water, and this liquid junction can contribute a considerable potential. In practice, no attempt is usually made to prevent H_2 from reaching the silver-silver chloride electrode, or to prevent soluble silver species from reaching the platinum electrode. Fortunately, the kinetics of the $H(ads) \mid H^+$ couple and the $Ag \mid Ag^+$ couple are so rapid that small amounts of dissolved silver do not appreciably shift the potential of the hydrogen electrode, and small amounts of dissolved hydrogen do not appreciably shift the potential of the silver electrode.

An analysis of the type we have just gone through can be made only when the mechanism of each electrode reaction as well as all the possible equilibria and transport phenomena within the electrolyte are quantitatively understood. With such a complete mechanistic understanding, we can predict not only what conditions (extremely dilute or extremely concentrated HCl, oxygen present in the solution, etc.) can interfere with the operation of the electrodes, but we can also predict quantitatively the extent to which various ions added to the solution can interfere with the specificity of the electrodes.

Equilibria have also been studied with this type of cell. If the concentration of chloride ion is fixed, then the hydrogen electrode responds to changes in the activity of hydrogen ion, and equilibrium constants for various acid-base reactions can be measured quite accurately, either in a medium of constant ionic strength, or in a series of media which allow extrapolation to infinite dilution.

The versatility of the hydrogen-silver chloride cell results from the high degree of specificity of the two electrodes used; and this cell has been exploited for a large variety of thermodynamic measurements. However, many substances interfere with its operation, particularly ammonia, cyanide, or thiosulfate, which convert AgCl to stable, soluble complexes; bromide, iodide, or sulfide, which convert AgCl to a less soluble salt; any organic or inorganic material reducible by hydrogen at a platinum electrode, or oxidizable by hydrogen ion or silver ion at either a platinum or silver electrode—which excludes a great many materials of interest to the biochemist, biologist, organic chemist, and analytical chemist.

Furthermore, it can measure only the mean activity of HCl in an electrolyte, and attempts to extend this kind of cell to other salts did not yield nearly such a wide variety of information.

The problem faced by the electrochemical thermodynamicist who had only a few classical electrodes at his disposal was quite clear: there were many systems for which he would like to have thermodynamic data which were quite inaccessible by means of any electrochemical cell he could devise. For example, measurement of the activity of $ZnCl_2$ in the presence of NaCl was simple and could be carried out with the cell

$$Zn(Hg) \mid ZnCl_2, \ NaCl, \ H_2O \mid AgCl;Ag$$

On the other hand, there was no way in which a cell could be set up which measured the activity of NaCl in the presence of $ZnCl_2$, until the advent of cation-sensitive glass electrodes.

One of the very important techniques for studying complex equilibria is to use a constant ionic medium consisting of a high concentration of inert salt (*e.g.*, $NaClO_4$) which keeps activity coefficients and liquid junction potentials constant provided the other ions (of interest) are at relatively low concentrations. Even though the constant ionic medium technique could have been applied to some studies of complex equilibria as early as 1900, it was not employed widely until the Debye-Hückel theory and studies of ion-pairing phenomena had made it clear that there were electrolytes which **were** relatively inert toward interaction with many ions, and which could be used to keep the activity coefficients constant while the equilibria were unraveled.

The development of the proton-sensitive glass electrode and its widespread adoption for the measurement of pH was the first really significant use of a membrane-type electrode for thermodynamic measurements. Even so, for a long time glass electrodes were mistrusted by thermodynamicists, because their potentials drifted with time and could not be referred to a primary standard redox couple. One of the first studies to make extensive use of glass electrodes for thermodynamic measurements was the work of Bjerrum [9] on the complexes of metal ions with ammonia. By using a constant ionic strength medium consisting of an ammonium salt, changes in glass electrode potential could be made to reflect changes in NH_3 concentration. The long succession of studies by Sillén and coworkers [3] of hydrolytic equilibria, and of Schwarzenbach and others on the formation of complexes between organic compounds and metal ions [3] has exploited both the constant ionic medium concept, and the measurement of hydrogen ion activity with a glass electrode to determine indirectly the activity of an acid or base which is the complexing ligand. Although initially there was a strong prejudice in favor of acid-base equilibrium constants measured in the hydrogen-silver chloride cell, within recent years many accurate studies have been made with glass electrodes [5,11].

The development of special glasses which could be used to make electrodes reversible to alkali metal cations gave a new dimension to thermodynamic studies [12]. Measuring the activity of NaCl in the presence of $ZnCl_2$, which we mentioned before as being impossible for the classical electrochemist, now became simple with a cation-sensitive glass electrode which showed highly specific response to Na^+ and essentially no response to divalent ions such as Zn^{++}. These cation-sensitive electrodes are now sufficiently stable, and the associated electronic measuring instruments sufficiently sensitive and noise-free that measurements have been made of the activity coefficients of, e.g., NaCl either alone [13,14] or in the presence of other electrolytes [15,16] which rival in accuracy the classical measurements using amalgam electrodes or the isopiestic vapor pressure method [6]. An important prerequisite for these accurate measurements is the availability of standard solutions in which the activity of NaCl is accurately known. This problem of establishing standards is a general one, and is discussed in detail in Chapter 6.

Finally, we come to the development of membrane electrodes made from materials other than glass, which are the subject of this volume. The origin, mechanism of operation [10,12] and uses of these electrodes are discussed in other chapters, and the remainder of this paper will be devoted to a review of their use in thermodynamic studies. Lest we lose perspective, however, let me summarize this introduction by saying again that these electrodes provide us with new tools for thermodynamic studies, but that these tools must be themselves thoroughly studied and their results compared with all other available methods, before we can trust them as we have learned to trust the classical and glass electrodes before them.

II. The Lanthanum Fluoride Electrode

Without doubt, the most unusual and probably the most significant of the solid-state membrane electrodes is the lanthanum fluoride electrode. First announced in 1966 by its inventors, Frant and Ross [17], it was of such immediate interest that by the end of 1968, more than 25 papers concerned with this electrode had appeared in print.

The unique property of a europium-doped lanthanum fluoride crystal to form a membrane apparently permeable to fluoride ion and virtually no other anion or cation, provided the first fluoride-reversible electrode, and indeed one of the few truly **specific** ion-selective electrodes. As we will see in detail below, this electrode gives Nernstian response to fluoride ion concentrations from above $1M$ to below $10^{-5}M$, and only OH^- seems to interfere with this response.

Essentially all the studies discussed in this section have been performed using the cell

$$Hg;Hg_2Cl_2(s) \mid KCl(sat) \mid\mid F^-, etc. \mid LaF_3(s) \mid NaF(0.1M), NaCl$$
$$(0.1M) \mid AgCl(s);Ag$$

The left hand half cell is a commercial saturated calomel electrode, and the right hand half cell is contained within the plastic body of the commercial (Orion Research, Inc.) "fluoride electrode." If the LaF_3 membrane is permeable only to fluoride ion, the potential of the cell should be given by

$$E = E_{AgCl:Ag} - E_{SCE} - \frac{RT}{F} \ln [F^-]\gamma_F + E_a + E_j. \tag{3}$$

Here E_a is the asymmetry potential of the membrane, and E_j is the liquid junction potential between saturated KCl solution and the test solution. Both these terms are usually combined with the potential of the internal silver-silver chloride electrode and the calomel reference electrode, and are found to be relatively constant with time and relatively independent of the test solution composition:

$$E = E^{\circ\prime} - \frac{RT}{F} \ln [F^-]\gamma_F \tag{4}$$

$E^{\circ\prime}$ is now a constant which is determined by calibration in a solution of known fluoride ion activity.

The use of a single ion activity coefficient introduces some ambiguity in relatively concentrated solutions, and for rigorous measurements, a cell without liquid junction, where the other electrode is reversible to a cation in the test solution, should be used. However, no such measurements have been published, although we will discuss below some work which is presently in progress. For solutions more dilute than $0.1M$, however, γ_F is usually taken to be equal to the mean activity coefficient $\gamma_\pm$ of NaF in a solution of the same ionic strength. Alternatively, γ_F may be calculated from some variant of the extended Debye-Hückel theory. For concentrations below $0.1M$, the error is of the same order of magnitude as the experimental measurement errors. At higher concentrations, the ambiguity becomes important. In a constant ionic medium, the actual value of the activity coefficient need not be known, since it is constant throughout the various experiments and can be included in the standard potential, $E^{\circ\prime}$, when calibrations are made.

A. SELECTIVITY

A number of studies have borne out the initial optimism about the unusual selectivity of this electrode. In their initial communication, Frant and Ross [17] stated that "Adding $0.1M$ NaCl or $NaNO_3$ to a solution containing $10^{-4}M$ fluoride ion results in a 7 mV decrease in potential . . ." and that $1M$ Cl^- or NO_3^- results in a 20 mV decrease in potential. These changes are approximately what would be expected from the change in ionic strength resulting from the addition of the other salt. Although no data were available from which to predict the effect of NaCl or NaNO$_3$ on either the mean activity coefficient of NaF or on the liquid junction potential of the solution with saturated KCl, estimations based on the Debye-Hückel theory and on the activity coefficient of pure NaF solutions at concentrations from 0.1 to 1.0M agreed within approximately 10% with the observed values. In the presence of $0.1M$ $SO_4^=$ the potential of the electrode in $10^{-4}M$ fluoride was observed to shift by 13 mV instead of the predicted 18 mV, but this is certainly within the possible error in estimating the activity coefficient of F^- in the presence of a divalent instead of a monovalent ion. Bicarbonate, phosphate (pH = 6.4) and acetate (pH = 4.9) apparently do not cause any interference either [18].

Although we will discuss deviations from the Nernst equation in more detail below, it is worth noting now that approximately the same (Nernstian) slope of the calibration curve (Fig. 1) is obtained in 0.1M KNO$_3$ [19], 1.0M NaCl [20], or 0.1M MgSO$_4$ [20] containing various amounts of KF or NaF as in solutions containing KF or NaF alone. This result confirms the lack of interference by K^+, Na^+, Mg^{++}, NO_3^-, Cl^-, and $SO_4^=$. Deviations in Figure 1 at the $10^{-1}M$ fluoride concentration are due at least in part to ionic strength changes.

Looking at the same type of measurement from another perspective, we have listed in Table 1 the response observed for a lanthanum fluoride electrode (*vs.* SCE) to $10^{-4}M$ NaF in a buffer consisting of 0.18M sodium potassium tartrate, 0.012M disodium citrate and 0.008M NaOH to which various substances were added [20]. In all cases, the pH was between 5.0 and 6.3, where there is expected to be no interference by OH^- or from the formation of protonated fluoride species (see below). The citrate and tartrate tend to complex transition metal ions, and thus to minimize any effects from the formation of complexes of these ions with fluoride.

An interfering ion would be expected to make the potential of the fluoride electrode more negative, and only in the silicate solution was this observed. There, the shift was only 0.3 mV for a 65-fold excess of silicate over fluoride, and can probably be attributed to fluoride impurities in the silicate. Other explanations may be a shift of the liquid junction potential, or possibly the formation of a slightly charged film of silicate-based material on the surface of the lanthanum fluoride membrane. This latter possibility is suggested because the potential becomes 5 mV more positive when the pH is changed from 7 to 4, when silicate is present, but not in solutions containing fluoride only.

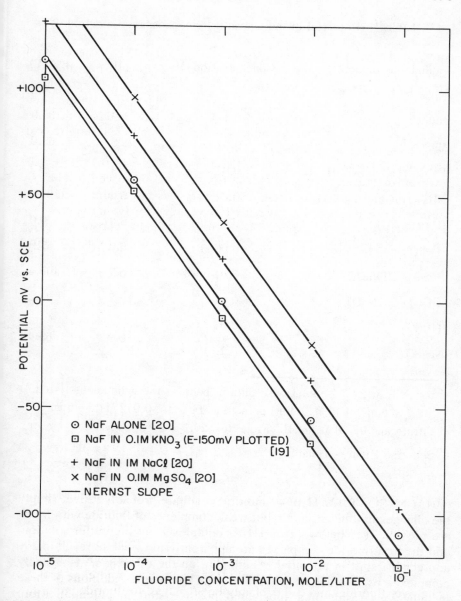

Figure 1.   Potential of LaF$_3$ membrane electrode as a function of fluoride concentration in various supporting electrolytes. Note that the zero of the potential scale depends on the internal filling solution and is different for data from References 19 and 20.

For all the other additions listed in Table 1, the potential becomes more positive, which is consistent with the formation of fluoride-containing complexes with the added ions. The shifts in the presence of 0.1M NaCl,

Table 1. Potential of lanthanum fluoride membrane electrode.[a]

Added substance	Concentration (M)	pH	E (mV)
None		5.9	+ 68.2
NaCl [b]	0.1	5.9	68.9
MgSO$_4$ [b]	0.01	5.8	69.0
Fe$_2$(SO$_4$)$_3$ + NaOH	0.01	5.4	69.0
NH$_4$Al(SO$_4$)$_2$ + NaOH	0.01	5.2	131.0
H$_3$BO$_3$	0.1	6.3	70.0
H$_2$SiO$_3$	0.0065	5.9	67.9
BeSO$_4$ + NaOH	0.01	5.7	100.4
ZrOCl$_2$ + NaOH	0.01	6.2	93.2
TiOSO$_4$	0.01 ⎫	6.2	69.4
Na$_2$SO$_4$	0.1 ⎭		

[a] $vs.$ SCE at 23 °C. Solutions contain, besides the substances listed, 10^{-4} M NaF, 0.18 M sodium potassium tartrate, 0.012 M disodium citrate and 0.008 M NaOH. From Ref. 20.

[b] See also Figures 1 and 9.

0.01M MgSO$_4$, 0.1M H$_3$BO$_3$, and titanyl sulfate probably reflect simply the changes in ionic strength, but weak complexes of fluoride with Mg^{++} are possible (see below). Iron(III) is complexed by the buffer solution, and the iron fluoride complexes are apparently too weak to result in any appreciable shift in potential. Aluminum, on the other hand, is strongly complexed by fluoride, as is beryllium and zirconium. Additions of these metallic ions result in a substantial positive shift in potential. More detailed studies of complex formation equilibria will be discussed later.

Only small shifts in potential [20] resulted from the addition of large concentrations of some non-ionic materials to $10^{-3}M$ NaF solutions, as can be seen in Table 2. These shifts can probably be accounted for by changes in the activity coefficient of NaF due to the salting-out effect. It is particularly worthy of note that hydrogen peroxide has the effect of making the potential more positive, which might indicate the formation of weak complexes between fluoride ions and the protons of H_2O_2.

Table 2. Influence of non–ionic compounds on the lanthanum
fluoride electrode.[a]

Additive	Concentration (M)	ΔE (mV)
None		0
Glucose	0.1	−1.1
	1.0	−0.4
Urea	0.1	−0.5
	1.0	−4.0
H_2O_2	0.1	+ 0.7
	1.0	+ 4.0

[a] Data from Ref. 20. Measurements $vs.$ SCE at 23 °C.
All solutions 10^{-3} M in NaF.

Baumann [21] showed that the slope of a curve of potential *versus* log NaF concentration had the same slope (59 mV) in 1, 5, and 10M phosphoric acid as in water alone, although the potentials shifted to more positive values as the acid concentration increased, because of the formation of protonated fluoride species. In 10M phosphoric acid, Fe(III), Al(III), UO_2^{2+} or Th(IV) showed only a slight effect on the potential, because they were complexed by the phosphoric acid and were not available to complex with fluoride ion (which was, of course, also highly complexed with H^+). In this same study, negligible interference was found for NO_3^-, Cl^-, and phosphoric acid at the 1M level, even though the fluoride level was as small as $10^{-5}M$. It was also pointed out that sodium silicate (1M, neutralized with phosphoric acid) contains small amounts of fluoride ($7 \times 10^{-5}M$ in the sample analyzed), which tends to confirm that the negative shift in potential in the presence of silicate (Table 1) resulted from fluoride impurity.

The most extensive test of the specificity of the electrode for fluoride in the presence of chloride was made by Mesmer [22]. Fluoride response was Nernstian in the presence of 1.00m chloride to below $10^{-4}m$ fluoride;

and when the different NaCl or KCl samples were corrected for an assumed fluoride impurity ($6 \times 10^{-6}M$ to $6 \times 10^{-5}M$), then Nernst behavior was obtained to below $10^{-5}M$, in agreement with results obtained in pure NaF solutions. These data emphasize the importance of using salts of ultra-high purity when doing experiments in a constant ionic medium.

Addition of HCl to a $1.00m$ NaCl solution, in which the fluoride content was estimated (from deviation of the Nernst plot for added fluoride) to be $5.6 \times 10^{-6}m$, gave potentials which corresponded well to those calculated from the dissociation constant for HF obtained by other methods (see below), confirming that the deviation was indeed due to a fluoride impurity and not to a chloride interference. Additional confirmation was obtained by adding Be^{++}, which decreased the measured free fluoride concentration. The upper limit for chloride interference was placed at $< 2 \times 10^{-8}m$ in the presence of $1.00m$ chloride. The selectivity of this electrode is thus extraordinarily good.

A similar conclusion was reached by Gatewood [23] who showed that the fluoride response in 12.5% HCl solutions ($3.64M$) was Nernstian (± 5 mV) to below $10^{-4}M$ fluoride concentrations.

B. STABILITY AND KINETIC RESPONSE

Because glass pH and cation-sensitive electrodes are known to drift in potential over long periods of time, it is of interest to inquire whether the lanthanum fluoride membrane electrode is subject to similar difficulties. The published evidence is not entirely consistent. Lingane [18] stated that the constant $E°$ in the equation

$$E = E° - \frac{RT}{F} \ln [F^-]\gamma_F \tag{5}$$

was constant within ± 1 mV for several weeks. Durst and Taylor [19] made measurements over a 1-week period on samples of their solutions and noted that the potential underwent only random variation during that time. In solutions of concentration $10^{-3}M$ or greater, the 95% confidence limits on the mean of 21 measurements (3 each day for 7 days) were ± 0.5 mV. Reproducibility on a given day was "only slightly better than that between days. . . . The long term deviation . . . was found to be random (bidirectional) and approximately 2 mV/week." Part of this variation was attributed to temperature changes, and to the variability of the liquid junction potential with the SCE reference.

Srinivasan and Rechnitz [27] noted that stirring sometimes had a substantial effect on the observed potential. In $10^{-3}M$ NaF solution, the potential changed from -61.5 mV in a quiescent solution to -55.5 mV in a rapidly stirred solution. This shift was less at high concentrations, and negligible in the presence of $1M$ $NaNO_3$ supporting electrolyte, even at fluoride concentrations as low as $5 \times 10^{-5}M$. They recommended that readings be taken with slow stirring (by a Teflon-coated magnetic bar), and that under these conditions reproducibility was excellent: "The potentials were found to be quite stable, changing not more than 0.1 mV even after an hour. The reproducibility on the same day for two different solutions of the same concentration was within 0.1 mV." In contrast to Durst and Taylor's results, Srinivasan and Rechnitz observed a monotonic change in potential with time: "After a period of 2 weeks, the electrode gave a reading 3 mV more negative, and after a month, 7 mV more negative for the same solution. The slope of the calibration curve was found to be unchanged."

Even more rapid drifts in potential have been observed. Although reproducibility was on the order of ± 0.2 mV, a shift of E° by 1.8 mV in 1 or 2 days has been observed [26]. Thus, it seems to be essential to calibrate the electrode at least every day and perhaps between each measurement if very precise results are desired. However, the rate of drift does not seem to be large enough to warrant continuous recording of the potential and extrapolation of measurements made in test and reference solutions to the same point in time, as is often done with glass electrodes [13-16,28].

The kinetic response of the electrode is "almost instantaneous" [27,29], limited by the recorder response time of 0.5 sec, at least in solutions containing fluoride concentrations greater than millimolar. In very dilute solutions, the response time has been reported to be very long. In a $10^{-6}M$ NaF solution, for example, a steady potential was reached only after approximately 1 hour [20]. This may have resulted from small amounts of more concentrated solution which accumulated in crevices near the edge of the LaF_3 crystal, and conceivably does not reflect the true response of the membrane. It has been reported that some pieces of the first model of the electrode produced (Orion Model 94-09 with a white plastic body) "had an interstice between the crystal and the body of the electrode. Slow diffusion of the test solution into the interstice was responsible for the slow rate at which the system came to equilibrium. The . . . new model . . . has its crystal cemented into the body to eliminate the interstice. . . . Equilibrium is attained in less than 3 minutes at $10^{-6}M$ fluoride concentration. The response is more rapid at higher concentrations" [30]. The ultimate response speed of the electrode has not yet been determined but may be diffusion controlled, and with rapid-mixing systems, kinetic studies in the millisecond range may be possible.

C. Acidity Effects

In their original communication, Frant and Ross [17] pointed out that there were changes in potential as the pH of fluoride solutions was changed. A diagram illustrating this effect is presented in Figure 2 [20].

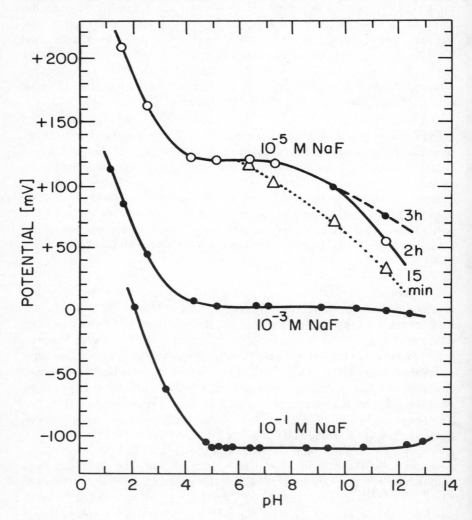

Figure 2.　Effect of pH on the potential of the LaF_3 membrane electrode in NaF solutions of various concentrations. Data from Reference 20.

Since that time, it has been well established that the positive shift in potential observed in acid solutions is due entirely to protonation of the fluoride ion, and that neither HF nor HF_2^- produces any interference.

The electrode obeys the Nernst equation (in terms of free fluoride ion activity) precisely in this region [27]. More details will be given below in a discussion of the HF equilibria.

The negative shift in potential in basic solutions is not so well understood. Frant and Ross [17] stated: "The only significant interference comes from hydroxide ion, which is not surprising in view of the similarities in charge and ionic radii. In pure solutions, significant hydroxide interference occurs when the concentration of hydroxide about equals the concentration of fluoride, and a tenfold excess of hydroxide will double the apparent fluoride content." This implies an interference of the simple additive type:

$$E = E° - \frac{RT}{F} \ln \{[F^-] + k_s [OH^-]\}$$ (6)

but k_s, the selectivity ratio, is not approximately 0.1, independent of fluoride concentration (as stated above), but varies from essentially zero in $10^{-1}M$ fluoride to greater than one in $10^{-5}M$ fluoride. Furthermore, the approach to a steady potential value has been reported [20] to be much slower in basic solutions. This is shown in Figure 2. At pH = 12 it takes as long as 3 hours to reach a steady potential in $10^{-5}M$ fluoride solution. Curiously, the interference is greater at short times than it is at steady state.

The mechanism of the hydroxide interference is still unexplored. Frant and Ross [17] implied that hydroxide ions took the place of fluoride ions in the LaF₃ crystal lattice because of their similarity of ionic radii. Bock and Strecker [20] made no hypotheses to explain the deviations at high pH values.

It is of interest to examine the possibility of the equilibrium formation of a lanthanum hydroxide complex or precipitate, which might set free fluoride ions, which could then cause a potential deviation in the direction observed; for example:

$$LaF_3(s) + 3 OH^- \rightleftarrows La(OH)_3(s) + 3 F^-$$ (7)

The solubility product, K'_{sp} for La(OH)₃ is approximately $10^{-21.7}$ [3]. Although for freshly precipitated LaF₃, the solubility product, K_{sp},[1] is approximately 10^{18} [24], the effective solubility product of the LaF₃ electrode crystal even in unstirred solutions is on the order of 10^{-22}, as we discuss below in connection with deviations from the Nernst equation at low concentrations. Thus the equilibrium represented by Equation (7) predicts that LaF₃ will dissolve to produce La(OH)₃ whenever

$$\frac{[OH^-]}{[F^-]} = \left(\frac{K'_{sp}}{K_{sp}}\right)^{1/3}$$ (8)

---

[1] K_{sp}, is equivalent to the IUPAC notation for the solubility product constant K_{s0}.

Depending on which value is chosen for K_{sp}, this ratio can be between 0.05 and 1.0. Note that this is close to the range of the observed ratios for which hydroxide interference is observed (Fig. 2).

The mechanism can be more complicated, however, since at high pH values, stable lanthanum hydroxide complexes are formed in solution [3]. At pH $= 11$, for example, the predominant species in equilibrium with $La(OH)_3$ is $LaOH^{++}$, with a concentration of $10^{-11.8}M$. Smaller concentrations of La^{+3} ($10^{-12.7}M$) and $La_2(OH)_2^{+4}$ ($10^{-13.3}M$) are also present. Thus, even if solid $La(OH)_3$ did not precipitate, high pH solutions would tend to lower the concentration of free La^{+3} and, if this was in equilibrium with the LaF_3 crystal, liberate excess F^- into the boundary layer region near the electrode. Since F^- would be continually removed from the electrode by stirring or diffusion under normal measurement conditions, but would build up in solution, one would predict that the potential would show a long-term drift to more negative values and that this drift would be faster with small solution volumes. However, the only time dependence data available (Fig. 2) show that the potential drifts in the opposite direction, to more positive potentials.

Studies of this phenomenon would probably be most clearly defined if a very small (*i.e.*, 50 μl) sample were used in the type of setup described by Durst and Taylor [19]. If care were taken to avoid convection, the kinetics of the hydroxide interference could possibly be interpreted using linear diffusion theory, and the mechanism could be elucidated. Radiotracer studies of lanthanum concentration, though difficult, might also be feasible, since the half-lives of the slowest-decaying radioactive isotopes of lanthanum are of the order of a few days.

D. DEVIATIONS FROM THE NERNST EQUATION

The most rigorous test of the Nernst equation would be best made in a cell without liquid junction, but such measurements have not yet been published. In our discussion of activity coefficients, below, we present some unpublished measurements made over a limited range of composition, in a cell without liquid junction, which apparently confirm the Nernst equation within the precision of the measurements. In this section, however, we will examine measurements made with the cell with liquid junction

$$Hg; Hg_2Cl_2(s) \mid KCl \text{ (sat)} \parallel F^-, etc. \mid LaF_3 \text{ membrane electrode}$$

both in solutions containing NaF or KF alone, and in various constant ionic media.

Quite a number of workers have verified that deviations from the Nernst equation are less than 1 or 2 mV in the range from 0.1M to below

$10^{-5}M$ [18,19,20,22], but the ultimate precision of measurement is considerably better than this, and some of the uncertainty arises because of the presence of a liquid junction (between saturated KCl and the test solution) of variable potential. Results obtained in a constant ionic medium are more likely to be free of liquid junction errors than results in a medium of varying ionic strength.

The potential of the LaF_3-SCE cell is expected to obey a Nernst equation of the form:

$$E = E^\circ - \frac{RT}{F} \ln [F^-]\gamma_F + E_j \qquad (9)$$

and it is important to recognize that γ_F and E_j cannot be measured independently. In a constant ionic medium, both γ_F and E_j are virtually constant and can be included in E°; but in a medium of varying composition, both can be expected to vary. Making measurements in a cell without liquid junction avoids this thermodynamic uncertainty, but most investigators have chosen to calculate γ_F according to some assumption, and thus to lump whatever additional deviations occur from the Nernst equation into E_j. Conversely, one may calculate E_j (e.g., by the Lewis-Sargent equation [5]) and lump additional deviations from the Nernst equation into the single ion activity coefficient.

Uncertainties in the activity coefficient of fluoride ion and the liquid junction potential are expected to be of most concern at high concentrations. At low concentrations, two additional problems arise: the presence of fluoride impurities in the salt used to prepare the constant ionic medium (if one is used) and fluoride contributed by the intrinsic solubility of LaF_3 in the test solution. These contributions may be expressed as follows:

$$[F^-] = C_F + C_F' + \frac{3K_{sp}}{[F^-]^3} \qquad (10)$$

where C_F is the concentration (moles/liter) of fluoride deliberately added to the test solution, C_F' is the (unknown) concentration of fluoride impurity in the supporting electrolyte, and K_{sp} is the solubility product of LaF_3.

To see deviations from the Nernst equation quantitatively, the best published data are those of Durst and Taylor [19], for which a statistical estimate of the error in potential at each concentration was made. In Figure 3 we have plotted values of the function

$$E' = E + \frac{RT}{F} \ln C_F\gamma_F \qquad (11)$$

calculated from the data of Durst and Taylor. If liquid junction potentials are constant, this function should approach E° at high concentrations. For these calculations γ_F was assumed to be equal to the mean activity coefficient of NaF at the same ionic strength. (Unfortunately, the ionic strength was not precisely constant, but varied between 0.1 and 0.2 in the high concentration range, because the concentration of NaF was varied and the concentration of KNO_3 supporting electrolyte was kept constant at $0.1M$.)

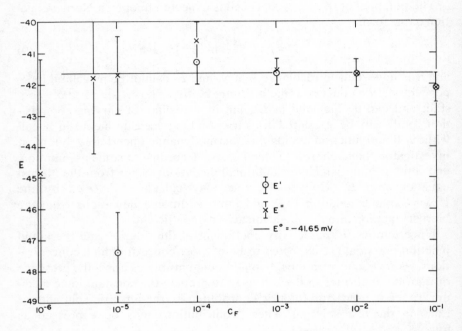

Figure 3.   Deviations from the Nernst equation according to various assumptions which are described in the text. Data from Reference 19.

For $C_F \geqslant 10^{-4}$, E' is constant within the experimental error (95% confidence limits, 21 measurements) calculated by Durst and Taylor. At $10^{-5}M$ and below, however, the deviations in E' are in the direction predicted above and are well outside the experimental error. To test whether these deviations are due to a fluoride impurity in the supporting electrolyte we have also plotted in Figure 3 the function

$$E'' = E + \frac{RT}{F} \ln \{(C_F + C'_F)\gamma_F\}$$

with C'_F chosen to be $2.5 \times 10^{-6}M$. This amounts to only 25 parts per million of fluoride in the KNO_3 supporting electrolyte, and is not unreasonable. The precise value of C'_F was chosen to make the calculated value of E'' at $10^{-5}M$ equal to the best estimate of $E°$. It turns out that this also causes the E'' value at $5 \times 10^{-6}M$ to be equal to $E°$, an excellent confirmation of the assumption.

Still, there are deviations of E'' to more negative potentials, at $10^{-6}M$, which could be due to the intrinsic solubility of LaF$_3$, even though the experimental error is large enough to account for such a deviation. If this deviation were due to fluoride from the LaF$_3$ crystal, the effective solubility product could not be greater than $K_{sp} = 10^{-23}$.

This observation is interesting since the value of K_{sp} measured by Lingane [24] by titration of fluoride with lanthanum nitrate, in a solution of ionic strength approximately $0.08M$, was $10^{-17.9}$. This much larger value is entirely inconsistent with the data of Figure 3. Durst and Taylor used a sample of only 50 μl, and one would expect that this small volume of solution would be more likely to have reached equilibrium with the LaF$_3$ crystal. The alternative hypothesis that $C'_F = 0$ and that all deviations of E' from constancy are due to the solubility product does not give good internal consistency at all. The value of K_{sp} obtained varies from $10^{-20.8}$ (fitting the $10^{-5}M$ point) to $10^{-22.2}$ (fitting the $10^{-6}M$ point).

Furthermore, the data of Frant and Ross [17], obtained in KF solutions without supporting electrolyte, and the data of Lingane [18], obtained in $0.100M$ NaNO$_3$ supporting electrolyte, tend to support the value of K_{sp} which we obtained from the deviations of E''. Here there is no question that C'_F is small, since there is no foreign salt present which could carry fluoride impurities. The curve given by Frant and Ross is consistent with a solubility product $K_{sp} = 10^{-24.5}$, in agreement with the result obtained from Figure 3. (Frant and Ross [17] gave the value $K_{sp} = 10^{-29}$, but this implies that the free fluoride concentration in a saturated LaF$_3$ solution is approximately $10^{-7}M$. From the curves displayed by both Frant and Ross [17] and Lingane [18], the free fluoride concentration is much closer to $10^{-6}M$.)

Turning now to the high-concentration region, we see from Figure 3 that the point at $10^{-1}M$ deviates slightly from the best estimate of $E°$. Although we have attempted to compensate for the fact that the ionic strength for this point was twice what it was in dilute solutions (by using a value of γ_F corresponding to $0.2M$ NaF instead of $0.1M$ NaF), and the deviation is within the 95% confidence limits for the measurements, it is worth pointing out that this magnitude of deviation corresponds to a 10% error in estimating the activity coefficient, in the direction of a larger activity for fluoride ion than that predicted purely from ionic strength considerations. Alternatively, a shift in liquid junction potential (because the test solution changed in composition from essentially $0.1M$ KNO$_3$ to $0.1M$ KNO$_3 - 0.1M$ NaF) of 0.5 mV could also account for the deviation. From our measurements of the activity coefficient of NaF in NaF-NaCl electrolytes (see below), one would expect that the mean activity coefficient of NaF in NaF-KNO$_3$ electrolytes could be somewhat larger than in NaF at the same ionic strength. This is in agreement with the deviations in Figure 3.

More recent work [26], using a constant ionic medium of high concentration in a cell where the liquid junction potential is almost certainly negligible, has confirmed the Nernstian behavior of the LaF$_3$ electrode. The cell used was

Ag; AgCl | KCl$(3M)$ || K$^+$, F$^-$, Cl$^-$ | LaF$_3$ membrane electrode

where the concentration of KF and KCl in the right-hand compartment were varied, but their total concentration was kept at $3M$. This assured that both the liquid junction potential and the activity coefficient of fluoride ion were kept constant (so long as the concentration of KCl was much greater than the concentration of KF). Under these conditions, the activity coefficient and liquid junction potentials are lumped with the standard potential. Figure 4 shows how the quantity

$$E^{\circ\prime} = E + 59.16 \log C_F \tag{13}$$

varies from $0.001M$ to $0.2M$ fluoride. The 95% confidence limits on $E^{\circ\prime}$ are ± 0.5 mV, in agreement with the results of Durst and Taylor [19] in the range from 10^{-2} to $10^{-4}M$.

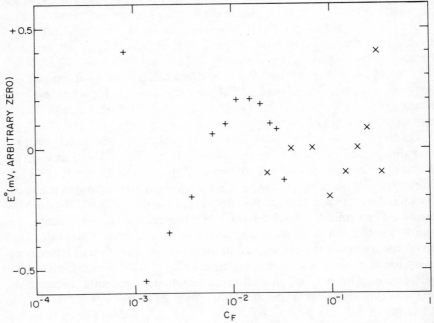

Figure 4.   Deviations from the Nernst equation in $3M$ KCl solutions, including any variation of activity coefficients or liquid junction potential. Data from Reference 26.

We may thus conclude from these studies that the Nernst equation is obeyed well within experimental error for all fluoride concentrations above $10^{-6}M$, and that any deviations in that region in the direction of negative potentials can probably be explained in terms of fluoride impurities. The effective solubility product of the LaF_3 crystal appears to be approximately 10^{-24}, which is in marked disagreement with the value of 10^{-18} obtained from freshly precipitated LaF_3, as described in the next section. A possible explanation for this discrepancy is that the freshly precipitated material is a hydrated form of considerably higher free energy than the massive crystal used to construct the electrode.

Deviations from the Nernst equation in the direction of more positive potentials are almost certainly due to the formation of complexes between fluoride and one of the other ions in the solution. Such phenomena are best treated within the framework of solution equilibria, and are discussed in detail in the next section.

E. EQUILIBRIA

The most important equilibria which the fluoride ion engages in are those with the hydrogen ion, and these have been the subject of considerable study before the advent of the LaF_3 membrane electrode [3]. However, this new electrode makes possible a new experimental approach, and since the analysis of the data obtained is typical of all equilibrium studies in constant ionic medium, we shall present the results in some detail. Further discussion of the approach used can be found in standard reference works [9,32,33].

As discussed above, in a constant ionic medium, the potential of a LaF_3 membrane electrode with respect to a reference electrode (*e.g.*, SCE) is given by the free fluoride concentration:

$$E = E° - \frac{RT}{F} \ln [F^-] \qquad (14)$$

The standard potential $E°$ is obtained by calibration in solutions containing NaF at pH values (*e.g.*, 5-7) where there is negligible protonation of fluoride. Then acid is added and the potential observed. For a complete study, the total fluoride concentration is changed by several orders of magnitude to test for polynuclear complexes (*e.g.*, $H_4F_4^+$ [34]). From the materials put into the solution, the total concentration of fluoride, C_F, and hydrogen ion, C_H, are known, and the most popular function to use in analyzing the data is the ligand number

$$\bar{n} = \frac{C_F - [F^-]}{C_H} \qquad (15)$$

This is the ratio of bound fluoride to total hydrogen. If HF were the only complex formed, ñ would vary between 0 and 1. The data of Figure 5 [27] show clearly that ñ exceeds unity at high fluoride concentration, and thus that species such as HF_2^- are important. The fact that all points fall on the same curve is evidence for the mononuclear (*i.e.*, HF_n) nature of the complexes, since the total fluoride concentration [27] was varied over the range from $0.001M$ to $0.5M$. The ionic strength was kept constant at $1.0M$ with $NaNO_3$ for these measurements.

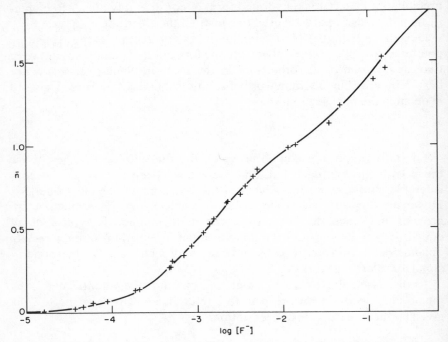

Figure 5. Bjerrum plot of experimental values for ligand number ñ as a function of free fluoride ion concentration. Note that ñ exceeds unity at high fluoride ion concentrations; a direct confirmation of the existence of complexes other than HF. Data from Reference 27.

Assuming the equilibria:

$$H^+ + F^- \rightleftharpoons HF \qquad K_1 \qquad\qquad (16)$$

$$HF + F^- \rightleftharpoons HF_2^- \qquad K_2 \qquad\qquad (17)$$

the ligand number may be expressed as

$$\bar{n} = \frac{\beta_1[F^-] + 2\beta_2[F^-]^2}{1 + \beta_1[F^-] + \beta_2[F^-]^2} \qquad\qquad (18)$$

where $\beta_1(=K_1)$ and $\beta_2(=K_1K_2)$ are overall formation constants. This expression can be cast into a linear form [32,33]:

$$\frac{\bar{n}}{(1-\bar{n})[F^-] \cdot 10^3} = \beta_1 \cdot 10^{-3} + \beta_2 \cdot 10^{-6}\left(\frac{2-\bar{n}}{1-\bar{n}}\right)[F^-] \cdot 10^3 \qquad (19)$$

which is of the form

$$y = a + bx \qquad (20)$$

with $a = 10^{-3}\beta_1$ and $b = 10^{-6}\beta_2$. The functions y and x are easily calculated from the experimental data of Figure 5, and are displayed in Figure 6. Note that $x \rightarrow \infty$ at $\bar{n} = 1$, and thus the value of β_2 is heavily weighted by

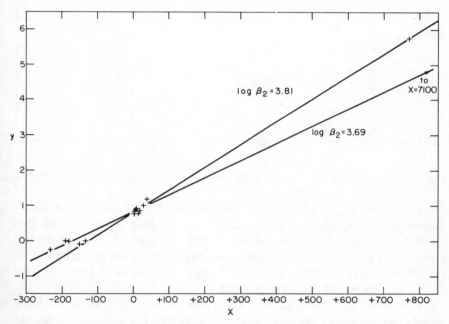

Figure 6. Linear plot to determine equilibrium constants for the formation of HF and HF_2^- as described in the text. Data from Reference 27.

points in that region. On Figure 6, two slopes have been indicated, and a "best value" is $\beta_2 = 10^{3.75}$. This slope has been used to draw the curve of Figure 7, which is an enlargement of the region of low x, and the intercept corresponds to $\beta_1 = 10^{2.89}$.

An independent study by Neumann and Sillén [26] has given the results which are partially shown in Figure 8. An analysis using considerably more data and the least squares valley search program LETAGROP [35] yielded the equilibrium constants $\beta_1 = 10^{3.31}$ and β_2

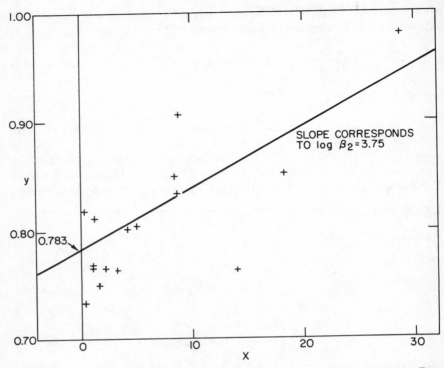

Figure 7. Expanded plot of Figure 6 in the region near x = 0, showing the intercept. Data from Reference 27.

$= 10^{4.03}$ in $3M$ KCl medium, with no evidence for polynuclear or higher mononuclear complexes. The results of a number of studies on this system by various methods are summarized in Table 3. The results obtained with a LaF_3 membrane electrode are in excellent agreement with results obtained by other methods. Compare particularly the two most recent studies in $3M$ KCl medium [26].

Three other fluoride equilibria have also been studied using the LaF_3 membrane electrode. We have already mentioned the determination [24] of K_{sp} for freshly precipitated LaF_3 by titration of $La(NO_3)_3$ with NaF, which gave a value $K_{sp} = 10^{-17.9}$ at the ionic strength of the titration ($\sim 0.08M$). Estimation of activity coefficients gave $K_{sp} = 10^{-18.5}$ at zero ionic strength. In the same study, the solubility product of EuF_3 was determined to be $10^{-16.65}$ at ionic strength ~ 0.1, considerably larger than for LaF_3. The large discrepancy between the K_{sp} for freshly precipitated LaF_3 and the effective K_{sp} for the solid LaF_3 crystal of the electrode ($\sim 10^{-24}$) has not yet been resolved.

The equilibrium constant for the reaction

$$Fe^{+3} + F^- \; \rightleftarrows \; FeF^{+3} \qquad\qquad K_1 \qquad\qquad (21)$$

Table 3. Equilibrium constants for the $H^+ - F^-$ system at 25 °C. [a]

Method	Ionic medium	$\log K_1$	$\log K_2$	Ref.
Conductance	HF (var)	3.14	0.74	36
Cond. & Transference	HF (var)	3.13	0.67	37
Solubility	dilute	3.78		38
Colorimetric pH	$\rightarrow 0$	3.62	1.52	39
Quinhydrone pH	0.53 KNO_3	2.94	0.57	40
Quinhydrone pH	0.53 NH_4NO_3	2.82	0.59	40
Quinhydrone pH	0.53 $NaNO_3$	2.91	0.57	41
Hydrogen pH	0 (corr)	3.17	0.59	42
	0.5	2.93	0.60	42
	0.102 $HClO_4$	3.15	0.59	42
Spectrophotometric pH	0.5 $NaClO_4$	2.91		43
Hydrogen pH	3 KCl	3.26	0.74	44
Quinhydrone pH	3 $NaClO_4$	3.28	1.08	44
LaF_3 Membrane	1.0 $NaNO_3$	2.90 ± .03	0.77 ± .05	27
LaF_3 Membrane	1.0 $NaNO_3$	2.89 ± .01	0.86 ± .04	27
LaF_3 Membrane	1.0 NaCl	3.11 ± .03		22
LaF_3 Membrane	3 KCl	3.31 ± .02	0.72 ± .03	26
Quinhydrone pH	3 KCl	3.32 ± .01	0.75 ± .06	26

[a] Errors are 95% confidence limits where quoted.
[b] Recalculated.

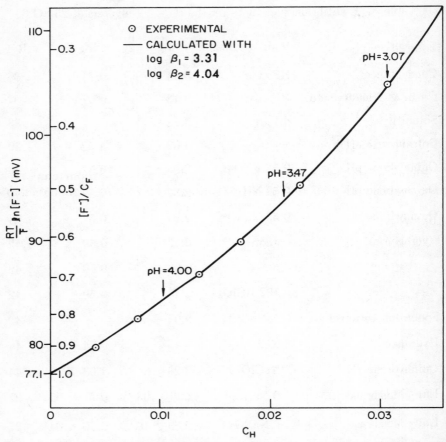

Figure 8.   Comparison of experimental with calculated values for fluoride concentration in HF solutions of varying acidity. Data from Reference 26.

was determined in the course of a kinetic study of complex formation between fluoride and Fe^{+3} or Al^{+3} [29]. The method of analysis was similar to that described for the HF complexes, except that hydrolysis of Fe^{+3} had to be taken into account. The theoretical equation was obeyed within experimental error, giving $K_1 = 10^{5.06}$, and $K_2 < 10^4$, since the intercept was zero within experimental error.

A study of the stability constants of Sn(II)-fluoride complexes has been carried out using the lanthanum fluoride electrode [73], and some more fragmentary studies deserve mention. Lingane [18] attempted to determine the solubility product of CaF_2 but this was not too successful. A similar attempt by Neumann and Sillén [26] also met with difficulty due to unexplained drifts in potential. Lingane's solubility product for CaF_2 was $10^{-8.27}$, which is much larger than the theoretical value calculated from free energy data by Latimer [4] ($10^{-9.77}$) or from conductance data by Kohlrausch [45] ($10^{-10.41}$). Clearly, more work is required on this system.

Some data have been published on the thorium fluoride complexes [18], and some work is in progress on niobium fluoride complexes [26]. Complexes with Be^{+2}, Zr^{+4}, Al^{+3}, and other ions have been noted [20, 22, 29] but detailed studies have not been carried out. For example, in $10^{-2}M$ $BeSO_4$ with $10^{-4}M$ NaF at pH = 5.3, the potential of the fluoride electrode is 125 mV more positive than in $10^{-4}M$ NaF alone [20].

Fluoroborate ion apparently hydrolyzes enough even at room temperature to produce sufficient fluoride ion for the electrode to respond, but the kinetics of hydrolysis are slow. For example [20], a solution of $2.5 \times 10^{-4}M$ $NaBF_4$ (which should produce $10^{-3}M$ fluoride on complete hydrolysis) showed a potential 137.4 mV more positive than a solution containing only $10^{-3}M$ NaF. After 24 hours, this difference had decreased to 110.8 mV, and after 73 hours, to 85.1 mV. This experiment suggests that the slow hydrolysis of BF_4^- would be simple to study kinetically using the fluoride electrode, but that studies of the hydrolysis equilibria would have to involve equilibration (if not measurement) at a higher temperature.

In contrast, fluosilicate ion showed essentially complete hydrolysis, giving the same potential as a NaF solution containing the same amount of total fluoride [20].

Deviations on the addition of more weakly complexed ions have also been observed. This is shown in Figure 9 where the potential of the lanthanum fluoride electrode (vs. SCE) in $10^{-4}M$ NaF together with additions of NaCl or $MgSO_4$ is plotted, as a function of ionic strength [17,20]. The broken line is the potential predicted by assuming the activity coefficient of the fluoride ion to be equal to the mean activity of NaF at the same ionic strength, and neglecting any changes in liquid junction potential at the reference electrode. The calculated potentials agree with the measured potentials in NaCl, $NaNO_3$ and Na_2SO_4 solutions within 2 mV up to ionic strength 0.1 and within 7 mV at ionic strength 1.0. Although the measured potentials are all slightly positive of the calculated potentials, and might be construed as showing some formation of NaF complexes or ion-pairs, the deviations are not outside the range expected from the approximations employed. On the other hand, the measurements in $MgSO_4$ and $MgSO_4$-NaCl solutions show deviations in the same direction of as much as 30 mV, which is a strong indication that fluoride ion is being removed from the solution by formation of complexes, probably MgF^+. The existence of this complex has been suggested by other studies [3], but the present data are too sparse for evaluation of an

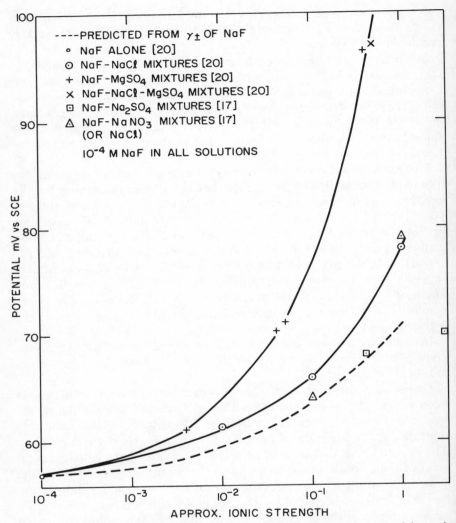

Figure 9.   Potential of LaF$_3$ membrane electrode in $10^{-4}M$ NaF solutions containing various added electrolytes.

equilibrium constant. However, this is certainly one system which could be studied profitably using a constant ionic medium. One important point to note is that an anionic interference by either Cl$^-$ or SO$_4^=$ would cause the measured potential to be more negative than the predicted potential; and the observed deviations are all in the opposite direction. A further point to note is that the points on Figure 9 obtained by Frant and Ross [17] in NaNO$_3$ and NaCl mixtures show experimental values close to those of Bock and Strecker [20] in NaCl alone. However, the values obtained in Na_2SO_4 [17] are almost precisely the predicted values, so that the large deviations observed in $MgSO_4$ must be due to the Mg^{++} ion and not to the sulfate ion.

F. Activity Coefficient Measurements

Although the stability and high selectivity of the lanthanum fluoride electrode makes it eminently suitable for accurate measurements of activity coefficients, no results have yet been published in this area. However, there are at least two studies in progress, and these will be briefly described here.

The most obvious experiment to perform is the measurement of mean activity coefficients in solutions containing only NaF by means of the cell:

Na glass electrode $|Na^+, F^-, H_2O|$ LaF_3 membrane electrode

and preliminary experiments of this type have been carried out [31,46]. The potentials obtained were consistent with the activity coefficients of NaF in water, as obtained by isopiestic measurements [2], but the reproducibility of the measurements (± 1 mV) was not as good as expected. At the time, it was not clear whether this irreproducibility resulted from instability in the sodium-sensitive glass electrode or in the LaF_3 electrode, but subsequent experiments have provided evidence (including visible etching of the glass surface) that the glass electrode is responsible for the poor reproducibility of these measurements.

In our laboratory [31], we have also carried out measurements on NaCl-NaF mixtures using the following cells:

Ag; AgCl $|$ Na^+, Cl^-, F^-, H_2O $|$ LaF_3 membrane electrode

Ag; AgCl $|$ Na^+, Cl^-, F^-, H_2O $|$ Na glass electrode

Measurements made with the first cell were much more reproducible than those made with the second cell, and after some time, the sodium glass electrode gave erratic response, required times as long as 1 hour to come to equilibrium, and showed visible signs of etching on the surface. In contrast, the LaF_3 membrane electrode cell came to equilibrium within a few seconds and showed no long-term signs of instability.

It is possible to obtain, from measurements of the AgCl-LaF_3 cell, the mean activity coefficients of both NaF and NaCl in NaCl-NaF mixtures. The potential of this cell is given by

$$E = E° + \frac{RT}{F} \ln \left(\frac{m_{Cl}}{m_F}\right) + \frac{2RT}{F} \ln \left(\frac{\gamma_{12}}{\gamma_{21}}\right) \tag{22}$$

where m_{Cl} and m_F are the molal concentrations of chloride and fluoride in the mixed electrolyte, γ_{12} is the mean activity coefficient of NaCl (component 1), and γ_{21} is the mean activity coefficient of NaF (component 2) in the mixed electrolyte. To eliminate long-term uncertainties in E°, the test solutions are compared with a calibration solution with $m_{Cl} = m_F$. In order that Harned's Rule be applied, all solutions are the same ionic strength (*e.g.*, $1.0m$). Since the concentrations of chloride and fluoride are known in both the test and reference solutions, and the temperature is known, the difference in potential between these solutions gives directly the quantity

$$R_{21} = \log \frac{\gamma_{21}^r \gamma_{12}^t}{\gamma_{12}^r \gamma_{21}^t} \qquad (23)$$

where the superscripts r and t indicate the reference and test solutions, respectively. Experimental values of this quantity, obtained at total ionic strength, $1.00m$, and $25.00\,°C$ are presented in Figure 10.

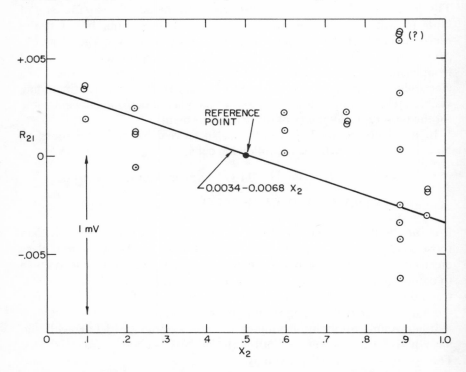

Figure 10.   Activity coefficient function R_{21} (defined in text) as a function of X_2, the ionic strength fraction of NaF in NaCl-NaF mixtures at constant total ionic strength $1.0m$. Data from Reference 31.

If Harned's Rule is assumed to be obeyed for both components [1,2]

$$\log \gamma_{12} = \log \gamma_{10} - \alpha_{12} X_2 I \tag{24}$$

$$\log \gamma_{21} = \log \gamma_{20} - \alpha_{21} X_1 I \tag{25}$$

will hold, where γ_{10} and γ_{20} are the activity coefficients of NaCl and NaF, respectively, in solutions containing only that salt, at ionic strength I which is the same as the mixed solution. The ionic strength fraction of NaF, X_2, is given simply by

$$X_2 = 1 - X_1 = \frac{m_F}{m_F + m_{Cl}} \tag{26}$$

Using these equations, one obtains

$$R_{21} = (\alpha_{12} + \alpha_{21})(0.5 - X_2) \tag{27}$$

where we have made use of the fact that $X_2 = 0.5$ in the reference solution.

Independently, from the Gibbs-Duhem relation, one obtains the relation [1,2]:

$$\alpha_{21} - \alpha_{12} = \frac{2}{2.303 I}(\phi_2^\circ - \phi_1^\circ) = -0.055 \tag{28}$$

where ϕ_2° and ϕ_1° are the osmotic coefficients of solutions containing only NaF and NaCl, respectively, at ionic strength I. Combining this with the above expression for R_{21}, we obtain two alternative expressions:

$$R_{21} = (2\,\alpha_{12} - 0.055)(0.5 - X_2) \tag{29}$$

$$R_{21} = (2\,\alpha_{21} + 0.055)(0.5 - X_2) \tag{30}$$

On Figure 10, a line has been drawn with the equation

$$R_{21} = 0.0034 - 0.0068\,X_2 \tag{31}$$

which leads to the Harned Rule coefficients

$$\alpha_{12} = +0.031; \; \alpha_{21} = -0.024 \tag{32}$$

This value of α_{12} is in good agreement with the results of measurements with the AgCl-sodium glass electrode (Fig. 11), provided the data obtained at high values of X_2 are discarded. This again confirms the interference of fluoride ion with the sodium glass electrode. Some rather sparse data (Fig. 12) on a sodium glass electrode-LaF$_3$ membrane electrode cell have been obtained, and these are in good agreement with the value $X_{21} = +0.031$.

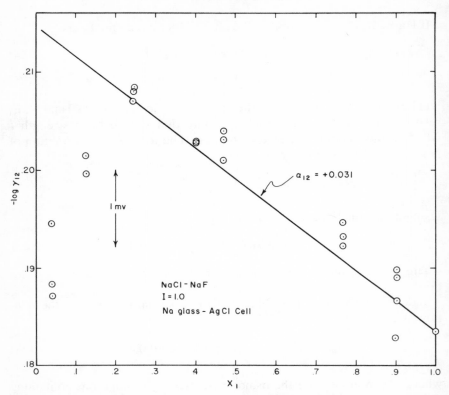

Figure 11. Mean activity coefficent of NaCl in NaCl-NaF electrolytes measured with a sodium-sensitive glass electrode and an Ag-AgCl reference electrode. X_1 is the ionic strength fraction of NaCl at constant total ionic strength $1.0m$. Data from reference 31.

From Figure 10 it is apparent that the data are also fit quite well by R_{21} $= 0$, the result which is expected on the basis of the Debye-Hückel theory if the sizes of the fluoride and chloride ions are approximately equal. If this assumption is made, one obtains

$$\alpha_{12} = -\alpha_{21} = 0.0275 \tag{33}$$

which is also in reasonable agreement with the other experiment.

Because of the apparent irreproducibility of the sodium glass electrode in fluoride-containing solutions, experiments are in progress [31] to determine the activity coefficients of NaF and NaCl in these mixed electrolytes using a sodium amalgam electrode. This will provide an independent check on the results presented above.

G. KINETICS

The logical extension of equilibrium measurements to kinetic studies of reactions involving fluoride ion has been made for three reactions by

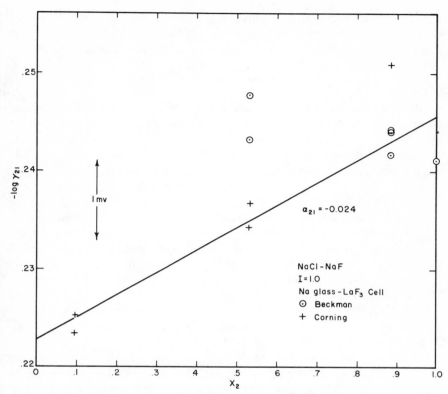

Figure 12. Mean activity coefficient of NaF in NaCl-NaF electrolytes measured with a sodium-sensitive glass electrode and a LaF_3 membrane electrode. Data from Reference 31.

Srinivasan and Rechnitz. In the reaction of Fe^{+3} with F^-, they showed that both the reaction paths

$$Fe^{+3} + F^- \rightarrow FeF^{+2} \tag{34}$$

$$Fe^{+3} + HF \rightarrow FeF^{+2} + H^+ \tag{35}$$

are possible at 25 °C, and depending on the pH, either F^- or HF is the primary reactant [29].

For the reaction of aluminum ion with F^-, the mechanism proposed [29] is

$$Al^{+3} + HF \rightarrow AlF^{+2} + H^+ \tag{36}$$

$$Al(H_2O)^{+3} + F^- \rightleftarrows AlOH^{+2} + HF \tag{37}$$

$$AlOH^{+2} + HF \rightarrow AlF^{+2} + H_2O \tag{38}$$

At high acidities the first reaction is rate limiting, and at lower acidities the third reaction becomes rate limiting. A study of the reaction between iron(III) fluoride complexes with iodide ion has also been made [47] in which it was shown that Fe^{+3} (but not the complex FeF^{+2}) reacts with iodide ion. These data are discussed in more detail in Chapter 9.

H. NON-AQUEOUS SOLUTIONS

Although the fluoride electrode has not been used for thermodynamic studies in solvents other than water, a few scattered observations seem to indicate that such studies can be done with a precision comparable to that obtained in aqueous solutions. Lingane [24] verified the Nernst equation for the lanthanum fluoride membrane electrode (with respect to an aqueous SCE) in 60% aqueous ethanol at ionic strengths ($NaNO_3$ supporting electrolyte) of 0.1 and 0.01M. The free fluoride ion concentration at which deviations were observed from the Nernst plots was close to that value ($10^{-6}M$) observed in aqueous solutions, but the potentials were approximately 100 mV more negative. This may be either a liquid junction or asymmetry potential effect, and quite possibly both.

Titration curves for fluoride with $La(NO_3)_3$ in 70% aqueous ethanol [24] and of fluoride with Th(IV) solutions in 60% aqueous ethanol [18] indicate that the fluorides of these two elements are much less soluble in aqueous ethanol than in water alone, but no quantitative analysis of these data to determine equilibrium constants was attempted.

Lithium has been determined by potentiometric titration with fluoride using the lanthanum fluoride membrane electrode as indicator, in a solvent containing approximately 95% ethanol and 5% water, and it is clear from the titration curves that LiF is considerably less soluble than NaF in this medium [48]. Again, no attempt was made to calculate equilibrium constants from the titration curve.

Some preliminary experiments [49] have been conducted using the lanthanum fluoride electrode in an aprotic organic solvent, dimethyl sulfoxide (DMSO). There appeared to be no visible attack or softening of the material (Calcon polyester) from which the electrode body was prepared in this solvent, and it seemed feasible to attempt potentiometric measurements. An aqueous SCE was used as the reference electrode. Lithium fluoride is known to be relatively insoluble in DMSO [50], and a sharp break was observed in a potentiometric titration curve of tetraethylammonium fluoride (Et_4NF) with LiCl, as shown in Figure 13. The solubility product obtained from this curve was within an order of magnitude of the value (4×10^{-4}) measured by direct solubility, but quantitative consistency was not observed. This is further shown in Figure 14, which is an attempt to construct a Nernstian calibration curve using varying concentrations of Et_4NF in DMSO, both with and without a supporting electrolyte. Although the electrode gave the expected calibration curve in aqueous solutions, the response in DMSO solutions

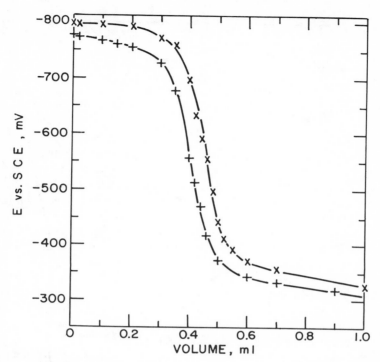

Figure 13. Titration of Et₄NF with LiCl in DMSO; +, with $0.1M$ Et₄NClO₄ supporting electrolyte; x, without supporting electrolyte. Data from Reference 49.

was not all what was expected, and indicates that some material is present which is removing free fluoride ion from the dilute solutions. Tetraethylammonium perchlorate supporting electrolyte tends to increase these deviations. Whether these mysterious results are due to impurities, or to some intrinsic difficulties with the LaF_3 membrane electrode cannot be resolved without further experiments.

III. The Silver Sulfide Membrane Electrode

The silver sulfide membrane electrode responds to either silver ion or sulfide ion in aqueous solutions. Nernstian response to Ag^+ has been observed down to $10^{-7}M$ in $AgNO_3$ solutions, and to calculated Ag^+ concentrations as low as $10^{-25}M$ in solutions of silver complexes. For silver ion concentrations below $10^{-4}M$, plastic vessels are used because of the strong adsorption of Ag^+ by pyrex glass [51]. The principal advantage of the silver sulfide membrane over a simple silver metal electrode for determination of silver ions is its freedom from interference by complexing and precipitating agents (such as thiosulfate and iodide) and by oxidizing or reducing agents.

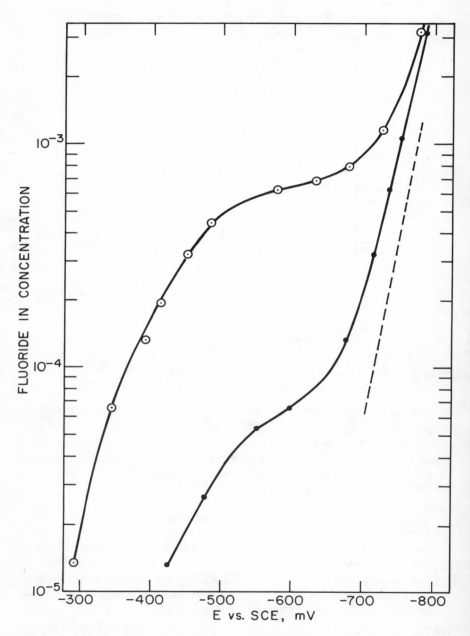

Figure 14.   Response of LaF$_3$ membrane electrode to fluoride ion in DMSO: O Et$_4$NF in 0.1M Et$_4$NClO$_4$ supporting electrolyte: ● Et$_4$NF without supporting electrolyte; – – –, Nernst slope of 60mV. Data from Reference 49..

There have been only two published studies of this electrode, but it seems possible to exploit it in studies of a large number of chemical systems involving either silver or sulfide. Hseu and Rechnitz [52], using an SCE reference electrode with an intermediate $0.1M$ $NaNO_3$ salt bridge to avoid reaction of sulfide with mercury ions or silver with chloride ions, verified the Nernstian response to Ag^+ over the range from 10^{-1} to $10^{-4}M$, and to sulfide ion from 10^{-2} to $10^{-7}M$. In the sulfide ion measurements, corrections had to be made for the reaction of sulfide ion with water

$$S^= + H_2O \rightleftarrows HS^- + OH^- \qquad (39)$$

which is a significant reaction even in relatively concentrated NaOH solutions. This effect (although well known) was verified by a study of the effect of pH at constant sulfide concentration. From the difference between potentials observed in Ag^+ solutions and $S^=$ solutions, the solubility product of Ag_2S was determined to be $(1.48 \pm 0.1) \times 10^{-51}$ at zero ionic strength and 25 °C, in good agreement with literature data obtained with silver electrodes and by calculation from free energy data.

The effect of a number of anions was found to be negligible: Cl^-, Br^-, I^-, SCN^-, $CrO_4^=$, NO_3^- and $SO_4^=$ did not affect the response to sulfide ion. Hg^{++} is probably the only cationic interference. The formation constant K_{s3} of the complex $SnS_3^=$ from $SnS_2(s)$ and $S^=$ was determined and found to be $(2.06 \pm 0.1) \times 10^5$ at ionic strength 0.1 and 25 °C, in agreement with the results of solubility measurements.

The response time of the silver sulfide electrode seems to be of the order of 1 to 10 seconds, and thus kinetic studies of slow reactions involving sulfide ions seem to be feasible, although none have yet been published [52]. On the other hand, if the electrode is first equilibrated with the solution, it takes only a few milliseconds to establish the equilibrium potential once the circuit is closed [53].

The response of the Ag_2S membrane to silver and sulfide ions has been verified by Light and Swartz [53], who also studied the temperature coefficient of the electrode. When the change in standard potential of the $Ag-Ag^+$ internal electrode is taken into account, the theoretical temperature coefficient in $0.1M$ $AgNO_3$ solution was calculated to be $(dE/dT)_{th}$ $= -0.42$ mV/deg, which is in good agreement with the experimental value of -0.4 mV/deg. In $0.1M$ Na_2S and $0.1M$ NaOH, the temperature coefficient is $+0.05$ mV/deg.

A comparison was made [53] between the silver sulfide membrane electrode and a classical $Ag-Ag_2S$ electrode of the second kind, made by coating a silver wire with silver sulfide. The membrane electrode was superior, particularly with respect to interference by oxidizing agents such as Fe^{+3} and nitric acid. The fundamental difference seems to be that the electrode of the second kind has a porous structure which allows the solution to come in contact with the silver electrode surface, whereas the membrane electrode prevents this secondary path of reaction while retaining the high ionic conductivity of the Ag_2S crystal.

IV. Miscellaneous Solid-State Electrodes

Although thermodynamic studies have not been made with other solid-state membrane electrodes, their ready availability may encourage many studies in the near future. Membranes of the silver halides have some advantage over the conventional electrodes of the second kind, since they are relatively unaffected by oxidizing agents, and can even be made to show response to complexing agents such as SCN^- and CN^-. Electrodes reversible to divalent cations such as Cu^{++}, Cd^{++}, and Pb^{++} can also be prepared using mixed sulfides, and the construction and properties of these electrodes are discussed in Chapter 2. Heterogeneous membrane electrodes may also be useful, but again, no serious thermodynamic studies have been undertaken. Chapter 3 summarizes their preparation, properties, and history, so they will not be discussed further in this section.

V. Calcium-Selective Electrodes

The calcium-selective liquid ion exchange electrode and a number of related membrane electrodes have been the subject of considerable research during the past three years. The calcium-selective properties of a liquid ion exchanger based on calcium didecylphosphate dissolved in dioctylphenylphosphonate were first described by Ross [54], and other membrane electrodes selective to calcium have been described by Gregor, et al. [55,56], Shatkay [57,58] and Schultz et al. [59]. Much earlier work is reviewed in these articles. Although the construction and detailed properties of these electrodes (particularly interferences by hydrogen, sodium, and other ions) vary, the general principles involved in evaluating them are similar to those we used in our discussion of the lanthanum fluoride membrane electrode, and we will not belabor those points here. Furthermore, calcium selective electrodes have been discussed in great detail in Chapters 2 and 7, so this section will merely indicate those studies which are concerned with thermodynamic properties.

In the case of the liquid ion exchange electrodes, the ion exchange phase, a water-insoluble organic liquid, is immobilized in a porous membrane which separates two aqueous phases. A cell without liquid junction, which we have used in our laboratory [60] may be represented as follows:

$$\text{Ag; AgCl}(s) \mid \text{CaCl}_2(m_1) \mid \text{organic} \mid \text{CaCl}_2(m_2) \mid \text{AgCl}(s); \text{Ag}$$
$$\text{(test)} \qquad \text{phase} \quad \text{(internal)}$$

and of course the organic phase may be a solid [59] as well as a liquid, provided the cell resistance is low enough to permit accurate measurements. Measurements obtained with a concentration cell such as the one described above are presented in Figure 15. Because there is no liquid

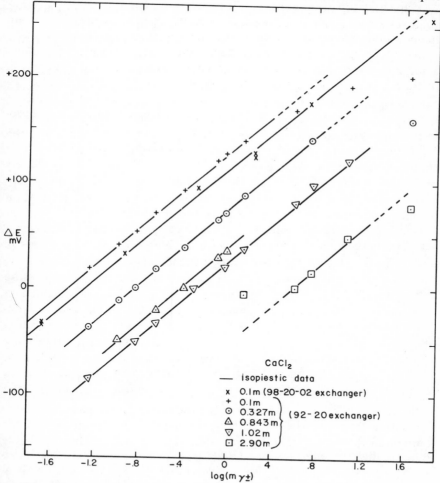

Figure 15.   Response of calcium-selective liquid ion exchange electrodes in CaCl₂ solutions of various concentrations. The different sets of data were obtained with different concentrations of internal filling solutions, as indicated. Data from References 31 and 60.

junction between the test phase and the reference electrode, there can be no ambiguity about the distinction between the liquid junction potential and a single ion activity coefficient, such as is found in Shatkay's [56] experiments. A number of internal filling solutions were used (m_2), and when isopiestic values of the mean activity coefficient for $CaCl_2(\gamma_\pm)$ were used, the Nernst equation

$$\Delta E = \frac{3RT}{2F} \ln \frac{m_1 \gamma_1}{m_2 \gamma_2} \tag{40}$$

was verified within experimental error over a wide range of concentration. With the calcium didecylphosphate ion exchanger (Orion 92-20) deviations from the Nernst equation were observed whenever the concentration gradient across the membrane was too large — either a test solution too concentrated for a dilute filling solution or a test solution too dilute for a concentrated filling solution. Such deviations were observed by Ross [54] with an $0.1m$ filling solution at concentrations above $0.1m$ for test solutions, and were verified in later work [60]. However, if the internal and external solutions are not too different in concentration, the Nernst equation is obeyed over a limited range of concentration even in solutions as concentrated as $6m$. A more recently available liquid ion exchanger (Orion 98-20-02 exchanger, used in the "flow-through" apparatus) showed a much wider range of Nernstian behavior, even when the internal solution was $0.1m$ and the external solution was $5m$.

Data such as are presented in Figure 15 can also be used to determine activity coefficients directly. In Figure 16 such a set of calculations is summarized. Using measurements on the most dilute solutions ($<$ $0.01m$) with a dilute filling solution ($0.1m$), it is possible to determine the activity coefficient γ_1 by extrapolation to infinite dilution. These data show some deviations at high concentrations, but can be matched with activity coefficient data obtained with a more concentrated filling solution over the range where both systems show Nernstian behavior. Proceeding in this way, one can build up piecemeal a curve of mean activity coefficient from a number of different measurements, and such a curve is shown in Figure 16. The solid line represents the isopiestic data for the mean activity coefficient of $CaCl_2$ [2].

In the above experiments, the pH of the test reference solutions was kept at 7.0 to avoid interference by hydrogen ion, and also to avoid the possible precipitation of $Ca(OH)_2$ or $CaCO_3$ (due to atmospheric CO_2). These pH-dependent effects are discussed in Chapters 2 and 7, and must be considered in any thermodynamic studies using calcium-selective electrodes.

The stability of potential is not as good as with solid-state membrane electrodes because the free charge at the organic-aqueous interfaces de-

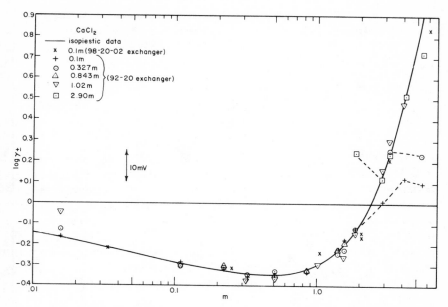

Figure 16.   Results of analyzing the data presented in Figure 15 to obtain mean activity coefficients for CaCl₂.

pends on the geometry of those interfaces, and even when the organic phase is immobilized in a membrane, hydrostatic pressure, stirring, or surface-active agents can disturb the charge distribution which gives rise to the observed potential. Although readings can be duplicated to 0.1 mV. overall errors are usually much larger. Thus, a system with carefully reproducible geometry is essential for accurate studies. The response time of the calcium-selective liquid ion exchange electrodes is of the order of 10 seconds [61], considerably slower than for the solid-state membrane electrodes, but still fast enough for studies of the kinetics of slow reactions.

Most divalent and monovalent cations interfere with the response of calcium-selective electrodes to some extent, but the description of these interferences is a complicated matter. In dilute solutions, the usual selectivity ratio concept is useful, and selectivity ratios are relatively constant over the range from $0.001M$ to $0.05M$. Above this concentration, however, complicated ion-exchange equilibria, which have not been thoroughly investigated, take place, and the selectivity ratio varies quite strongly with solution composition. For example, the selectivity ratio of the Orion 92-20 exchanger for calcium over sodium is approximately 5000 in dilute solutions [62], but this same exchanger in NaCl-CaCl₂ solutions of ionic strength $6m$ showed only about a 3-to-1 selectivity ratio, and this varied strongly with solution composition [60]. Selectivity ratios

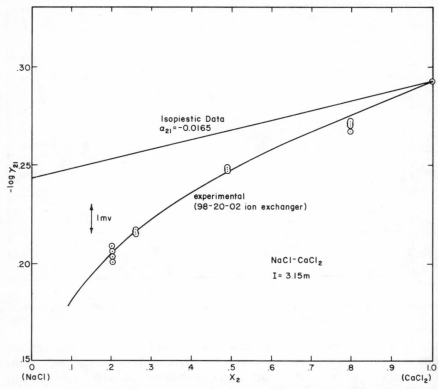

Figure 17.   Results of an attempt to measure the activity coefficient of CaCl₂ in NaCl–CaCl₂ electrolytes using a liquid ion exchange electrode. Deviations from the isopiestic data [63] are in the direction expected if the electrode responded partially to sodium ion. Data from Reference 31.

for dilute solutions are given in Chapter 2, but these should be checked in detail for concentrated solutions.

The Orion 98-20-02 exchanger, which showed better performance than the 92-20 exchanger in concentrated CaCl₂ solutions, was used in an attempt to measure the activity coefficients of CaCl₂ in NaCl-CaCl₂ electrolyte mixtures [31]. The results are shown in Figure 17. The straight line at the top of the figure is obtained from the isopiestic data of Robinson and Bower [63], which have been confirmed by measurements with sodium glass electrodes and sodium amalgam electrodes [64]. The experimental measurements obtained with the calcium-selective electrode are in error by an amount well outside the random deviations of individual measurements, and in the direction predicted if the electrode responded to Na⁺ as well as to Ca⁺⁺. These deviations are of the order of a few millivolts, and although this electrode system is not satisfactory for activity coefficient measurements, it is still quite useful for analytical purposes.

Calcium-selective electrodes have also been used to measure equilibrium constants in a number of systems. Nakayama and Rasnick [65] measured the solubility product of calcium sulfate dihydrate and the dissociation constant of the complex $CaSO_4$ in aqueous solutions of varying ionic strength containing NaCl and Na_2SO_4. Their results were in good agreement with literature data obtained by solubility and conductimetric methods [3].

Rechnitz and Lin [61] evaluated the equilibrium constants for the association of Ca^{++} with the chelating agents ethylenediaminetetraacetic acid (EDTA) and nitrilotriacetic acid (NTA) using the Orion 92-20 liquid ion exchanger. They also made a kinetic study of the exchange between Ca^{++} and Mg^{++} with their EDTA complexes, which is described in more detail in Chapter 9. Rechnitz and Hseu [66], using the Beckman 39068 calcium ion exchanger (which has a solid organic matrix [59]), studied the formation constants of various complexes: calcium malate, calcium citrate, and calcium *trans*-1,2-diamino-cyclohexane-N,N,N',N'-tetraacetic acid (DCTA). In these studies, the electrode used had an advantage over the Orion liquid ion exchanger type in that it was much less sensitive to hydrogen ion, and measurements could be made in much more acidic media. However, its selectivity for calcium over sodium was poorer.

Thompson [67] has measured the concentration of free magnesium ion in a solution approximating sea water, using the Orion 92-32 ("divalent ion") liquid ion exchanger, and obtained results in agreement with the calculations of Garrels and Thompson on their chemical model of sea water [68]. A similar measurement of the concentration of ionized calcium in sea water was reported by Thompson and Ross [69].

Although measurement of activity coefficients for calcium salts in most multicomponent electrolytes probably cannot be made with sufficient accuracy to compete with other thermodynamic approaches to such systems, calcium ion activity measurements in such systems **can** be made with sufficient accuracy and precision that the determination of equilibrium constants and the evaluation of the relative amount of ionized calcium (or other divalent ions) compared to the total concentration in complex mixtures may provide useful data, and in some cases, may provide the only data available on a given system. The development of new and more selective ion exchangers will continue to expand the field of measurements for which the calcium-selective ion exchange electrodes can be used.

VI. Miscellaneous Liquid Ion Exchange Electrodes

Although there are almost an infinite number of possible studies which could be carried out with the various liquid ion exchange electrodes available and yet to be developed, not much work of a thermodynamic character has yet been published. A few studies will be briefly mentioned here.

Rechnitz and Lin [70] used a cupric ion-sensitive exchanger (Orion 92-29) to measure the formation constants of copper(II) with the ligands glycine, glutamic acid, tris(hydroxymethyl)aminomethane, and acetate. Hseu and Rechnitz [71] used a perchlorate-sensitive exchanger (Orion 92-81) to determine the solubility products of $KClO_4$, $[Co(NH_3)_6](ClO_4)_3$, $[Cu(C_5H_5N)_4](ClO_4)_2$, and $[Fe(C_{12}H_8N_2)_3](ClO_4)_2$, where the latter two ligands are pyridine and 1,10-phenanthroline, respectively. Potterton and Shults [72] evaluated the precision (approximately ± 1 mV), working range, response time (10 sec) and memory effects of the nitrate-selective ion exchange electrode (Orion 92-07). The Nernst equation was verified in $NaNO_3$ solutions over the range of concentration from $10^{-4.5}$ to 10^{-1}, but no further thermodynamic measurements were made.

VII. Conclusions

The ready availability of solid-state and liquid ion exchange electrodes which are more or less specific for certain ions has expanded enormously the scope of experimental thermodynamic measurements in aqueous solutions. The solid-state electrodes (particularly the LaF_3 membrane electrode) are stable and precise enough, and free enough of interferences by other ions, that activity coefficient and equilibrium constant measurements should be possible in systems of quite varied complexity. Studies of the coordination chemistry of fluoride compounds in aqueous and non-aqueous solutions should burgeon with the advent of a fluoride ion sensing device. Studies of equilibria and activity coefficients of halides and pseudo-halides in the presence of oxidizing and reducing agents may now be possible using appropriate solid-state membrane electrodes. Similar restrictions on the use of silver electrodes and amalgam electrodes of cadmium, lead, copper, and other metal ions, may be removed by the use of mixed sulfide solid-state electrodes.

Similarly, the liquid ion exchange electrodes reversible to ions such as perchlorate, nitrate, and tetrafluoroborate, greatly expands the scope of thermodynamic measurements on compounds containing these anions, and on their solutions. Although the precision and selectivity of these electrodes is not as good as for the solid-state electrodes, it may be possible to make significant contributions to activity coefficient data as well as to equilibrium constant data. The calcium-selective membrane electrodes have already made extraordinary contributions to our understanding of calcium in physiological systems, and it seems likely that they will continue to be of service in this area. In addition, the similar ion exchangers which respond to other divalent cations may be employed in equilibrium constant measurements on systems which would otherwise require quite indirect approaches.

This brief summary is only a beginning. We can look forward to many years of exciting innovations in electrochemical thermodynamics as a result of the application of ion-selective electrodes.

VIII. Acknowledgments

The author thanks Mrs. Rima Huston for her continual assistance throughout the preparation of this review. Professor Lars Gunnar Sillén, Dr. Roger G. Bates, and Dr. Martin S. Frant contributed to important discussions. This work was supported in part by the U. S. Department of the Interior, Office of Saline Water.

IX. References

[1] Harned, H. S., and Owen, B. B., The Physical Chemistry of Electrolytic Solutions, 3rd ed., Reinhold Publishing Corp., New York, New York, 1958.

[2] Robinson, R. A., and Stokes, R. H., Electrolyte Solutions, 2nd ed., revised, Butterworth and Cox, Ltd.,London, 1965.

[3] Sillén, L. G., and Martell, A. E., Stability Constants of Metal-ion Complexes, Spec. Publ. No. 17, The Chemical Society, London, 1964.

[4] Latimer, W. M., Oxidation Potentials, 2nd ed., Prentice Hall, Englewood Cliffs, New Jersey, 1952.

[5] Ives, D. J. G., and Janz, G. J., Reference Electrodes, Academic Press, New York, 1961.

[6] Harned, H. S., and Robinson, R. A., Multicomponent Electrolyte Solutions, Vol. 2, Topic 15 of the International Encyclopedia of Physical Chemistry and Chemical Physics, Pergamon Press, London,1968.

[7] Butler, J. N., Adv. Electrochem. and Electrochem. Eng. Vol. 7 (in press).

[8] Smyrl, W. H., and Tobias, C. W., Electrochim. Acta 13, 1581 (1968); Smyrl, W. H., and Newman, J., J. Phys. Chem. 72, 4660 (1968).

[9] Bjerrum, J., Metal Ammine Formation in Aqueous Solution, P. Haase and Son, Copenhagen, 1941.

[10] Buck, R. P., Anal. Chem. 40, 1432, 1439 (1968).

[11] Bates, R. G., Determination of pH, Theory and Practice, John Wiley and Sons, Inc., New York, 1964.

[12] Eisenman, G., Ed., Glass Electrodes for Hydrogen and Other Cations, Marcel Dekker, Inc., NewYork, 1967.

[13] Truesdell, A. H., Science 161, 884 (1968).

[14] Moore, E. W., and Ross, J. W., Jr., J. Appl. Physiol. 20, 1332 (1965).

[15] Lanier, R. D., J. Phys. Chem. 69, 3992 (1965).

[16] Synnott, J. C., and Butler, J. N., J. Phys. Chem. 72, 2474 (1966).

[17] Frant, M., and Ross, J. W., Jr., Science 154, 1553 (1966).

[18] Lingane, J. J., Anal. Chem. 39, 881 (1967).

[19] Durst, R. A., and Taylor, J. K., Anal. Chem. 39, 1483 (1967).

[20] Bock, R., and Strecker, S., Z. Anal. Chem. 235, 322 (1968).

[21] Baumann, E. W., Anal. Chim. Acta 42, 127 (1968).
[22] Mesmer, R. E., Anal. Chem. 40, 443 (1968).
[23] Gatewood. J., Halliburton Services, Duncan, Oklahoma 73533, private communication.
[24] Lingane, J. J., Anal. Chem. 40, 935 (1968).
[25] Durst, R. A., Anal. Chem. 40, 931 (1968).
[26] Neumann, G., and Sillén, L. G., Royal Institute of Technology, Stockholm, Sweden, private communication.
[27] Srinivasan, K., and Rechnitz, G. A., Anal. Chem. 40, 509 (1968).
[28] Zielen, A. J., J.Phys. Chem. 67, 1474 (1963).
[29] Srinivasan, K., and Rechnitz, G. A., Anal. Chem. 40, 1818 (1968).
[30] Raby, B., and Sunderland, W. E., Anal. Chem. 40, 939 (1968).
[31] Huston, R., and Butler, J. N., Tyco Laboratories, Inc., unpublished data (This work was supported by the U. S. Dept. of the Interior, Office of Saline Water).
[32] Rossotti, F. J. C., and Rossotti, H., The Determination of Stability Constants, McGraw Hill, New York, 1961, Chapter 5.
[33] Butler, J. N., Ionic Equilibrium, Addison-Wesley, Reading, Mass., 1964, Chapters 8 and 9.
[34] Ciavatta, L., and Liberti, A., International Conference on Coordination Chemistry, London, 1959, pp. 133-4.
[35] Sillén, L. G., Acta Chem. Scand. 16, 159 (1962); ibid. 18, 1085 (1964); Ingri, N., and Sillén L. G., Acta Chem. Scand. 16, 173 (1962); Arkiv Kemi 23, 97 (1964).
[36] Ostwald, W., J. Prakt. Chem. 32, 300 (1885); Duessen, E., Z. Anorg. Chem. 44, 300 (1905).
[37] Davies, C. W., and Hudleston, L. J., J. Chem. Soc. 125, 260 (1924).
[38] Aumeras, A., Compt. Rend. 184, 1650 (1927).
[39] Roth, W. A., Annalen 542, 35 (1939).
[40] Brosset, C., Svensk Kem. Tidskr. 54, 155 (1942).
[41] Brosset, C., and Wahlberg, U., Svensk Kem. Tidskr. 55, 335 (1943).
[42] Broene, H. H., and DeVries, T., J. Amer. Chem. Soc. 69, 1644 (1947).
[43] Connick, R. E., and Tsao, M. S., J. Amer. Chem. Soc. 76, 5311 (1954), ibid. 78, 1827 (1956).
[44] Ciavatta, L., Arkiv, Kemi 21, 129 (1963).
[45] Kohlrausch, F., Z. Phys. Chem. 64, 129 (1908).
[46] Bates, R. G., National Bureau of Standards, private communication.
[47] Srinivasan, K., and Rechnitz, G. A., Anal. Chem. 40, 1955 (1968).
[48] Baumann, E. W., Anal. Chem. 40, 1731 (1968).
[49] Holleck, G., and Butler, J. N., Tyco Laboratories, Inc., unpublished data (This work was supported by the U. S. Air Force, Cambridge Research Laboratories).
[50] Butler, J. N., J. Electroanal. Chem. 14, 89 (1967).
[51] Ross, J. W., and Frant, M., paper presented at Eastern Analytical Symposium, New York, Nov. 1968. See also Bulletin No. 3 and Instruction Manual for Model 94-16 electrode, Orion Research Corp., Cambridge, Mass., 1967 and 1968.
[52] Hseu, T. M., and Rechnitz, G. A., Anal. Chem. 40, 1054 (1968).
[53] Light, T. S., and Swartz, J. L., Anal. Lett. 1, 825 (1968).
[54] Ross, J. W., Science 156, 1378 (1967).
[55] Gregor, H. P., and Schonhorn, H., J. Amer. Chem. Soc. 79, 1507[1957]; ibid. 81, 3911 (1959); ibid. 83, 3576 (1961).
[56] Bagg, J., and Gregor, H. P., J. Amer. Chem. Soc. 86, 3626 (1964).
[57] Shatkay, A., Anal. Chem. 39, 1056 (1967). See also discussion Anal. Chem. 40, 456 (1968).
[58] Shatkay, A., J. Phys. Chem. 71, 3858 (1967); Biophys. J. 8, 912 (1968).

[59] Schultz, F. A., Peterson, A. J., Mask, C. A., and Buck, R. P., Science 162, 267 (1968).
[60] Huston, R., and Butler, J. N., Anal. Chem. 41, 200 (1969).
[61] Rechnitz, G. A., and Lin, Z. F., Anal. Chem. 40, 696 (1968).
[62] Moore, E. W., Ann. N. Y. Acad. Sci. 148 (1) 93 (1968).
[63] Robinson, R. A., and Bower, V. E., J. Res. Nat. Bur. Stand. 70A, 313(1966).
[64] Butler, J. N., and Huston, R., J. Phys. Chem. 71, 4479 (1967).
[65] Nakayama, F. S., and Rasnick, B. A., Anal. Chem. 39, 1022 (1967).
[66] Rechnitz, G. A., and Hseu, T. M., Anal. Chem. 41, 111 (1969).
[67] Thompson, M. E., Science 153, 866 (1966).
[68] Garrels, R. M., and Thompson, M. E., Amer. J. Sci. 260, 57 (1962).
[69] Thompson, M. E., and Ross, J. W., Jr., Science 154, 1643 (1966).
[70] Rechnitz, G. A., and Lin, Z. F., Anal. Lett. 1, 23 (1967).
[71] Hseu, T. M., and Rechnitz, G.A., Anal. Lett. 1, 629 (1968).
[72] Potterton, S. S., and Shults, W. D., Anal. Lett. 1, 11(1967).
[73] Hall, F. M., and Slater, S. J., Australian J. Chem. 21, 2663 (1968).

CHAPTER 6

ACTIVITY STANDARDS FOR ION-SELECTIVE ELECTRODES

Roger G. Bates and Marinus Alfenaar[1]

Division of Analytical Chemistry
National Bureau of Standards
Washington, D.C. 20234

I. Introduction. Electrode Response and Ionic Activity

Measurement of the electromotive force of reversible galvanic cells is one of the most attractive means available for studying the properties of the electrolytes participating in the cell reaction and, by extension, of the ions of which they are composed. Difficulties are encountered, however, in separating the emf, a **potential difference**, into its two electrode potentials. There is a corresponding difficulty in separating the well-defined properties of an electrolyte into those for the individual ions; here thermodynamics can offer no unique guide or formula.

Nevertheless, the concepts of the single electrode potential and the individual ionic activity are useful. In this connection, it is interesting to note that the utility of a conventional scale of electrode potentials has been recognized for many years, although many thermodynamic purists continue to oppose the concept of single ion activities.

In essence, the indeterminacy of electrode potentials and single ion activities stems from the indeterminate character of the surface potential of any real phase and of the inner electric (Galvani) potential Φ, [1,2]. The outer (Volta) potential Ψ of the phase, a measurable quantity, is defined by the work required to bring a unit point charge very slowly from an infinite distance up to a point close to the surface of the phase. To obtain the inner potential of the phase, however, it would be necessary to know the surface potential χ, or the work of moving the point charge through the surface. These quantities are related by

$$\Phi = \Psi + \chi \qquad (1)$$

The surface potential χ is not measurable. For this reason, the Galvani potential Φ within a single phase cannot be determined exactly, nor can the difference of Galvani potentials between points in different phases (on which the single electrode potential depends) be measured. On the other hand, Galvani potential differences corresponding to the transfer of ions

---

[1] Present address: Analytical Chemistry Laboratory, University of Utrecht, Croesestraat 77A, Utrecht, Netherlands.

between internal parts of the same phase can be measured readily because they do not involve the indeterminate surface potential.

The electrochemical process at an electrode always involves a transfer of charge from one phase to another. When two electrodes are immersed in the same liquid phase, however, the surface potential cancels out. Consequently, the electric potential difference, under zero current conditions, between two pieces of the same metal attached to the electrodes depends solely on the chemical potentials of the substances participating in the electrode reaction. This potential difference is termed the electromotive force (emf).

Cell reactions are oxidation-reduction processes. It is convenient to think of two half reactions, one (an oxidation) supplying electrons which, on closing an external circuit, pass to the other electrode and are consumed in a reduction process. Consider a cell represented by the scheme

$$Zn(s) \mid ZnI_2(m) \mid AgI(s); Ag(s)$$

where (s) denotes a solid phase and (m) represents the molality of zinc iodide in the solution phase. Clearly zinc and silver both exist in two oxidation states in the two electrode compartments. The half reactions are

$$Zn^{2+} + 2e^- \leftrightharpoons Zn \tag{2}$$

and

$$AgI + e^- \leftrightharpoons Ag + I^- \tag{3}$$

These half reactions are reversible, and it is impossible to tell, without further information, which will proceed toward the right (reduction) and which toward the left (oxidation) when the zinc and silver electrodes are connected with an external conductor. Hence, by international convention [3], cell reactions are written as if oxidation occurs spontaneously at the left electrode of the cell scheme and reduction at the right on closing the external connection. This situation would make the right electrode positive to the left, and, when these conditions are met, the emf is given a positive sign. If, in actuality, the left electrode is found to be the positive electrode, the emf is given a negative sign [3].

The cell reaction for the cell given in the above example is therefore

$$Zn + 2\ AgI \leftrightharpoons ZnI_2 + 2\ Ag \tag{4}$$

Thus, Equation (2) is assumed to proceed spontaneously from right to left (oxidation) while Equation (3) proceeds from left to right (reduction). According to the Nernst equation, the emf, E, of the cell is given by

$$E = E^\circ - \frac{RT}{2F} \ln (a_{Zn^{2+}} a_{I^-}^2) \tag{5}$$

where R, T, and F are respectively, the gas constant, the thermodynamic temperature, and the faraday.

Furthermore, conceptually it may be said that the potential of the zinc electrode is determined by the activity of zinc ions and that the potential of the silver-silver iodide electrode is determined by the activity of iodide ions, even though only the mean activity of these ions is measurable. Formally, the potentials of the two electrodes can therefore be written [compare Eq. (2) and Eq. (3)]

$$E_{Zn^{2+};\ Zn} = E^{\circ}_{Zn^{2+};\ Zn} + \frac{RT}{2F} \ln a_{Zn^{2+}} \qquad (6)$$

and

$$E_{AgI;\ Ag} = E^{\circ}_{AgI;\ Ag} - \frac{RT}{F} \ln a_{I^-} \qquad (7)$$

By convention, the emf of the complete cell is $E_r - E_l$, where r and l denote the right electrode and left electrode, respectively.

II. Operational Definition of the pA Value

The convenience and practicality of routine pH measurements were assured by the development of the glass electrode. The potential difference between this electrode and the solution in which it is immersed responds rapidly and precisely to changes in the activity of hydrogen ions in the solution. The pH cell consists of a glass indicator electrode combined with a stable reference electrode of substantially constant potential.

The development of other ion-selective electrodes responding satisfactorily to ions other than hydrogen makes possible a similar solution of the problems of measuring the concentrations or activities of these ions in solution. An ion-selective electrode $A(sel)$ reversible to the cation A^{n+}, for example, can be made a part of the cell

$$A(sel)\ |\ A^{n+}\ ||\ KCl(conc)\ |\ Hg_2Cl_2;Hg$$

where the electrode on the right is a standard calomel reference electrode. An electrode reversible to the anion A^{n-} can be used similarly:

$$A(sel)\ |\ A^{n-}\ ||\ KCl(conc)|\ Hg_2Cl_2;Hg$$

The reactions for the two cells are:

$$A + \frac{n}{2}\ Hg_2Cl_2 \rightleftharpoons A^{n+} + n\ Hg + n\ Cl^- \text{ (in conc KCl)} \pm \text{ion transfer} \qquad (8)$$

and

$$A^{n-} + \frac{n}{2}\ Hg_2Cl_2 \rightleftharpoons A + n\ Hg + n\ Cl^- \text{ (in conc KCl)} \pm \text{ion transfer} \qquad (9)$$

Inasmuch as the chloride activity in the reference electrode is constant (barring temperature changes), the term (RT/F) $(\ln a_{Cl^-})$ can conveniently be included in the standard potential of the reference electrode (as is often done in discussions of pH cells [4]), the combination being termed $E^{o\prime}_{ref}$. Hence, for the emf, E, of the cell with an electrode reversible to a cation, one can write

$$E = (E^{o\prime}_{ref} + E_j) - E^o_A - \frac{RT}{nF} \ln a_{A^{n+}}$$ (10)

where E_j is the liquid-junction potential, and, for the corresponding cell containing an electrode reversible to an anion,

$$E = (E^{o\prime}_{ref} + E_j) - E^o_A + \frac{RT}{nF} \ln a_{A^{n-}}$$ (11)

It is evident that the emf of the first cell [compare Eq. (10)] decreases with increasing activity of A^{n+}, while that for the second [compare Eq. (11)] increases as the activity of A^{n-} becomes greater.

The operational definition of pH [5] was a necessary consequence of the inability to evaluate terms such as $E^{o\prime}_{ref} + E_j$ and of a recognition of the day-to-day drifts in E^o_A. For this reason, the pH is defined in terms of the difference of emf between the "unknown" solution, X, and a standard, S, of similar composition, the two measurements preferably being made at nearly the same time. It is logical to extend this approach to the measurement of "pA." From Equation (10), $E^{o\prime}_{ref}$, E_j, and E^o_A remaining unchanged, the difference of E observed when a standard solution is replaced by an unknown solution is a quantitative measure of the difference of pA:

$$pA(X) = pA(S) + \frac{n(E_X - E_S)F}{RT \ln 10}$$ (12)

when A is a cation. Similarly, from Equation 11, for an anion A,

$$pA(X) = pA(S) - \frac{n(E_X - E_S)F}{RT \ln 10}$$ (13)

III.   The Residual Liquid-Junction Potential

Tentatively, Equations (12) and (13) may be regarded as definitions of the pA value when the selected ion is a cation, A^{n+} [Eq. (12)] and an anion, A^{n-} [Eq. (13)]. However, the likelihood that the residual liquid-junction potential in pA measurements may be larger than in pH measurements must not be overlooked. This quantity, expressed in pA or pH units, will be designated ΔE_j. It arises from differences in the concentrations and mobilities of the ionic species in the standard (S) and unknown (X) solutions.

Because of the buffer effect, wide changes of pH are not necessarily accompanied by appreciable changes of ionic strength; they may be achieved by the substitution of other buffer species of much the same molality. On the contrary, it is often difficult to vary pA without producing a corresponding change in the total concentration of ions. For example, an "unknown" solution of sodium chloride with pCl about 1 will have 10 times the ionic strength of a standard NaCl solution of pCl(S) = 2. These differences, which must be regarded as the rule rather than the exception, make it imperative to include $\Delta \bar{E}_j$ on the right side of Equations (12) and (13) at this stage in the development of definitions of the pA value. The magnitude of $\Delta \bar{E}_j$ can be estimated by the classical formulas for the liquid-junction potential or by comparing the "experimental" pA(X) with the "true" -log a_A(X) given by the convention adopted. Thus,

$$\Delta \bar{E}_j = pA(X) + \log a_A (X) \tag{14}$$

It is to be expected that later work will show how large a separation of pA(X) and pA(S) can be tolerated before "greater than negligible" liquid junction errors are encountered.

IV. Performance Tests for Ion-Selective Electrodes

The electrode potential of a well-behaved reversible ion-selective electrode responds to changes in the activity of the selected ionic species in conformance with the Nernst equation. In view of the fact that the variations in the liquid-junction potential may well be large enough to obscure the proper behavior of the indicator electrode, it is very desirable that the electrode response be examined in a cell without liquid junction, if possible. In many instances, this can be accomplished by comparing mean activity coefficients for electrolytes, determined by the use of the ion-selective electrode, with accepted values obtained with electrodes of proved reliability or by other thermodynamic methods. For example, ion-selective electrodes reversible to metal ions can often be combined with the reliable silver-silver chloride electrode in solutions of the metal chloride. If the activity coefficients obtained from the measured emf values agree with the accepted literature values, it may safely be assumed that the electrode is responding satisfactorily over the concentration range covered by the measurements. Electrodes reversible to anions may be combined in a similar way with the hydrogen electrode or with a metal electrode known to be dependable.

This procedure is useful not only for affirming the Nernst response of the electrode but also for examining the selectivity. For the latter purpose, the mean activity coefficients of a salt of the selected ion in mixtures of electrolytes are needed.

V. Conventional Activity Scales

Although the potential of a single electrode is believed to reflect changes in the activity of a single ionic species, it is quite clear that a) only potential **differences** between individual electrodes can be measured, and b) activities of **ion combinations** alone can be exactly determined. If the reference electrode potential and its associated liquid-junction potential are hopefully assumed to remain constant, however, emf measurements lead to changes of ionic activity. The usefulness of practical pH measurements depends on such a procedure and on a defined or **conventional** scale of hydrogen ion activity on which reference standards for the pH scale are based.

A. THE pH CONVENTION

In the NBS procedure, standard pH(S) values are assigned to selected buffer solutions with the aid of emf measurements of cells without liquid junction. The cells contain hydrogen electrodes and silver-silver chloride electrodes; therefore, they yield values of the acidity function $p(a_H\gamma_{Cl})$ for the buffer solution with added chloride and, by suitable extrapolation, also for the chloride-free buffer solution. A non-thermodynamic step, the estimation of γ_{Cl^-}, is necessary to derive values of pa_H, which are, in turn, identified with pH(S) for the reference standards in the operational pH definition. With international concurrence [6], the following convention for γ_{Cl^-} was adopted:

$$-\log \gamma_{Cl^-} = \frac{AI^{1/2}}{1+1.5I^{1/2}} \tag{15}$$

where A is the Debye-Hückel slope constant and I is the ionic strength. It was intended that this formula be used at ionic strengths of 0.1 and below.

At this point it should be emphasized that, in theory, the activity coefficients of other ions become fixed when a scale of numerical values for the activity coefficients of any one species is selected. If γ_{Cl^-} in a solution of sodium chloride is defined, for example, γ_{Na^+} becomes fixed through the mean activity coefficient $\gamma_\pm$ of sodium chloride obtainable by a variety of thermodynamic methods. In a similar way, $\gamma_{Ca^{2+}}$ and γ_{K^+} in solutions of calcium chloride and potassium chloride, respectively, acquire numerical values when γ_{Cl^-} in these solutions is evaluated. Mean activity coefficients can also be measured in mixtures of electrolytes. Furthermore, certain combinations and ratios of ionic activity coefficients, such as $\gamma_{Cl^-}/\gamma_{Ac^-}$ (where Ac^- is acetate ion) and $(\gamma_{Cl^-} \cdot \gamma_{H_2PO_4^-})/\gamma_{HPO_4^{2-}}$ can be determined by experimental means. The number of arbitrary non-thermodynamic formulas or conventions adopted in an effort to facilitate and improve the interpretation of analytical measurements made with ion-selective electrodes (hydrogen and glass electrodes must be included in this class) should evidently be kept as small as possible. Otherwise a truly chaotic situation would result. It is therefore highly desirable that standard reference data for the activities of the ions to which the newer ion-selective electrodes respond be made as consistent as possible with the convention already adopted in the assignment of standard pH values.

B. COMPARISON OF REASONABLE CONVENTIONS

The pH convention is usually applied to the estimation of γ_{Cl^-} in buffer solutions containing relatively small amounts of an alkali chloride. The chloride ion activity coefficients derived by Equation (15) are, however, nearly the same as the mean activity coefficients of sodium chloride in its pure aqueous solutions, up to an ionic strength exceeding 0.1. Thus, in practice, the pH convention is substantially equivalent to a convention which is based on the equality of γ_{Na^+} and γ_{Cl^-} in these solutions of sodium chloride. Consequently it is completely analogous to the MacInnes convention [7] which asserts the equality of γ_{K^+} and γ_{Cl^-} in aqueous solutions of potassium chloride. The MacInnes convention has been widely used in the estimation of single ionic activity coefficients. Garrels [8] has proposed that it be adopted as a basis for establishing activity standards for ion-selective electrodes.

Both the pH convention proposed by Bates and Guggenheim [6] and the earlier MacInnes convention offer a means of achieving a certain amount of consistency among the activity coefficients of a number of single ionic species. In practice, they are not completely successful in fulfilling this desired objective. Nevertheless, they may be expected to have some advantages over approaches based solely on a splitting of the mean activity coefficients of all electrolytes according to a predetermined formula. For uni-univalent electrolytes, the simplest convention of this type is $\gamma_+ = \gamma_- = \gamma_\pm$. For 2-1 electrolytes such as calcium chloride, it is reasonable, as Butler has pointed out [9], to interrelate the activity coefficients of the ions according to the valence relationships set forth in the Debye-Hückel equation, namely $\gamma_{2+} = \gamma_+^4 = \gamma_-^4$. This convention, in turn, appears somewhat more reasonable than equating γ_{2+} to $\gamma_\pm$ as Shatkay has proposed for calcium chloride [10].

Table 1 compares the values of pa_A for several cations and anions in aqueous salt solutions at ionic strengths of 0.1 and 1.0, as derived by three of these conventions. It is evident that these "reasonable" conventions give closely comparable results at ionic strengths of 0.1 or less but that the differences become appreciable when the ionic strength is as high as 1.0.

Table 1. Comparison of values of pa_A based on three different conventions.

Salt	pH convention		MacInnes convention		Debye-Hückel convention	
	pa_A		pa_A		pa_A	
	cation	anion	cation	anion	cation	anion
		Ionic strength = 0.1				
KCl	1.118		1.114		1.114	
		1.110		1.114		1.114
NaF	1.108		1.106		1.116	
		1.124		1.126		1.116
NaCl	1.108		1.106		1.110	
		1.112		1.114		1.110
NaI	1.108		1.106		1.104	
		1.100		1.102		1.104
NaClO$_4$	1.108		1.106		1.111	
		1.114		1.116		1.111
CaCl$_2$	1.887		1.880		1.898	
		1.286		1.291		1.282
		Ionic strength = 1.0				
KCl	0.234		0.219		0.219	
		0.204		0.219		0.219
NaF	0.160		0.145		0.242	
		0.324		0.339		0.242
NaCl	0.160		0.145		0.182	
		0.204		0.219		0.182
NaI	0.160		0.145		0.133	
		0.106		0.121		0.133
NaClO$_4$	0.160		0.145		0.201	
		0.242		0.257		0.201
CaCl$_2$	1.105		1.075		1.168	
		0.381		0.396		0.349

C. Self-Consistent Scales of Ionic Activity

In the application of the pH convention a further problem — that of internal consistency — arises. The same difficulty must be faced in applying the MacInnes convention. This dilemma is illustrated by the following diagram:

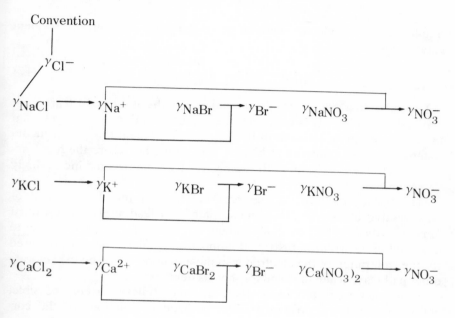

The activity coefficient of chloride ion in solutions of varying ionic strengths is defined by the convention embodied in Equation (15). With a knowledge of mean activity coefficients, it is then possible to obtain the activity coefficients of sodium, potassium, and calcium ion, for example, in solutions of their chlorides. If the activity coefficients of these cations were taken, by extension, to be the same in bromide or nitrate solutions, for example, three or more pathways to γ_{Br^-} and $\gamma_{NO_3^-}$ would be available. Without doubt, these multiple values of γ_{Br^-} and $\gamma_{NO_3^-}$ would differ from one another at higher ionic strengths. One value, of course represents γ_{Br^-} in a sodium bromide solution, another in a potassium bromide solution, and so forth. It is quite reasonable that these should be different, but it must not be forgotten that the separate values of γ_{Br^-} were derived by taking γ_{Na^+} (or γ_{K^+}) to have the same value in the chloride and bromide salt solutions of the same ionic strength.

According to this approach, multiple pathways to the activity coefficients of single ions exist. For example, γ_{A^-} could be calculated by a number of independent paths from the convention for γ_{Cl^-} and the mean activity coefficients of MA and MCl, where M represents any one of a number of univalent cations:

$$\log \gamma_{A^-} = \log \gamma_{Cl^-} + 2 \log \frac{\gamma_{MA}}{\gamma_{MCl}} \qquad (16)$$

Similarly, γ_{A^-} could be derived from data for the salts of bivalent cations M^{2+}:

$$\log \gamma_{A^-} = \log \gamma_{Cl^-} + \frac{3}{2} \log \frac{\gamma_{MA_2}}{\gamma_{MCl_2}} \qquad (17)$$

The individual values obtained at ionic strengths of 0.1 and 1.0 are summarized in Table 2. It is clear that the choice of pathway is not very significant at an ionic strength of 0.1. Again it is evident that larger inconsistencies are encountered at higher ionic strengths, where the mean activity coefficients of salts of the same valence type become increasingly divergent.

We are not inclined, at the present stage in the development of ion-selective electrodes, to propose pathways leading to single-valued ionic activities for all ions in all of their salt solutions. We prefer rather to deal first of all with the restricted number of standard solutions required for the calibration of the electrodes in most common use and to elaborate other pathways when the need for them is demonstrated.

It is therefore proposed that, to the fullest extent possible, cation-responsive electrodes be standardized in solutions of the corresponding completely dissociated chloride salts and that anion-responsive electrodes be standardized in solutions of the completely dissociated sodium salts of the anions. Activity coefficients for the "reference" ions chloride and sodium would be derived from the pH convention directly and from its combination with the known mean activity coefficients of sodium chloride in its aqueous solutions:

$$\log \gamma_{Na^+} = 2 \log \gamma_{\pm}(NaCl) - \log \gamma_{Cl^-} \qquad (18)$$

It is further suggested that these rules apply without restriction as to ionic strength.

Table 2. Values of $-\log \gamma_A$ for anions at 25 °C, derived from the pH convention by different pathways.

Cation	Anion (A)					
	Cl^-	F^-	Br^-	I^-	ClO_4^-	NO_3^-
	Ionic strength = 0.1					
Li^+	0.110	–	0.10	0.08	0.09	0.11
Na^+	0.110	0.12	0.11	0.10	0.12	0.13
K^+	0.110	0.10	0.11	0.10	–	0.14
Rb^+	0.110	–	0.11	0.11	–	0.14
Cs^+	0.110	–	0.11	0.11	–	0.14
Mg^{2+}	0.110	–	0.10	0.09	0.09	0.11
Ca^{2+}	0.110	–	0.11	0.10	0.10	0.14
Sr^{2+}	0.110	–	0.11	0.10	0.11	0.14
Ba^{2+}	0.110	–	0.09	0.08	0.09	0.13
	Ionic strength = 1.0					
Li^+	0.204	–	0.17	0.06	0.09	0.24
Na^+	0.204	0.32	0.16	0.11	0.24	0.36
K^+	0.204	0.15	0.19	0.15	–	0.47
Rb^+	0.204	–	0.21	0.22	–	0.47
Cs^+	0.204	–	0.21	0.22	–	0.42
Mg^{2+}	0.204	–	0.15	0.09	0.07	0.22
Ca^{2+}	0.204	–	0.16	0.10	0.09	0.30
Sr^{2+}	0.204	–	0.17	0.10	0.14	0.33
Ba^{2+}	0.204	–	0.16	0.09	0.14	0.46

VI. Standard Reference Solutions

Standard reference values for pa_{Cl} and pa_{Na} in sodium chloride solutions and for pa_{Ca} in calcium chloride solutions and pa_F in sodium fluoride solutions have been based on the procedures set forth in the preceding section. The results are given in Table 3 for several molalities of the reference salt solution. By definition, the conventional pa_A in these selected standard reference solutions will be identified with pA(S) in the operational definitions set forth in Equations (12) and (13). The mean activity coefficients needed in the calculation of pa_A were taken from data in the literature (NaCl [11,12]; NaF [13]; $CaCl_2$ [14,15]). In view of the likelihood that sodium fluoride is not completely dissociated in the range of molality 0.1 to 1.0, it was not possible to assign a standard value for pF in $1m$ sodium fluoride.

VII. Comparison of Experimental and Defined pA Values

We have examined the behavior of chloride electrodes as well as those responsive to sodium, calcium, and fluoride ions in relation to the scales of ionic activity proposed in the previous sections. In each case, the response of the electrode was determined in a cell without liquid junction, in combination with a "norm" electrode known to behave reliably in the solution in question. After the response of the electrode had been affirmed in this way, pA values were obtained experimentally over a wide range of electrolyte concentration. The "experimental" values of $- \log \gamma_A$, that is, $pA + \log m_A$, were compared with $- \log \gamma_A$ defined by the conventions set forth above. For the measurements, the electrode was standardized at an ionic strength of 0.01. The pA values at this reference point can be found in Table 3.

Table 3. Suggested reference standard values, pA(S), at 25 °C.

Material	Molality mol kg^{-1}	pNa(S)	pCa(S)	pCl(S)	pF(S)
NaCl	0.001	3.015		3.015	
	0.01	2.044		2.044	
	0.1	1.108		1.110	
	1.0	0.160		0.204	
NaF	0.001	3.015			3.015
	0.01	2.044			2.048
	0.1	1.108			1.124
$CaCl_2$	0.000333		3.537	3.191	
	0.00333		2.653	2.220	
	0.0333		1.887	1.286	
	0.333		1.105	0.381	

The emf measurements of cells without liquid junction were made in U-type cells, the two compartments of which were joined by capillary tubing. Another cell vessel accommodated two ion-selective electrodes in a main chamber provided with a magnetic stirrer. Two side compartments, separated from the main chamber by stopcocks, housed the calomel reference electrodes. This vessel was immersed in a water bath for temperature control. The measurements in sodium fluoride solutions were made in beakers and other laboratory ware fabricated of polyethylene. Three commercial saturated calomel reference electrodes were used in this work. Two junctions were of the fiber type, and the third was of the sleeve type. The measuring equipment consisted of a precision potentiometer, a high-impedance electrometer of the vibrating reed type, and a recorder.

It should be emphasized that the observations on electrode behavior recorded in the succeeding sections were made on a single electrode of each type studied. Individual variations among electrodes of the same type certainly exist. Furthermore, improved types of ion-selective electrodes are being developed continually by a rapidly advancing technology.

A. CHLORIDE-SELECTIVE ELECTRODES

Two commercial types of chloride-selective electrodes (Orion Research, Inc.), namely the solid-state type (Model 94-17), consisting of a silver chloride membrane, and the liquid ion-exchanger type (Model 92-17) were used. These were compared in sodium chloride solutions directly against a silver-silver chloride electrode, with the results shown in Figure 1. The response of the solid-state electrode was found to be superior to that of the liquid ion-exchanger electrode. The measurements were usually made in stirred solutions, and equilibrium was ordinarily attained in less than 15 minutes, provided that the silver-silver chloride electrode had been suitable conditioned. The results obtained below a molality of 5×10^{-4} mol kg^{-1}, where the silver-silver chloride electrode is poorly reproducible, are not to be considered significant.

In repeated measurements of cells containing a chloride-selective electrode and a silver-silver chloride electrode in 0.01 m sodium chloride, the solid-state electrode was found to require 15 min to achieve equilibrium at 10 °C. Shorter response times, of the order of 3 to 7 min, were observed at 25 and 45 °C. Reproducibility was about 0.01 pCl unit. In sodium chloride solutions, the reproducibility and response time of the liquid ion-exchanger electrode were slightly superior to those of the solid-state electrode at all three temperatures. Prior to each measurement, the ion-selective electrodes were soaked in distilled water and dried with absorbent tissue.

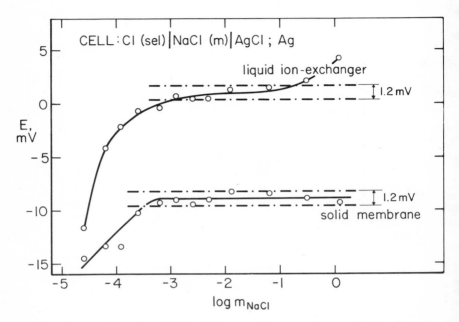

Figure 1. Comparison of two types of chloride-selective electrodes with the silver-silver
chloride electrode in solutions of sodium chloride.

When pA values were measured with the chloride-selective electrode
(solid-state type) standardized at $I = 0.01$ in sodium chloride solutions,
the results shown in Figure 2 were obtained. The curves represent
theoretical values of $-\log \gamma_{Cl-}$ calculated by the pH convention set forth
in Equation (15) [curve 1], by the MacInnes convention as proposed by
Garrels [curve 2], and setting γ_{Cl-} equal to the mean activity coefficient
of sodium chloride in these solutions [curve 3]. Inasmuch as the response
of the solid-state chloride-selective electrode was shown to follow closely
that of the silver-silver chloride electrode from $5 \times 10^{-4}m$ up to $1.0m$,
the departure of the experimental points from the curves of Figure 2
must be due either to residual liquid-junction potentials or to inadequacies
in the three conventions.

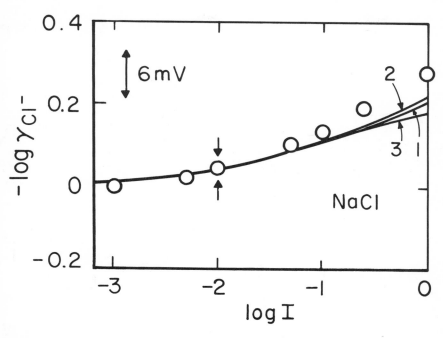

Figure 2. "Experimental" values (circles) of -log γ_{Cl^-}, derived from emf measurements with a chloride-selective electrode and a calomel reference electrode, compared with values defined by three conventions. Curve 1, pH convention; curve 2, MacInnes convention; curve 3, $\gamma_{Cl^-} = \gamma_{\pm}(NaCl)$. Arrows mark point of standardization.

B. SODIUM-SELECTIVE ELECTRODE

A sodium glass electrode of composition NAS_{11-18} (obtained from Corning Glass Works, Inc.) was combined with the silver-silver chloride electrode in sodium chloride solutions; the cell had no liquid junction:

$$Na(gl) \mid NaCl(m) \mid AgCl;Ag$$

The standard potential was calculated from the emf at $m = 0.01$ and the activity coefficient for sodium chloride at this molality [12]. Results of the emf measurements are shown in Figure 3. The mean activity coefficients of sodium chloride calculated from the measured emf are shown by the circles, and the curve is drawn through the accepted activity coefficients given in the literature [12,13]. The accuracy of the response of the sodium electrode seems to have been confirmed in the range of sodium chloride molalities from 0.001 to 1.0 mol kg^{-1}.

At 25 and 45 °C, the sodium glass electrode reached equilibrium in about 3 min. Its behavior at 10 °C was inclined to be sluggish, probably because of the increased electrical resistance of the glass membrane when

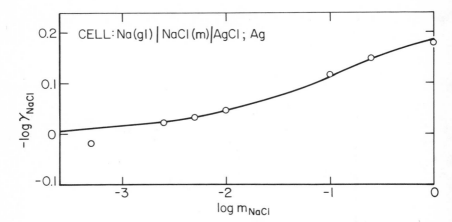

Figure 3.   Determination of -log γ_{NaCl} with the sodium glass electrode in a cell without liquid junction. The curve is drawn through the accepted literature values.

the temperature was lowered. At the two higher temperatures, the reproducibility of repeated measurements was very good, being of the order of 0.1 to 0.2 mV(0.002 to 0.003 pNa unit).

The response of the sodium glass electrode in mixtures of sodium chloride and calcium chloride at a constant ionic strength of 1.0 was also confirmed by emf measurements of the cell

$$\text{Na}(gl) \mid \text{NaCl,CaCl}_2 (I = 1.0) \mid \text{AgCl;Ag}$$

at 25 °C.   The values of log $(\gamma_{NaCl}/\gamma^\circ_{NaCl})$, where γ°_{NaCl} is the activity coefficient of sodium chloride in its pure aqueous solution of molality 1.0 mol kg^{-1}, agreed within 0.001 unit of those calculated by Robinson and Bower [16] from isopiestic vapor pressure measurements.

The "experimental" values of pNa were obtained by means of a cell with liquid junction, consisting of the sodium glass electrode in combination with a saturated calomel reference electrode, the cell being standardized as before in a sodium chloride solution of molality 0.01 mol kg^{-1}. The results are shown in Figure 4. As in Figure 2, curve 1 was derived from the convention proposed here, curve 2 represents the MacInnes convention, and curve 3 is based on $\gamma_{Na+} = \gamma_\pm(\text{NaCl})$. It may be observed that the experimental points lie below the theoretical curves at high ionic strengths, whereas they fell above the curves in Figure 2. This behavior suggests an error caused by the residual liquid-junction potential which, as shown by Equations (10) and (11), has opposite effects on the experimental values of pCl and pNa, raising one and lowering the other.

C. CALCIUM-SELECTIVE ELECTRODE

The response of a calcium-selective electrode of the liquid ion-exchanger type (Orion Research, Inc., Model 92-20) was studied in

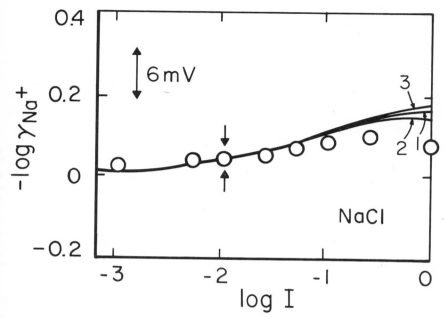

Figure 4. "Experimental" values (circles) of -log γ_{Na^+}, derived from emf measurements with the sodium glass electrode and a calomel reference electrode, compared with values defined by three conventions.

a cell without liquid junction of this following type:

$$\text{Ca}(sel) \mid \text{CaCl}_2(I) \mid \text{AgCl;Ag}$$

The cell was standardized at $I = 0.01$, using the known activity coefficient of calcium chloride at this molality [14]. The mean activity coefficients of calcium chloride at 25 °C obtained experimentally are plotted in Figure 5 as a function of ionic strength (I). The curve is again drawn through the mean activity coefficients obtained by other thermodynamic methods and recorded in the literature [13]. The agreement is quite satisfactory, confirming the accuracy of the response of the calcium electrode in solutions of calcium chloride.

In order to examine the response of the calcium-selective electrode in mixtures of sodium chloride and calcium chloride, emf measurements of this same cell with aqueous salt mixtures of a total molality of 1.0 mol kg^{-1} were made. Poor reproducibility was observed, especially in solutions of high sodium content. This result suggests that the selectivity ratio Ca^{2+}/Na$^+$ is not sufficiently high for this particular application of the calcium electrode. In calcium chloride solutions at 25 °C, however, the calcium-selective electrode was found to be reproducible to 0.2 to 0.3 mV (0.01 pCa unit) and to reach equilibrium in about 1 min after immersion in the solution.

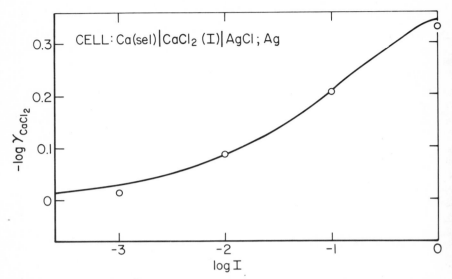

Figure 5.   Determination of -log γ_{CaCl_2} with a calcium-selective electrode in a cell without liquid junction. The curve is drawn through the accepted literature values.

The response of the calcium-selective electrode in calcium chloride solutions was also explored by measurements of a pCa cell with a saturated calomel reference electrode and a liquid junction. The cell was standardized as before at $I = 0.01$. The results are shown in Figure 6, where $- \log \gamma_{Ca^{2+}}$, that is, $pCa + \log m_{Ca^{2+}}$, is plotted as a function of the logarithm of the ionic strength. Once again, curve 1 was calculated by the convention proposed here, curve 2 by the MacInnes convention, and curve 3 by assuming the z^2 relationship embodied in the Debye-Hückel formula, which leads to $\gamma_{Ca^{2+}} = \gamma_{\pm}^2 (CaCl_2)$. Curve 4 resulted from setting $\gamma_{Ca^{2+}}$ equal to the mean activity coefficient of calcium chloride, as suggested by Shatkay [10]. As expected, curve 4 differs considerably from those curves that are consistent with the Debye-Hückel theory.

D.   FLUORIDE-SELECTIVE ELECTRODE

The accuracy of the response of a sodium-selective electrode having been affirmed, this electrode was used in combination with the fluoride-selective electrode, (Orion Research, Inc., Model 94-09) of the solid-state (lanthanum fluoride) type, to study the response of the fluoride electrode in solutions of sodium fluoride at 25 °C. The cell did not have a liquid junction; it is represented as follows:

$$Na(gl) \mid NaF(m) \mid F(sel)$$

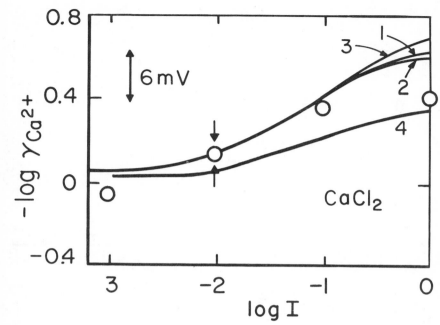

Figure 6. "Experimental" values (circles) of -log $\gamma_{Ca^{2+}}$, derived from emf measurements with a calcium-selective electrode and a calomel reference electrode, compared with values defined by four conventions.

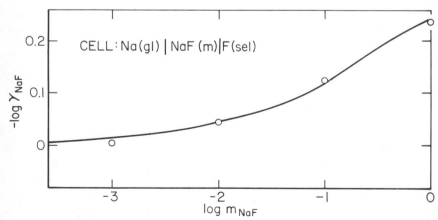

Figure 7. Determination of -log γ_{NaF} with a sodium glass electrode and a fluoride-selective electrode in a cell without liquid junction. The curve is drawn through accepted literature values.

The cell was standardized in a solution of NaF of molality 0.01 mol kg⁻¹.
   The results are shown in Figure 7, where the curve is drawn once again through the known activity coefficients of sodium fluoride in its aqueous

solutions. The response of the fluoride electrode over a considerable range of sodium fluoride concentration seems to be very satisfactory. From a limited number of measurements, it appeared that the reproducibility of the fluoride-selective electrode is 0.2 to 0.3 mV (0.005 pF unit) in solutions of sodium fluoride.

Experimental values of the activity coefficient of fluoride ion, derived from pF measurements in the cell with liquid junction, are shown as circles in Figure 8. Curve 1 again represents the convention proposed in this

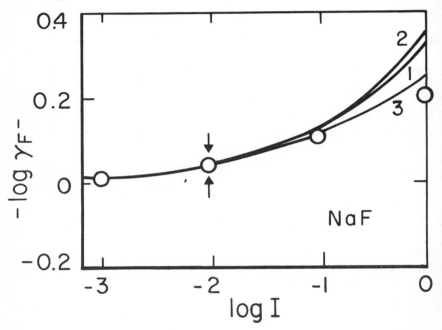

Figure 8. "Experimental" values (circles) of -log γ_{F-}, derived from emf measurements with a fluoride-selective electrode and a calomel reference electrode, compared with values defined by three conventions.

paper, curve 2 is derived from the MacInnes convention, and curve 3 is based on the Debye-Hückel convention $\gamma_{F-} = \gamma_{\pm}(NaF)$. Contrary to the situation with chloride ion illustrated in Figure 2, the experimental points in Figure 8 fall below the curves at $I = 1$. This is probably because sodium fluoride is incompletely dissociated at this high concentration. The mean activity coefficient is therefore low and the conventional -log γ_{F-} is too high. For the same reason, the points lie closer to curve 3 than to curves 1 or 2.

VIII. Limitations of Practical pA Measurements

It is evident that the practical application of ion-selective electrodes is successful only when certain conditions are met. First of all, the response of the electrode to changes in the activity of the ion to which it is selective must be demonstrated, over the range in which the electrode is to be used, by suitable measurements in a cell without liquid junction in the manner outlined in earlier sections. Secondly, there must be assurance that other ions that may interfere with this response are not present in sufficient concentration to affect the results. Finally, the experimental conditions must be such that the residual liquid-junction potential error will be small relative to the required accuracy of the measured pA.

We have seen in earlier sections that the response of the four types of electrodes studied here is excellent over a range of at least three decades of concentration. A listing of the chief interferences can usually be found in the literature provided by the manufacturer of the electrodes. In general, interferences are likely to be more serious with electrodes of the liquid ion-exchanger type than with the solid-state type of electrode. Glass electrodes designed for the measurement of cation activities usually have a marked response to hydrogen ion, and therefore the pH of the solutions under study may have to be controlled at values 3 or 4 units higher than pA. Furthermore, sodium aluminum silicate glasses often show a strong response to silver ion [17].

The uncompensated liquid-junction potential may cause some of the most serious errors encountered in the experimental pA measurement. As shown by Equation (14), the residual liquid-junction potential (expressed in pA units) is defined as the difference between the measured operational pA value and the defined $- \log a_A$ for the same solution. It may therefore be estimated from plots such as those of Figures 2, 4, 6, and 8, representing the difference between the experimental points (circles) and the solid curve labeled 1. Table 4 summarizes these approximate values of $\Delta \bar{E}_j$ when the cell had been standardized in each case at an ionic strength of 0.01 in a pure aqueous solution of the salt concerned (sodium chloride, calcium chloride, or sodium fluoride). In deriving the data given in the table, it was assumed that sodium fluoride (like the other salts) is completely dissociated at molalities up to 1.0 mol kg^{-1}.

The influence of the composition and concentration of the solution on the liquid-junction potential error is shown in Figure 9 (ΔE_j of 3 mV corresponds to $\Delta \bar{E}_j$ of 0.05 unit). The cell consisted of a silver-silver chloride electrode used in conjunction with the saturated calomel electrode. It was standardized in a sodium chloride solution of molality 0.01 mol kg^{-1}, and all of the measurements were made at 25 °C. The "true" activity coefficients of chloride ion in each of the four salt solutions or aqueous salt mixtures were calculated by Equation (15). It is seen that the variation of the liquid-junction potential error with ionic strength is about the same for all four types of solutions, but for the solutions of calcium chloride and the two mixtures it is 1 to 2 mV different from that for pure

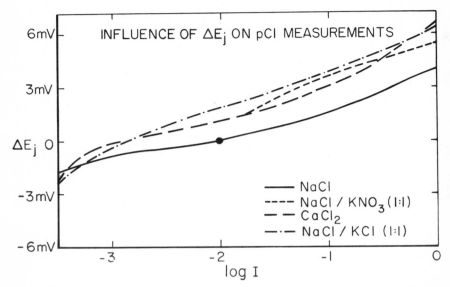

Figure 9. Residual liquid-junction potentials in a cell with a chloride-selective electrode and a calomel reference electrode for four types of solutions. The cell was standardized in 0.01 *m* sodium chloride.

solutions of sodium chloride. The corresponding error of 0.02 to 0.04 pCl unit could be eliminated only by standardizing the cell in a solution containing the same salt or salt mixture as is present in the "unknown" solutions.

On the other hand, an error of about 4 mV (0.07 pCl unit) is incurred when the cell is standardized in $0.01m$ sodium chloride and used for measurements in solutions of the same salt at a molality of 1.0 mol kg^{-1}. These estimates are consistent with calculated liquid-junction potentials [18]. To eliminate this concentration effect on the liquid-junction potential, it would be necessary to have a series of standard solutions of concentrations spaced over the entire range in which the electrode gives useful results. For example, if the electrode were standardized in $0.5m$ sodium chloride, the error in $1.0m$ sodium chloride would be reduced to about 1 mV (0.017 pCl unit).

Further measurements of electrode responses and residual liquid-junction potentials will be necessary before ideal standardization procedures can be recommended. It is nonetheless possible at the present time to suggest certain general procedures that promise to increase the accuracy of routine pA measurements. These are:

1.   The pretreatment of the electrode should be identical for both the "unknown" measurement and the standardization. (Soaking in distilled water for a few minutes and drying with soft absorbent tissue constitutes a satisfactory pretreatment.)

Table 4. Residual liquid–junction potential errors, ΔE_j in practical pA cells standardized at $I = 0.01$.

I	$\Delta \bar{E}$
	Cell: Na(gl) | NaCl (I) || KCl(sat) | Hg_2Cl_2;Hg
0.001	0.01 pNa unit
0.01	(0)
0.1	−0.02
1.0	−0.07
	Cell: Cl(sel) | NaCl (I) || KCl(sat) | Hg_2Cl_2;Hg
0.001	−0.01 pCl unit
0.01	(0)
0.1	0.02
1.0	0.07
	Cell: F(sel) | NaF (I) || KCl(sat) | Hg_2Cl_2;Hg
0.0001	0 pF unit
0.001	0
0.01	(0)
0.1	−0.02
1.0	−0.10
	Cell: Ca(sel) | $CaCl_2$ (I) || KCl(sat) | Hg_2Cl_2;Hg
0.001	−0.10 pCa unit
0.01	(0)
0.1	−0.03
1.0	−0.22

2. Stirring conditions should be identical in both the measurement and the standardization.

3. The same length of time should be allowed for equilibrium in the "unknown" measurement as in the standardization. (The time interval should be at least 2 min, but 5 to 10 min may be necessary for the most reproducible results.)

4. Standardization with two standard solutions bracketing the pA of the "unknown" solutions is desirable. (This procedure diminishes errors introduced by non-theoretical electrode response and by the residual liquid-junction potential.)

IX. Acknowledgment

The authors are grateful to the Foxboro Company for support of the initial stages of this work.

X. References

[1] Van Rysselberghe, P.,Electrochim. Acta **9**, 1343 (1964).

[2] Kortum, G., Treatise on Electrochemistry, 2nd ed., Elsevier Publishing Co., Amsterdam, 1965, Chapt. 8.

[3] Manual of Physicochemical Symbols and Terminology, Commission on Symbols, Units, and Terminology, International Union of Pure and Applied Chemistry, revised version, 1968.

[4] Bates, R. G., Determination of pH, John Wiley and Sons, Inc., New York, N. Y., 1964, Chapts. 3 and 4.

[5] Smith, E. R., and Bates, R. G., Compt. Rend. 15me Conf. IUPAC, 118 (1949).

[6] Bates, R. G., and Guggenheim, E. A., Pure Appl. Chem. **1**, 163 (1960).

[7] MacInnes, D. A.,J. Amer. Chem. Soc. **41**, 1086 (1919).

[8] Garrels, R. M., in Glass Electrodes for Hydrogen and Other Cations, G. Eisenman, Ed., Marcel Dekker, Inc., New York, N. Y., 1967, Chapt. 13.

[9] Butler,J. N.,J. Appl. Physiol. (in press).

[10] Shatkay, A., Anal. Chem. **39**, 1056 (1967).

[11] Harned, H. S., and Nims, L. F.,J. Amer. Chem. Soc. **54**, 423 (1932).

[12] Brown, A. S., and MacInnes, D. A.,J. Amer. Chem. Soc. **57**, 1356 (1935).

[13] Robinson, R. A., and Stokes, R. H., Electrolyte Solutions, 2nd ed., Butterworths, London, 1959, Appendix 8.10.

[14] Shedlovsky, T., and MacInnes, D. A.,J. Amer. Chem. Soc. **59**, 503 (1937).

[15] Robinson, R. A., Trans. Faraday Soc. **36**, 735 (1940).

[16] Robinson, R. A., and Bower, V. E.,J. Res. Nat. Bur. Stand. **A70**, 313 (1966).

[17] Eisenman, G., in Glass Electrodes for Hydrogen and Other Cations, G. Eisenman, Ed., Marcel Dekker, Inc., New York, N. Y., 1967, Chapt. 9.

[18] Shatkay, A., Anal. Chem. (in press).

CHAPTER 7

STUDIES WITH ION-EXCHANGE CALCIUM ELECTRODES IN BIOLOGICAL FLUIDS: SOME APPLICATIONS IN BIOMEDICAL RESEARCH AND CLINICAL MEDICINE

Edward W. Moore

Metabolic and Gastrointestinal Research Unit
Lemuel Shattuck Hospital
Commonwealth of Massachusetts
Departments of Medicine and Physiology
Tufts University Medical School
Boston, Massachusetts

I. Introduction

About four years ago I was preparing a chapter for Eisenman's book on cation-selective glass electrodes [1]. In the summary of that chapter it was stated: "It would seem that such electrodes have opened a veritable 'Pandora's Box' for investigators in the biological sciences. The specific studies which can be effected by this new methodologic tool will depend on the ingenuity of investigators and on improved fabrication of both macro- and microelectrodes with high specificity for specific ions. Electrodes with divalent-ion sensitivity will be of particular interest." Having spent the previous four years in search of calcium electrodes suitable for measurements in biologic fluids, we (like so many before us) had become rather pessimistic about the prospects for workable divalent-ion electrodes.

Only a few months later, however, we obtained from Orion Research, Inc., the first ion-exchange electrode with high specificity for calcium ion and began testing it in various biologic fluids. The present chapter will be concerned with some of the results obtained in our laboratory during the past four years with these and subsequent "generation" calcium-ion electrodes. Except for several abstracts and some preliminary data presented three years ago at a symposium on bioelectrodes [2], the data to be presented here have not been published previously. The reason for this is that we have felt it absolutely essential to have extensive data in several biologic systems and under pathologic as well as normal conditions before recommending general usage of these electrodes. It is now quite clear that the calcium-ion electrode is providing a powerful new tool in biomedical research and also in clinical medicine; its potential usefulness is very great indeed.

At the outset it should be pointed out, however, that since these electrodes have become commercially available, the response of biological investigators who have tried them has varied from great enthusiasm to considerable dismay. Much of the disillusionment is probably due to the fact that the first commercial version of the electrode (Orion Research, Model 92-20) did not work satisfactorily in serum, a problem related to the presence of protein and to the specific membrane used in that electrode. While this problem was subsequently resolved in the Orion flow-through system, the fabrication of the latter electrode requires a certain amount of skill and practice.

A. PHYSIOLOGIC IMPORTANCE OF CALCIUM

The physiologic importance of calcium is broad and complex. Classical frog heart experiments of McLean and Hastings [3-5] 35 years ago clearly demonstrated that **ionized** calcium, Ca^{++}, is the physiologically active species, and a large number of important physiologic processes are now known to be critically dependent on calcium ion activity (or concentration). These include: bone formation and resorption, nerve conduction, muscle contraction, cardiac conduction and contraction, cerebral function, renal tubular function, intestinal secretion and absorption, blood coagulation, membrane and capillary permeability, enzyme function and hormonal release from various endocrine glands. Great interest is currently focused on two particular hormones with calcium ion regulatory functions: 1) parathyroid hormone (parathormone) and 2) thyrocalcitonin (calcitonin) of the parafollicular cells of the thyroid gland. There is little doubt that Ca^{++} is one of the most important electrolytes in human physiology.

One of the greatest difficulties in both physiological and physiochemical studies of calcium metabolism has been the lack of a practical method for the direct determination of ionized calcium. The development by Ross [6] of ion-exchange calcium electrodes with high specificity for Ca^{++} allows study of numerous problems which would otherwise be quite difficult or impossible.

B. SOME HISTORICAL NOTES

Previous attempts at electrode measurements of calcium ion activity in biologic fluids have been largely unsuccessful. Early studies with calcium amalgam electrodes by Fosbinder [7] showed that such electrodes were reliable only in aqueous solutions of calcium salts; the electrodes were poisoned by very small amounts of protein, presumably due to formation of a protein film on the metallic surface. Joseph [8] subsequently interposed a cellophane membrane between such electrodes and various protein solutions. As noted by Greenberg [9], these measurements gave only changes in activity coefficients of the salt caused by altered solvent properties in the presence of protein. In recent years, investigators have therefore turned to other types of electrodes.

In the 1940's Sollner and coworkers [10-12] developed collodion membrane electrodes for measurement of several ions, a technique later worked out in detail by Gregor and Sollner [13]. Studies of particular physiologic note with this type of electrode were those of Carr [14] which we shall refer to later. The difficulty with these electrodes was that other ions gave rise to potentials across the membrane, the electrodes behaving reversibly to a given ion when only that ion was present. More recently, multilayer membrane electrodes with selectivity for Ca^{++} have been carefully studied by Gregor and associates [15].

Following Eisenman, Rudin and Casby's [16] development of sodium-selective glass electrodes, there was hope for a time that a glass electrode could be perfected suitable for Ca^{++} measurements in biologic fluids. Again, some success was achieved in pure aqueous solutions, as recently noted by Truesdell and Christ [17], but little or no success was achieved in biologic fluids. The selectivity of glass electrodes developed to date for Ca^{++} is probably too low for accurate measurements in biologic systems.

Of all the methods developed to date for measuring Ca^{++}, the one most widely used in biologic fluids is probably that using metal ion indicators, particularly ammonium purpurate (murexide) [18-21]. There are several restrictions with this method, however, including the necessity for removing proteins (i.e., precipitation, ultrafiltration, dialysis) and heavy metals prior to analysis.

To quote Neuman and Neuman [22]: "We can say, however, without fear of contradiction, that whoever develops a simple, accurate method for the estimation of calcium ion activities will truly be a hero to clinician and researcher alike."

C. INTEREST IN SERUM IONIZED CALCIUM

Since much of the following presentation will be concerned with electrode measurements in serum, it is reasonable to ask: Why are we particularly interested in **serum** ionized calcium? I believe the answer is apparent from the model shown in Figure 1. According to this model, Ca^{++} in serum (via interstitial fluid Ca^{++}) is in a state of dynamic interaction with the interface calcium of bone and cartilage. Parathyroid hormone, through mechanisms not fully understood, has bone-resorbing effects, with liberation of calcium to the extracellular pool, while calcitonin appears to have

BONE

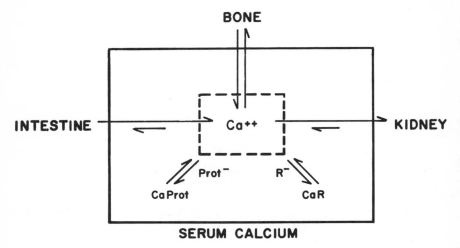

SERUM CALCIUM

Figure 1.   A model for the interactions of serum ionized calcium.

an opposite effect.[1] Absorption of calcium from the intestine is influenced by dietary intake and is enhanced by both Vitamin D and parathormone. Excretion of calcium occurs by both urinary and fecal routes. Parathormone reduces renal tubular reabsorption of phosphate and, despite enhanced proximal tubular reabsorption of calcium, results in an increased excretion of both calcium and phosphate [24-26].

Finally, Ca^{++} of serum is in a state of dynamic interaction ("equilibrium") with the plasma proteins and various anionic ligands in serum. In 1911, Rona and Takahashi [27] found from dialysis experiments that serum total calcium represents both diffusible and non-diffusible fractions. Numerous studies [19-22, 28-40] have subsequently shown that there are three distinct calcium fractions in normal serum: 1) non-diffusible (protein-bound) calcium, CaProt, which, depending on pH and temperature, represents about 30-55 percent of the total; 2) diffusible, non-ionized calcium (complexes and chelates), CaR, comprising some 5-10 percent of the total; and 3) ionized calcium, Ca^{++}

In normal man, serum Ca^{++} and total calcium concentrations are maintained within rather narrow limits (about ± 10 percent). Whether this is affected primarily by actions of parathormone on kidney or on bone is a subject of some controversy at the present time. In any case, it is evident from Figure 1 that calcium ion in serum plays a very central role in the overall scheme of calcium metabolism.

_____

[1]The importance of calcitonin as a regulator of serum Ca^{++} in man has not yet been clearly defined, although it appears to be of considerable importance in certain lower species such as fish, which often live in a high-calcium environment. As another link between man and the primordial ocean, it is therefore of interest that the parathyroid glands first appear phylogenetically in amphibians. The reader is referred to a recent review on calcitonin by Copp [23].

II. Electrode Characteristics and Analytical Techniques

Two types of electrodes have been employed: 1) "static" or "membrane" electrodes, *i.e.*, without sample-flow through the electrode, and 2) "flow-through" electrodes.

A. STATIC-TYPE ELECTRODE

A diagram of the "first generation" static electrode is shown in Figure 2. This electrode was prepared in the laboratory as follows: glass or

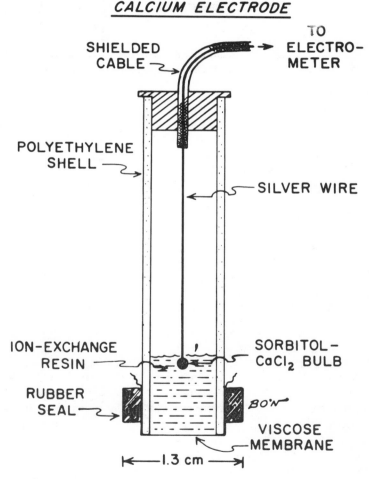

Figure 2.   Static-type calcium electrode, prepared in the laboratory.

plastic tubes were sealed at one end with Viscose dialysis tubing, held in place by a silicone rubber sleeve. The tube was then filled with 2-3 ml of a liquid ion-exchanger composed of the calcium salt of didecyl phosphoric acid dissolved in didecylphenyl phosphonate, obtained from Orion Research, Inc. (Cambridge, Mass.). Electrical contact was made with a chloridized silver wire coated with a solution of $0.1M$ KCl or $CaCl_2$ in fused sorbital. The volume of sample required was about 3 ml, and equilibrium time was usually 1-3 minutes. Average life-span of these electrodes was about 3 weeks. This electrode, which worked quite well in serum, is not to be confused with the "second generation" static electrodes marketed by Orion Research (Model 92-20), which employed a Millipore rather than cellulose membrane and did not work satisfactorily in serum. Another version of such "static" electrodes has been marketed by Corning Glass Works (Corning, N. Y.), but we have not had experience with this electrode.

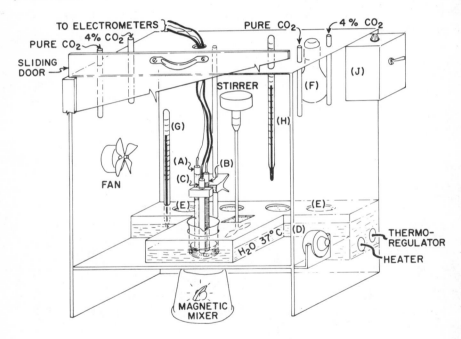

Figure 3.   Plexiglass CO_2 chamber for Ca^{++} measurements with static-type electrodes. Both [Ca^{++}] and pH are continuously monitored with separate electrometers. The calcium electrode (A) and pH electrode (B) are introduced into a standard or test solution with a calomel half-cell (C) as common reference electrode. Continuous stirring is achieved by a magnetic stirrer. Sample is maintained at 37 °C by circulating water (D). Additional samples may be pre-warmed (E). Air temperature is maintained at 37 °C by a light bulb (F) connected to a rheostat. Water and air temperatures are monitored by thermometers (G) and (H), while (J) is the thermoregulator control box. Sample pH is varied by alteration in chamber pCO_2.

The static electrode, while being rather crude, had the distinct advantage of allowing direct study of pH effects on ionized calcium. This required the construction of a suitable Plexiglass CO_2 chamber, shown in Figure 3, in which pCO_2 and sample pH could be carefully controlled.

Both ionized calcium and pH were continuously monitored through separate electrometers, using a calomel half-cell as common reference. Continuous stirring was achieved by a magnetic stirrer, and both water and air temperature were maintained at 37 °C. Virtually instantaneous changes in sample pH could be achieved by variation in chamber pCO_2. Because of the pH dependency of ionized calcium, all values given subsequently for the static electrode are those at the original whole blood pH.

B. Flow-Through Electrode

The "third generation" electrode, and the second type to be used in the present studies, was a flow-through electrode marketed by Orion Research, Inc. (Model 98-20), shown diagrammatically in Figure 4.

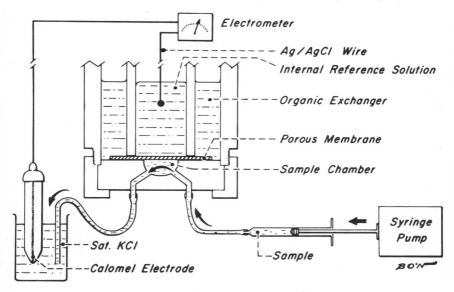

Figure 4.   Diagram of a flow-through electrode obtained from Orion Research, Inc. (Cambridge, Mass.).

This electrode became available about two years after the static electrode studies had begun. The sample flows through the electrode chamber at about 0.05 ml/min, using a gear-driven syringe pump. All measurements with this electrode were made at 25 °C.

The flow-through system has several advantages over static-type electrodes: 1) equilibration time is quite rapid, usually 30-60 seconds; 2) it is more stable, with typical drift of 2-5 mV during the course of a day, as compared with 3-10 mV/day with static electrodes; 3) less sample volume is required, several measurements being possible with a 1 ml sample; 4) the measurement is anaerobic, analogous to a blood pH measurement.

We now use only this type of electrode in our laboratory, but it should be noted that it has two disadvantages: 1) pH effects on ionized calcium, to be described below, cannot be directly monitored, as is readily done with the static-type electrode; and 2) it has not yet been thermostated, so that measurements are most conveniently made at room temperature.

Since the binding of calcium to serum proteins is both temperature and pH dependent, some difference between serum $[Ca^{++}]$ at 37 °C (static electrode) and 25 °C (flow-through electrode) would be expected. This difference will be noted below in studies of sera from normal subjects.

C. Electrode Selectivity

For a perfect electrode, sensitive to only one ion species, the electrode potential, E, is given by the Nernst equation:

$$E = E° + \frac{2.3\,RT}{nF} \log a \tag{1}$$

where a is the activity of the cation or anion being measured, $E°$ is a constant and R, T, n and F are the gas constant, absolute temperature, number of transferred electrons and the faraday constant, respectively.

In actual practice, no glass or ion-exchange electrode behaves perfectly, inasmuch as all electrodes will respond to more than one species (as illustrated by the so-called "alkaline error" or "sodium error" for glass pH electrodes at high pH). Thus, one is necessarily concerned with the "selectivity" of a given electrode, i.e., the potential which will be generated by one ion species in preference to other ion species.

In their work with sodium-selective glass electrodes, Eisenman, Rudin and Casby [16] developed the following empirical equation to describe electrode potentials in mixtures of two univalent cations:

$$E = E° + \frac{2.3\,RT}{nF} \log \left[(A^+)^{1/n_{AB}} + k_{AB}^{1/n_{AB}}(B^+)^{1/n_{AB}} \right]^{n_{AB}} \tag{2}$$

where (A^+) and (B^+) are the activities of ions A and B, respectively, and k_{AB} and n_{AB} are adjustable parameters which are constant for a given electrode and cation pair. The selectivity constant (k_{AB}) denotes how well the electrode "sees" one cation (A^+) in preference to the other cation (B^+). Ross [6] has found that the potential of ion-exchange calcium electrodes is similarly given by the empirical equation:

$$E = \text{constant} + \frac{2.3\,RT}{nF} \log\left[(Ca^{++}) + \sum_i k_i (A_i)^{2/z_i} \right] \tag{3}$$

where A_i and z_i are the activity and charge of an interfering ion i.

As shown in Table 1, the major interfering ions of concern in serum and other extracellular fluids are Na^+ and Mg^{++}. The selectivity for Ca^{++} over Na^+ (and also K^+) is so high that precise selectivity measurements are rather difficult to obtain. Ross [6] has found k_{CaNa} and k_{CaMg} values of 10^{-4} and 0.014, respectively. Similar results have been obtained in our laboratory [2]. Thus, in serum containing $1mM$ Ca^{++}, the presence of $150mM$ Na^+ would result in approximately 1-2 percent enhancement of apparent calcium ion concentration. The presence of $0.5mM$ Mg^{++} in serum would also yield an error of about $+1$ percent. Overall Na^+ and Mg^{++} error is thus believed to be about $+2$ percent. Hydrogen ion and K^+ errors must be considered in gastric juice and intracellular fluids respectively, but are of no consequence in extracellular fluids. The electrodes have been found to be unresponsive to anions and to chelates of calcium, and are thus highly specific for calcium ion. Below a pH of about 5.5, the electrodes no longer show Ca^{++} selectivity but behave as pH electrodes [6]. We have obtained very reproducible $[Ca^{++}]$ values in gastric juice, however, following alkalinization to pH 6-7 with NaOH [41].

Table 1. Selectivity constants (k_i) of ion—exchange calcium electrodes with respect to principal cations in extracellular (ECF) and intracellular (ICF) fluids.

$$E = \text{constant} + \frac{2.3\,RT}{nF} \log\left\{ [Ca^{++}] + \sum_i k_i\,[A_i]^{2/z_i} \right\}$$

Ion	k_{CaA_i} (approximate)	Ratio: $\dfrac{[A_i]}{[Ca^{++}]}$ Serum and ECF	ICF
Na^+	$10,000/1$	150	$10-15$
K^+	$10,000/1$	$4-5$	150
Mg^{++}	$100/1$	$0.5-1$	$1.5-20$
H^+	$\infty > $ pH 6	10^{-4}	10^{-4}

D. ELECTRODE CALIBRATION

Neglecting the effects of other cations, the observed electrode potential is a function of calcium ion activity (Ca^{++}). According to the Nernst equation, a 10-fold change in (Ca^{++}) should yield a potential change of 30.8 mV at 37 °C and 29.6 mV at 25 °C. These theoretical slopes have been observed occasionally; more typical values have been about 29 mV and 27 mV, respectively. Electrode response has been found to be linear over the Ca^{++} concentration range 1.0-10mM. Since the entire standard curve may shift several millivolts during the course of a day, possible errors resulting from such drift were minimized in the present studies by calibration in standard solutions before and after each unknown solution.

While electrode response is a function of calcium ion **activity**, the absolute value of this activity in any given solution is uncertain since individual ion activity coefficients cannot be experimentally determined. Using a Na-electrode, Ag-AgCl electrode system, Moore and Ross [42] have estimated γ_{CaCl_2} in mixed $CaCl_2$-NaCl solutions to be about 0.54 when NaCl = 0.15M. The development of a Ca^{++} activity scale by Bates, reported in this volume, represents an important advance in the application of calcium electrodes to biologic investigations.

In the following studies, all Ca^{++} values will be given in **concentration** terms, [Ca^{++}], relative to mixed $CaCl_2$-NaCl standard solutions with total ionic strength near that of serum, i.e., $\simeq 0.16M$. In so doing, it is assumed that $\gamma_{Ca^{++}}$ is similar in standard and unknown solutions. This assumption is probably reasonable, since activity coefficients are primarily related to total ionic strength [1,42-44].

Electrodes were therefore calibrated with solutions containing 150mM NaCl and 0.5-10.0mM $CaCl_2$; ionic strength thus varied from 151.5mM to 180mM. The fact that electrode response was linearly related to concentration over the indicated range suggests that $\gamma_{Ca^{++}}$ was similar in the different solutions, in accordance with Harned's rule [1,45]. The pH of these standards varied from about pH 6.0-7.0; no buffers were employed because: (1) the buffer would have uncertain effects on Ca^{++} activity, and (2) there is, as noted above, no detectable H^+ error with these electrodes above about pH 5.5. We would therefore suggest that buffers not be employed unless their possible effects on (Ca^{++}) are studied specifically. (For example, both bicarbonate and phosphate form calcium complexes, as will be noted later.)

Neglecting the effect of other cations on the electrode potential, the potentials in unknown and standard solutions are given by:

$$E_{unk} = E° + S \log (Ca^{++})_{unk} \qquad (4a)$$

$$= E° + S \log ([Ca^{++}] \cdot \gamma_{Ca^{++}})_{unk} \qquad (4b)$$

$$E_{std} = E° + S \log ([Ca^{++}] \cdot \gamma_{Ca^{++}})_{std} \tag{4c}$$

where S is the Nernst slope factor; 2.3 RT/nF. Assuming

$$\gamma_{Ca^{++}_{unk}} = \gamma_{Ca^{++}_{std}}$$

the potential difference, ΔE, between unknown and standard is given by:

$$\frac{\Delta E}{S} = \log \left(\frac{[Ca^{++}]_{unk}}{[Ca^{++}]_{std}} \right) \tag{5a}$$

(or)

$$[Ca^{++}]_{unk} = [Ca^{++}]_{std} \cdot 10^{\Delta E/S} \tag{5b}$$

While Equation (5) is easily solved graphically, we have found it convenient to record ΔE directly with an IBM Selectronic typewriter using a suitable interfacing device between the electrometer (Orion 801 digital pH meter) and typewriter. $[Ca^{++}]_{unk}$ is then obtained by manually feeding ΔE into an Olivetti-Underwood Programma 101 computer, with direct printout of $[Ca^{++}]_{unk}$. The entire operation takes 10-15 seconds and is somewhat more accurate than graphical interpolation.

Although it is implicit in Equation (5), it should be emphasized that small errors in electrode potential measurements may yield rather large errors in estimated $[Ca^{++}]$ in unknown solutions. Thus, with an electrode slope of 28 mV, an error of 1 mV in measured potential at 25 °C would yield about an 8 percent error in apparent $[Ca^{++}]$.

All potential measurements with static-type electrodes, in both standards and unknowns, were made at 37 °C in a Plexiglass chamber (Fig. 3), in which sample pH was varied by alteration in pCO_2. Electrode potentials were monitored with either a Corning Model 12 pH meter (Corning Scientific Instruments, Medfield, Mass.) or Orion Model 801 digital pH meter. Ionized calcium measurements in each serum, whole blood and ultrafiltrate were made over the pH range 6.8 to 7.8. This resulting curve was bracketed by standard curves obtained in $CaCl_2$-NaCl solutions. Duplicate measurements were similarly made. Because of the pH dependency of ionized calcium levels in sera and ultrafiltrates, all $[Ca^{++}]$ values given subsequently for the static electrode are those at the original whole blood pH. In the flow-through electrode studies, $[Ca^{++}]$ was either determined immediately (anaerobically at 25 ± 2 °C) or in samples frozen under oil, reequilibrated with 5 percent CO_2 prior to analysis.

It should be emphasized that no pH effect on $[Ca^{++}]$ was observed in standard solutions.

E. Ultrafiltration and Other Methods

Ultrafiltrates of sera were obtained at 25 ± 2 °C with a high-pressure dialysis cell obtained from National Instrument Laboratories (Rockville, Md.) shown in Figure 5.

Viscose (Union Carbide Co.) dialysis tubing with an approximate mean pore diameter of 25Å was used in all experiments and was soaked in running water and then distilled water for about 20 minutes prior to use. After insertion of the dialysis tubing, the chamber was well-aerated with 5 percent CO_2. Serum (10 ml), which had been separated under oil and its pH determined, was then introduced anaerobically into the Viscose bag and pressure applied with pure nitrogen gas at 4-45 psi (pounds per square inch).

The rate of ultrafiltration, at given pressure, is a function of wetted bag surface area and should thus decrease exponentially. This was found to be the case. Preliminary studies showed that the average time required to reduce serum volume to one-half was about 10 hours at 4 psi and about 3 hours at 45 psi.

In early studies of sera from normal subjects, it was found that ultrafiltrate pH was somewhat higher (0.1-0.2 pH units) than that of the original serum; the chamber was therefore modified to allow continuous gassing with moisturized 5% CO_2 during ultrafiltration. With this small modification, pH regulation was quite close; average ΔpH between ultrafiltrate and original serum in 9 normal and 10 pathologic sera was 0.039 ± 0.013(SE) units.

After formation of 2-3 ml of ultrafiltrate, each sample was removed anaerobically from the cell and immediately introduced into the Plexiglass chamber (which had also been pre-aerated with 5% CO_2) for electrode analysis of ionized calcium. All ultrafiltrates were clear; occasional cloudy samples were discarded and the experiment terminated.

Total calcium concentrations [Ca] were determined in duplicate by EDTA titration in $1M$ KOH using Cal-Red (K.& K Chemicals, Plainview, N. Y.) as indicator [20,46]. Twenty-five normal samples (20 sera, 5 ultrafiltrates) were also analyzed by atomic absorption (AAS) spectroscopy (Model 290, Perkin-Elmer Corp., Norwalk, Conn.). A close correlation (r = 0.96) between EDTA (y) and AAS (x) values was observed in both sera and ultrafiltrates; the two were related by the function: y = 0.16 + 0.96 x. Atomic absorption values thus averaged about 0.1mM lower than corresponding EDTA values in serum and about 0.06mM lower in ultrafiltrates. Unless otherwise indicated, all subsequent values will be those obtained by EDTA titration. Serum total protein was measured by the biuret method [47]; albumin and globulin were determined by electrophoresis.

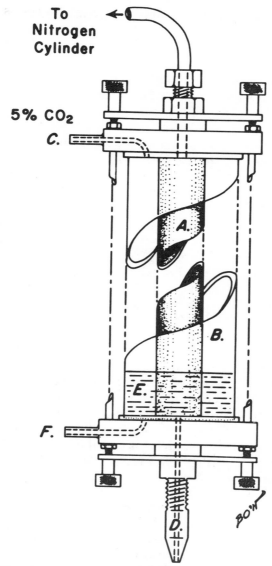

Figure 5.   Ultrafiltration cell employed in all studies. Viscose dialysis tubing is inserted
into a fritted stainless steel cylinder (A). The chamber is pre-aerated (C) with 5%CO$_2$,
95% O$_2$; serum is then introduced at (D) into the dialysis tubing and pressure applied
with pure nitrogen gas. Ultrafiltrate (E) collects between the steel cylinder and an outer
plastic jacket (B), and is removed without exposure to air by a syringe attached at (F).
Not shown is a modification made to allow more precise pH regulation during ultrafiltration. This consisted of drilling a small hole in the outer jacket about 2 inches from
the bottom to allow egress of moisturized 5% CO$_2$, introduced through the upper side arm
throughout ultrafiltration.

The following symbols and methods of calculation are used:

[Ca^{++}]   = electrode ionized calcium concentration (mM)
[Ca]   = total calcium concentration (mM)
[Alb]   = serum albumin concentration (g/l)
[Glob]   = serum globulin concentration (g/l)
[CaProt]   = concentration of calcium bound to serum proteins, calcu-
             lated as the difference in serum [Ca] and ultrafiltrate [Ca]
             (mM)
[CaR]   = concentration of diffusible complexes and chelates of cal-
             cium (mM). [CaR] was calculated as the difference
             in ultrafiltrate [Ca] and ultrafiltrate [Ca^{++}], or in a few
             instances, as the difference in ultrafiltrate [Ca] and serum
             [Ca^{++}].

III.   Results in Normal Subjects[2]

A. Do Ca^{++} Electrodes Work in Biologic Fluids?

There are several ways in which it can be shown that the calcium electrodes respond to changes in ionized calcium levels. In protein-free solutions such as ultrafiltrates, this is indicated by quantitative recovery upon
addition of CaCl$_2$-NaCl solution at constant total ionic strength. A
representative study is shown in Figure 6; virtually identical results were
obtained in 6 additional subjects. A quantitative linear increase in [Ca^{++}]
was observed in all studies.

In serum, the "recovery" of added calcium is not quantitative because
of partial binding of added calcium to the serum proteins. This will be
developed more fully in Section IV below.

That the electrodes respond specifically to ionized calcium has also
been shown by using the electrodes as monitors or end-point detectors for
chelating titrations. As shown in Figure 7, upon addition of an excess of
EDTA to serum or ultrafiltrate, there was a rapid decrease in ionized calcium, followed by a further decrease upon addition of NaOH. Virtually
identical results were obtained in 4 additional studies. Note that the
decline in [Ca^{++}] in serum was less abrupt than in ultrafiltrate. Note
particularly that the residual [Ca^{++}] value was quite small, suggesting that there was little or no extraneous potential in these fluids, $i.e.$, of
non-Ca^{++} origin; the residual value of about 0.04mM probably reflects
Na$^+$ error in the electrode potential.

Another way of showing that the electrode responds to calcium ion is
to measure the dissociation constant (K_d') of an important calcium
complex, such as calcium citrate. A single experiment, using the
flow-through electrode at 25 °C, was therefore performed as follows: to
an aqueous solution containing 1.0mM CaCl$_2$ and 120mM NaCl, 0.1 ml

---

[2] Preliminary reports of these studies have been published [2,48].

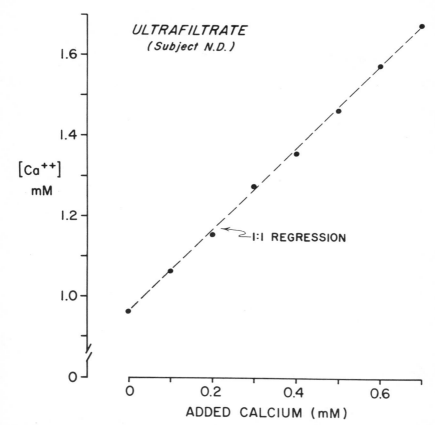

Figure 6. Representative recovery study in an ultrafiltrate of serum from a normal subject. Pure CaCl₂ (10.0mM) was added serially (30 µl) to a 3.0 ml ultrafiltrate sample at constant pH (pH 7.37). Resulting abscissa values are expressed as mM concentration. The dashed line is the theoretical 1:1 regression.

increments of 10.0mM citric acid were serially added and the final pH adjusted to 7.0 by addition of NaOH. Calculated total ionic strength for each solution was about 0.15M. With each serial addition of citrate, [Ca⁺⁺] was measured with the calcium ion electrode.

Results are shown in Figure 8. Upon 8 serial additions of citrate, there was a progressive decrease in observed [Ca⁺⁺]. Corresponding total citrate concentrations, corrected for volume, varied from 0.20mM to 1.67mM. Values for K'_{CaCit} calculated for each point in the left-hand side of Figure 8, varied from 0.332 to 0.453, with a mean of 0.398. In negative log terms, this corresponds to pK' values of 3.34 to 3.48. with a mean pK' of 3.40. The ratio [CaCit]/[Cit⁻] as a function of pCa is shown in the right-hand side of the figure.

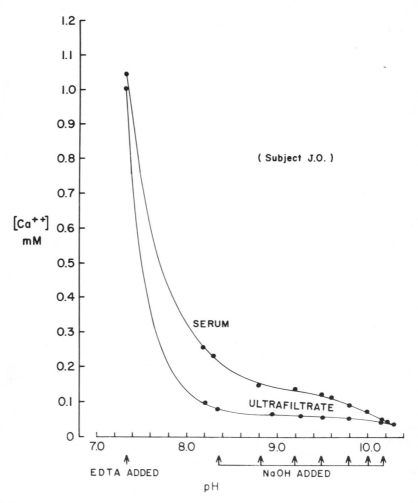

Figure 7. Effect of EDTA on ionized calcium concentrations in serum and ultrafiltrate as monitored with the static-type calcium electrode. 10 μmoles (in 30 μl) of di-sodium EDTA was added to 3.0 ml samples, yielding final EDTA concentrations of about 3.3 mM. Sample pH was then increased by addition of 1M NaOH in 10-20 μl increments.

The value of 3.40 for pK'_{CaCit} is somewhat higher than most reported studies [49] in which, by various methods, pK' values of about 3.2 have been obtained at this ionic strength and temperature.

B. Serum Ionized *vs.* Total Calcium

Ionized and total calcium concentrations were measured in 91 sera from 60 normal subjects. Of these, 72 studies in 52 subjects were made with static-type electrodes; the remainder were made with the more

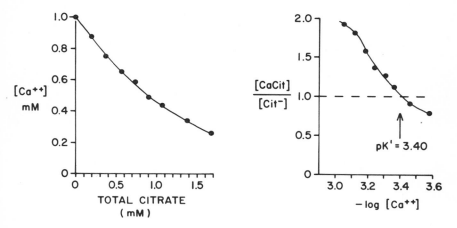

Figure 8.   Determination of the dissociation constant of calcium citrate by serial addition of citrate to a 1mM CaCl$_2$ solution (25°C, pH 7.0, I $\cong$ 0.15M).

recently obtained flow-through electrode. As shown in Figure 9, there was considerable variability in total serum calcium, with a range of 2.12 to 2.88mM [mean: 2.477 ± 0.286 (2 SD) mM]. Absolute variability in ionized calcium was only about one-half that of total calcium, with a range of 0.94 to 1.33mM. Percentage variability was thus similar for ionized and total calcium. Overall mean serum ionized calcium concentration for both static and flow-through electrodes was 1.136 ± 0.126 (2 SD) mM. Thus, 95 percent of normal subjects would be expected to lie in the range: 1.01mM to 1.26mM.

[Ca^{++}] measurements were made in 11 subjects with both static-type and flow-through electrodes, with an intervening period of 1 to 10 months. Mean values for the two electrodes were almost identical: 1.169 ± 0.05 (2 SE) mM and 1.161 ± 0.012mM, respectively. For all studies with the flow-through electrode (19 studies in 18 subjects), mean [Ca^{++}] was 1.163 ± 0.014 (2 SE) mM, which was not significantly different from the mean value of 1.127 ± 0.019 (2 SE) mM obtained with static-type electrodes in 52 subjects.

As noted in Section II.B. above, small differences in mean [Ca^{++}] values for the 2 types of electrodes might be expected, due to pH and temperature effects. Thus, static electrode [Ca^{++}] values were obtained at 37 °C and at the original whole blood pH; flow-through [Ca^{++}] values were at 25 °C and at the pH of serum after separation under oil. For all studies, the arithmetic average of venous pH was 7.34 ± 0.01 (2 SE) while for separated serum it was 7.42 ± 0.01 (2 SE). Serum pH, when

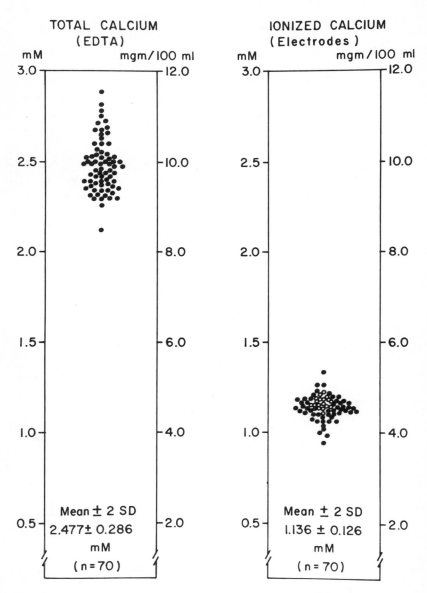

Figure 9.   Serum ionized and total calcium concentrations in 52 subjects studied with static-type electrodes ● and 18 subjects studied with flow-through electrodes O. Notice the narrow range of ionized calcium values. The 95 percent confidence limits for the population are indicated by respective means ±2SD:2.19-2.76m*M* for total calcium and 1.01-1.26m*M* for ionized calcium.

analyzed for $[Ca^{++}]$ with the flow-through electrode, thus averaged 0.08 pH units higher than blood pH. From observed pH effects on $[Ca^{++}]$, (Fig. 11) this difference would be expected to yield $[Ca^{++}]$ values with the flow-through electrode about 3 percent lower than with the static electrode. That the mean $[Ca^{++}]$ with the flow-through electrode was 0.04mM higher than with static electrodes probably reflects a temperature effect on the binding of calcium to serum proteins. Thus, from ultracentrifugation studies of Loken et al. [37], free $[Ca^{++}]$ in serum is about 5-6 percent higher at 25 °C than at 37 °C at this pH. Since the pH and temperature effects are opposite in direction, $[Ca^{++}]$ values with the flow-through electrode would thus be expected to be about 2-3 percent greater than with the static electrode, almost exactly the difference observed.

In these 60 normal subjects, a finding of particular note was a complete lack of correlation between serum ionized and total calcium concentrations, as shown in Figure 10. Ionized calcium was within a narrow range, irrespective of the total calcium level. This finding is potentially of great

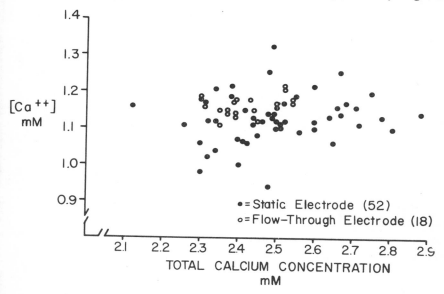

Figure 10. Relation between ionized and total calcium concentrations in 52 subjects studied with static-type electrodes ● and 18 subjects studied with flow-through electrodes O. Note the complete lack of correlation.

clinical importance since serum ionized calcium is the physiologically-active species, yet serum total calcium is measured routinely in hospitals throughout the world. The discrepancy between serum ionized and total calcium concentrations reflects variation in serum protein (mainly albu-min) concentrations. Thus, as will be noted in Section VI below, variation in serum total calcium concentration in normal subjects was almost quan-titatively accounted for by a corresponding variation in protein-bound cal-cium. In other words, it will be shown that **a serum total calcium measure-ment in the normal is an indirect measurement of the serum albumin level.**

In an effort to determine the variability of serum ionized and total calci-um concentrations within a given individual, 39 studies were performed in 15 subjects over a period of 2 years. The average interval between stu-dies was 7.6 months. The average difference between $[Ca^{++}]$ levels for each study was determined for each subject. For example, if $[Ca^{++}]$ values of 1.10, 1.15, and 1.20mM were obtained in 3 studies, the average difference between studies 1-2, 2-3 and 1-3 would be:

$$\frac{0.05 + 0.05 + 0.10}{3} = 0.067 \ mM.$$

Ionized calcium concentrations were remarkably constant within a given individual. The average difference between replicate studies for the 15 subjects was 0.07 ± 0.03 (2 SE) mM. Since mean $[Ca^{++}]$ for the 39 studies was 1.13 ± 0.01 (2 SE) mM, the average difference between re-peated studies was about 6 percent. Absolute variability in total serum calcium was about three times as great as with ionized calcium: mean total calcium for all studies was 2.52 ± 0.06 (2 SE) mM with an average difference between repeated studies of 0.23 ± 0.06 (2 SE) mM.

As a practical clinical or research tool, the value of the electrodes would be considerably enhanced if reliable measurements could be made in samples previously frozen and stored. This was therefore investigated early in the present studies (Table 2). Ionized calcium was measured in serum from 7 normal subjects before and after freezing for 24-72 hours. No significant differences were observed. Upon freezing of ultrafiltrates, however, a decrease in $[Ca^{++}]$ was frequently observed; some samples became cloudy and occasional precipitates were noted. It is concluded that $[Ca^{++}]$ may be reliably determined in previously frozen serum, but not in ultrafiltrates previously frozen. The apparent lack of precipitation in serum may reflect solubilizing properties of the serum proteins.

C. pH EFFECTS ON IONIZED CALCIUM

Clinically, it has long been recognized that alkalosis may precipitate hypocalcemic tetany. It is also known that the binding of calcium to serum proteins increases with increasing pH [35,37,39]. The static elec-trode and CO_2 chamber have allowed, for the first time, a direct study of such pH effects. In all studies with static electrodes (52 subjects), the ef-

Table 2. Effect of freezing on serum ionized calcium concentration.

Subject	Ionized calcium concentration (mM)		
	Before	After	Δ
1. R.C.	1.15	1.16	+0.01
2. C.G.	1.15	1.17	+0.02
3. N.G.	1.06	1.06	0
4. S.K.	1.12	1.16	+0.04
5. N.L.	1.26	1.26	0
6. L.M.	1.16	1.20	+0.04
7. S.S.	1.19	1.19	0
Mean	1.155	1.171	+0.016

fect of pH on serum $[Ca^{++}]$ was investigated over the range pH 6.8 to pH 7.8. Similar studies were also made in ultrafiltrates from 16 normal subjects. A representative study in a single normal subject is shown in Figure 11.

As expected, there was a pronounced pH effect in serum, with a linear or slightly sigmoid decrease in ionized calcium with increasing pH. The 4 curves represent duplicate runs, each duplicate being bracketed by standard curves. (The maximum variability between duplicate serum measurements in Figure 11 corresponds to about 1 mV in measured potentials.) The pH effect presumably results from competition between Ca^{++} and H^+ for negative sites on serum proteins and was considerably accentuated in residual "bag serum" following ultrafiltration, *i.e.*, upon concentration of the serum proteins. The pH effect was virtually instantaneous and was completely reversible.

In each of 16 subjects studied, a pH effect was also observed in serum ultrafiltrates, often almost identical to that in corresponding sera, as in the subject shown in Figure 11. This was quite unexpected and has since been studied rather extensively by Dr. Joel Jacknow in our laboratory. We will return to this problem below, in considering the diffusible calcium complexes of serum.

D. COMPONENTS OF SERUM TOTAL CALCIUM

It is well-recognized that the total calcium concentration in serum represents the sum of 3 distinct fractions: 1) protein-bound calcium $[CaProt]$, 2) diffusible calcium complexes $[CaR]$, and 3) ionized calcium $[Ca^{++}]$. Total ultrafiltrable (diffusible) calcium, representing both

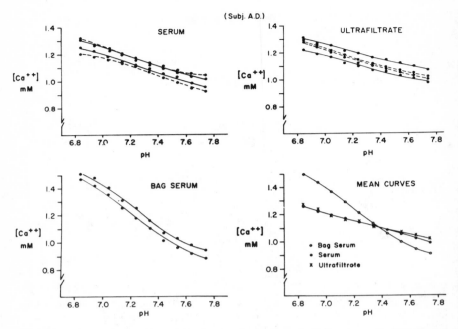

Figure 11.   Ionized calcium concentration as a function of pH in serum, ultrafiltrate and bag serum from a normal subject. In serum and ultrafiltrate, each [Ca++] curve was bracketed by measurements in standard CaCl₂-NaCl solutions; the 4 curves therefore represent duplicate runs. (The range of variability corresponds to about 1mV.) The 2 curves for bag serum represent a single run bracketed by standards. Note that the mean curves for serum and ultrafiltrate were virtually identical, while an accentuated pH effect was observed in residual bag serum, *i.e.,* upon concentration of the serum proteins.

ionized and complexed calcium, has been widely used as an index of serum ionized calcium.

In the 16 subjects from whom ultrafiltrates were obtained, mean serum [Ca] was 2.54 ± 0.04 (SE) mM and mean ultrafiltrate [Ca] was 1.52 ± 0.04mM. Average [CaProt] was thus 1.02mM and 59.6 percent of serum [Ca] was ultrafiltrable, a figure in general agreement with previous studies [21,29-31,35,39,40]. Ionized calcium concentrations in sera and ultrafiltrates were almost identical, with means of 1.16 and 1.17mM, respectively. Mean [CaR] was 0.35 ± 0.03mM. Of the total ultrafiltrable calcium, the ionized fraction varied considerably (range: 66.7-90.2 percent) with a mean of 76.7 percent. Total ultrafiltrable calcium was thus not a reliable index of serum ionized calcium in normals. Resulting fractions of the serum total calcium are summarized in Figure 12.

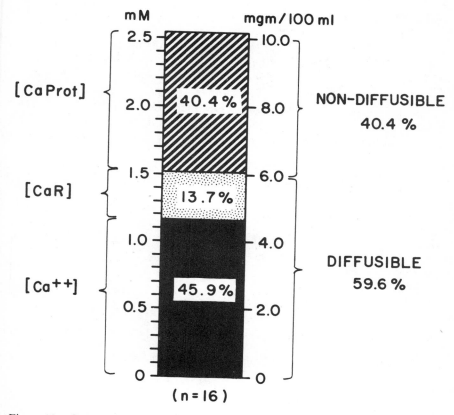

Figure 12. Components of serum total calcium obtained from ultrafiltration data in 16 normal subjects. Indicated percentages are the mean values for the group.

E. DIFFUSIBLE CALCIUM COMPLEXES [CaR] OF NORMAL SERUM

In their studies with the frog heart, McLean and Hastings [4] found 0.15-0.34mM of the serum total calcium could not be accounted for as [Ca⁺⁺] or [CaProt]; similar results were later obtained by Morison *et al.* [33]. Neuman and Neuman [22] have given 0.3mM as the estimated value for the concentration of diffusible calcium complexes of normal serum. More recent studies by Walser [21], however, have yielded considerably lower values, about 0.16mM, using murexide for measurement of [Ca⁺⁺]. Rose and associates [19,50] have reported values somewhat lower than those of Walser.

Our value of 0.35mM for [CaR] is therefore at least twice as high as that obtained in recent studies. At least half of the difference, however, may be related to the different chemical methods employed. Thus, if we had used atomic absorption spectroscopy (AAS) for measuring total calcium, rather than EDTA, our [CaR] value would have been about 0.29mM (Section II.E. above). Similarly, ultrafiltrate [Ca^{++}] values reported for murexide are higher (0-0.3mM) than those obtained here with the electrode. This would yield [CaR] values proportionately lower than those obtained from electrode data.

This problem has been studied by Dr. Jacknow in our laboratory. His results in 5 aqueous solutions, each containing 1.5mM CaCl$_2$ and 150mM NaCl, are shown in Table 3.

Table 3. Complexed calcium in 5 aqueous solutions each containing 1.50 mM/l [Ca^{++}] and 150 mM/l NaCl.

Solution	Free [Ca^{++}] mM/l	Complexed [Ca^{++}] mM/l
Phosphate 1.0 mM	1.48 – 1.50	0.00 – 0.02
Lactate 1.0 mM	1.48 – 1.49	0.01 – 0.02
Citrate 0.12 mM	1.41 – 1.43	0.07 – 0.09
Bicarbonate 25 mM	1.34 – 1.37	0.13 – 0.16
Mixture		
Mean	1.27	0.25
Range	1.25 – 1.29	0.21 – 0.29

Solutions of phosphate, lactate, citrate and bicarbonate were each prepared at the average concentration of these ions in normal serum, and also a mixture of all of these ions. Resulting Ca^{++} and complex concentrations are indicated, the average sum of the complexes being 0.25mM. Notice that about half the total was accounted for by bicarbonate.

At a Ca^{++} concentration of 1.15mM, i.e., the average value in normal serum, the sum can be calculated to be about 0.21mM. This would therefore appear to be the minimum value for [CaR] in serum, about 0.08mM less than that observed by AAS in our normal subjects by ultrafiltration. While this difference may reflect ultrafiltration error, it would appear that a calcium sulfate complex must also be considered. Nakayama and Rasnick [51] have recently obtained a K_d' for CaSO$_4 \cdot$2H$_2$O of 5.9 × 10^{-3}. At a normal serum SO$_4^=$ level of 0.5mM, a calcium sulfate complex of about 0.08-0.1mM might be expected. This would be just enough to account for the difference between our ultrafiltration and pure solution (Table 3) values.

Why then was there a pH effect on Ca^{++} in serum ultrafiltrates? Calculations indicate that the dissociation of each of these complexes — phosphate, lactate, citrate, and bicarbonate, should not vary with pH over the pH range compatible with life and this was experimentally confirmed by Dr. Jacknow in these solutions, *i.e.*, no pH-effect was observed. Calculations do indicate, however, that ultrafiltrates are probably supersaturated with calcium carbonate and perhaps also hydroxy-apatite. While unmeasured pH-dependent polyelectrolytes may also be present, we believe the observed pH effect in ultrafiltrates most likely represents a kinetic problem related to variable precipitation of certain calcium complexes.

F. WHOLE BLOOD Ca^{++}

Ionized calcium was determined in serum and in simultaneously-drawn heparinized whole blood from 6 normal subjects (Fig. 13). pH effects on $[Ca^{++}]$ in whole blood were roughly similar to those in corresponding sera. In all cases, however, $[Ca^{++}]$ was less in whole blood than in serum at normal venous pH (7.3-7.4). Although the average difference was small (mean $\Delta = -0.045 mM$ at pH 7.32), it was significant ($p < 0.01$).

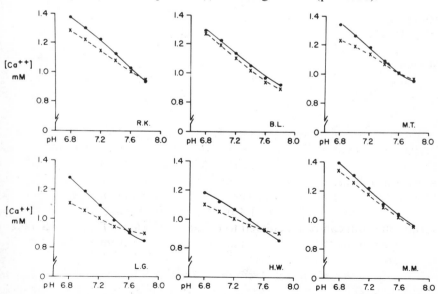

Figure 13. Comparison of ionized calcium concentrations in serum ● and heparinized whole blood × as a function of pH in 6 normal subjects. Note that below pH 7.6, whole blood $[Ca^{++}]$ was less than corresponding serum $[Ca^{++}]$ in all subjects.

G. Calcium-Heparin Complex

Because of the significant reduction in heparinized whole blood $[Ca^{++}]$, the effects of heparin on $[Ca^{++}]$ were studied as follows: sodium heparin (10,000 units per ml) was added in 0.02 ml increments to an aqueous solution (1.0 ml) containing 5mM CaCl$_2$ and 150mM NaCl, with continuous monitoring of ionized calcium by the electrode. As shown in Figure 14, there was a progressive decrease in the observed ionized calcium concentration, amounting to about 45 percent reduction upon addition of 0.1 ml heparin. Similar addition of 0.05 ml and 0.2 ml, respectively, of heparin to 2 normal sera (1.0 ml) resulted in a 13 percent decrease and 45 percent decrease in ionized calcium, respectively. Thus, it appears that observed differences in $[Ca^{++}]$ in sera and whole blood can be accounted for by the heparin used as anticoagulant. Possible effects of erythrocytes on $[Ca^{++}]$ have not been studied, however.

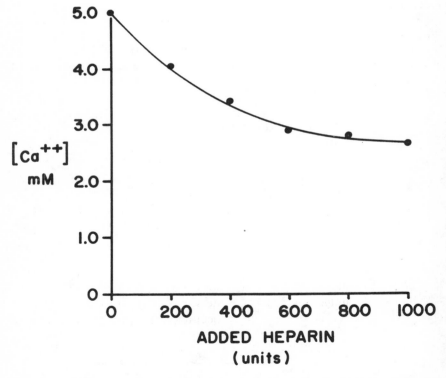

Figure 14. Effect of heparin on ionized calcium concentration in aqueous solution. To 1.0 ml of standard solution containing 5.0mM CaCl$_2$ and 150mM NaCl was added 0.02 ml increments of a commercial sodium heparin solution containing 10,000 units/ml. Data were obtained with static-type calcium electrode.

Heparin is a sulfated polysaccharide; although its ability to complex calcium has long been suspected, these data appear to be the first actual demonstration of such a complex. No formation constant can be given since the molecular weight of heparin is unknown.

H. Accuracy of Electrode Measurements

As with any laboratory method, an important aspect of electrode analysis is the accuracy of the method, both in relative and absolute terms. An estimate of the **relative** accuracy of both electrode (ionized) calcium and EDTA (total) calcium measurements was obtained by analysis of variance for duplicate measurements and expressed as the 95 percent confidence limit for the "true" value in any given sample. As may be seen in Table 4, variability of ionized calcium measurements with the static electrode was somewhat greater in serum than in ultrafiltrates. Replicate variability with the flow-through electrode was one-third that of the static electrode and was comparable to that for total calcium by the EDTA method. For a single value of 1.16mM in serum with the flow-through electrode, the 95 percent confidence limit for the "true" value in that sample (±2 SD) would be between 1.13 and 1.19mM.

Table 4. Variability of replicate calcium determinations.

| | Ionized calcium mM (Electrode) | | | Total calcium mM (EDTA) | |
	Static electrode[47]	Serum Flow–through [17]	Ultrafiltrate Static electrode[16]	Serum [83]	Ultrafiltrate [16]
Mean	1.14	1.16	1.17	2.50	1.52
2 SD	0.09	0.03	0.07	0.03	0.06

The present studies indicate that ionized calcium may be readily and rapidly determined in serum, whole blood and ultrafiltrates with a high degree of reproducibility. Relative accuracy therefore appears to be quite satisfactory, as judged by low duplicate variability, reproducible [Ca^{++}] curves as a function of pH, high specificity for calcium ion, lack of response to anions and chelates of calcium, quantitative recovery studies, usefulness as end-point detectors in chelating titrations, and low variability within a given individual over extended periods of time. There is no doubt that the electrodes respond to calcium ion in biologic fluids.

Absolute accuracy is much more difficult to assess, for there is no absolute appeal or independent method of direct corroboration. There appear to be 3 major considerations in this regard: 1) electrode response to other ions or non-ionic constituents of plasma, 2) variation in calcium ion activity coefficients in biologic fluids as compared with calibrating standards, and 3) variation in residual liquid junction potentials.

The first of these, i.e., response to other ions, would not appear to be of great importance in most biologic fluids because of the very high specificity for calcium ion over Na^+, K^+, and Mg^{++}. Absolute error resulting from these ions is probably well below 5 percent.

It is possible that errors in apparent Ca^{++} could be produced by uptake of plasma or ultrafiltrate constituents by the liquid ion-exchanger. While such a possibility cannot be completely excluded, there are at least 3 findings which strongly argue against it: 1) observed electrode $[Ca^{++}]$ values were within 5-10 percent of those reported for other methods, 2) $[Ca^{++}]$ values were very reproducible within a given individual over extended periods of time, presumably when other plasma constituents were variable, and 3) the EDTA data in Figure 7 argue strongly against a potential of non-calcium origin; upon addition of EDTA to serum or ultrafiltrate, $[Ca^{++}]$ fell to a very low level. This would not be expected if there were a significant non-Ca^{++} potential present.

Differences between calcium ion activity coefficients in biologic fluids as compared with calibrating standards are quite possible, but again are probably of no great significance. Although there is no experimental means by which individual ion activity coefficients can be determined, Garrels [52] has found close agreement between $\gamma_{Ca^{++}}$ values from electrode measurements and those from Debye-Hückel theory up to total ionic strength 0.3M. Since ionic activity coefficients are primarily related to total ionic strength, the use of calibrating standards with total ionic strength similar to that of plasma (i.e., $\simeq 0.16M$) should minimize $\gamma_{Ca^{++}}$ differences. Nevertheless, serum proteins may have effects on water activity and apparent activity coefficients.

Variation in residual liquid junction potentials (E_j), particularly in protein-containing solutions, must always be considered in electrode measurements using a reference (calomel) electrode with liquid junction. As noted by Bates [53], such potentials will generally be small when ionic strengths of unknown and standard are similar. There is some evidence which suggests that variation in E_j was not very great under the conditions of the present study. Thus, ultrafiltrates are essentially simple salt solutions and little difference in junction potentials, as compared with standard $CaCl_2$-$NaCl$ solutions, would be expected. That $[Ca^{++}]$ values were identical in serum and ultrafiltrates, as predicted from the generally accepted monoligand dissociation of calcium-proteinate, suggests that junction potentials in sera and ultrafiltrates were not greatly different. Also, we have shown previously that Na^+ activity in serum, as determined with sodium-selective glass electrodes, is almost identical to that of pure NaCl solutions at corresponding concentrations after correction for serum water content [54]. Nevertheless, it should be noted that with an electrode slope of 30 mV, a variation in liquid junction potential of 0.5 mV could produce an error of about 4 percent in apparent ionized calcium concentration.

It is of interest to compare electrode [Ca^{++}] values with those obtained previously by other methods. At least 3 methods have been used in the past to estimate ionized calcium: 1) the frog heart method [3-5], 2) rachitic cartilage bioassay [55], and 3) metal ion indicators [18-21,36,50,56]. Each of these has yielded average [Ca^{++}] values of about 1.1-1.4mM in normal serum, which is rather close to the present mean electrode value of 1.14mM.

IV. Studies of Calcium-Binding by Normal Serum Proteins

We turn now to *in vitro* studies of protein-binding of calcium in normal serum. Eight studies were made in 6 pooled normal serum samples at room temperature (25 ± 2 °C), pH (7.3-7.4) and ionic strength (0.15-0.16M). In two studies, pooled serum was serially diluted with NaCl and in six studies $CaCl_2$-NaCl was serially added at constant total ionic strength. Ultrafiltrates of each serial sample were obtained as described above, with measurement of both total calcium [Ca] (EDTA method) and ionized calcium [Ca^{++}] (flow-through electrode) concentrations in each serum and ultrafiltrate. Serum proteins were also measured as before in the six calcium-addition studies and in one of the two serum-dilution studies.

A. [CaProt] *Vs.* [Ca]

Resulting levels of protein-bound calcium [CaProt] are shown in Figure 15. Upon addition of calcium there was, as expected, a progressive and slightly curvilinear increase in protein-bound calcium, rising to about 2.7mM at a total calcium level of 8.0mM. Similarly, upon dilution with NaCl, [CaProt] decreased progressively, falling to zero concentration at a total calcium level of about 1mM. This intercept, rather than the expected intercept of zero, may reflect experimental error; since serum proteins, as well as calcium, were diluted to about 40 percent of their original level, resulting [CaProt] levels were probably too low (*i.e.,* 10-20 percent of original values) to accurately measure by ultrafiltration.

B. Calcium Fractions of Serum

Figure 16 shows the changes in each of the calcium fractions of normal serum upon dilution, or upon addition of calcium to serum. [CaR] levels were calculated as before, *i.e.,* as the difference in ultrafiltrate [Ca] and ultrafiltrate [Ca^{++}].

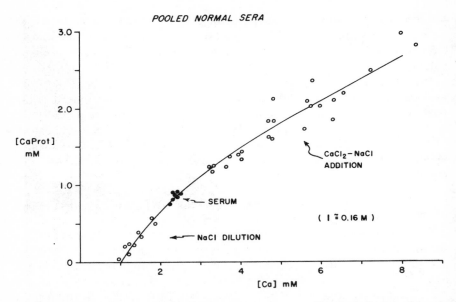

Figure 15.   Observed calcium-proteinate concentrations as a function of total calcium in pooled normal sera upon dilution with NaCl or addition of $CaCl_2$-NaCl at pH 7.3-7.4, 25°C and I $\cong 0.16M$.

If it is assumed that electrode measurements in ultrafiltrates were accurate, *i.e.*, in simple protein-free salt solutions, these data then allow an evaluation of the accuracy of electrode measurements in serum. "Calculated" or expected ionized calcium concentrations in serum are indicated in the figure.

C. PREDICTED *Vs.* OBSERVED SERUM $[Ca^{++}]$

A comparison of the predicted $[Ca^{++}]$ values in Figure 16 and those actually observed in serum with the electrode is shown in Figure 17. The close correspondence between observed and predicted values provides rather strong evidence that the electrode is not poisoned by protein in serum and suggests that residual liquid junction potentials and activity coefficients may be quite similar in sera and ultrafiltrates. This is in accord with the previous finding of virtually identical Ca^{++} values in sera and corresponding ultrafiltrates, as predicted by the generally accepted monoligand dissociation of calcium proteinate.

D. DISSOCIATION CONSTANT OF CALCIUM-ALBUMINATE

In their frog heart studies, McLean and Hastings [3-5] showed that the binding of calcium to serum proteins obeys the mass-law equation:

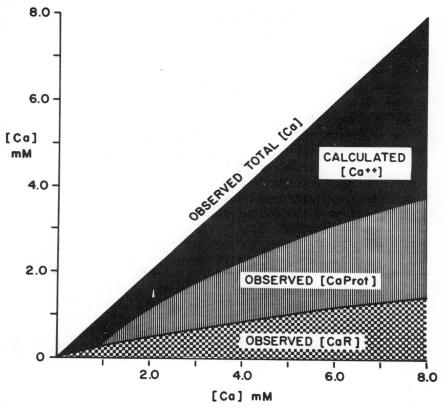

Figure 16.   Variation in the 3 calcium fractions of pooled normal sera upon dilution with NaCl or addition of $CaCl_2$-NaCl at pH 7.3-7.4, 25 °C, $I \cong 0.16M$. Methods for obtaining [CaProt] and [CaR] values are given in the text. Calculated [Ca⁺⁺] values were obtained as the difference in total calcium and the sum: [CaProt] + [CaR].

$$CaProt^{-n} \rightleftharpoons Ca^{++} + Prot^{-(n+2)} \tag{6}$$

Valency in the above reaction is not critical and the equation for the dissociation constant (K'_{CaProt}) may be written as:

$$K'_{CaProt} = \frac{[Ca^{++}][Prot^-]}{[CaProt]} \tag{7}$$

If we assume for the moment that calcium is quantitatively bound to albumin, $i.e.$, [CaProt] = [CaAlb], this is simplified to:

$$K'_{CaAlb} = \frac{[Ca^{++}][Alb^-]}{[CaAlb]} \tag{8}$$

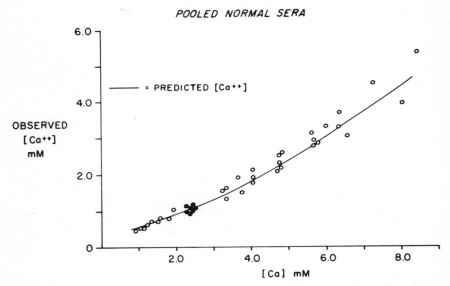

Figure 17. Relation between predicted [Ca++] values, obtained from Figure 16, and those observed with the flow-through calcium electrode in pooled normal sera upon dilution with NaCl or addition of CaCl₂-NaCl. (pH 7.3-7.4, 25 °C, I ≅ 0.16M.)

where $[Alb^-]$ is the total negative-site concentration available for calcium-binding and is equal to:

$$[Alb^-] = n[Alb] - [CaAlb] \qquad (9)$$

where $[Alb]$ is the molar albumin concentration and n is the average maximum number of negative sites available for calcium-binding per albumin molecule. Substituting (9) in (8):

$$K'_{CaAlb} = \frac{[Ca^{++}](n[Alb] - [CaAlb])}{[CaAlb]} \qquad (10)$$

We now have two unknowns: K' and n. As noted by Greenberg [9], if the range in observed $[Ca^{++}]$ values is sufficiently large, values for (K'_{CaProt}) and n may be obtained by rearrangement:

$$\frac{[Alb]}{[CaAlb]} = \frac{1}{n} + \frac{K'}{n} \cdot \frac{1}{[Ca^{++}]} \qquad (11)$$

If the equation holds, a plot of $\dfrac{[Alb]}{[CaAlb]}$ against $\dfrac{1}{[Ca^{++}]}$ should yield a straight line with intercept of $\dfrac{1}{n}$ and slope of $\dfrac{K'}{n}$, from which K' is readily calculated.

Actually, the above equations are an oversimplification, since it is implicitly assumed that successive dissociation (negative) sites on the protein molecule are identical and independent. From protein-binding studies of Scatchard, Klotz and others [57-60], the assumption is probably not strictly correct. This, however, is beyond our scope here. Loken et al. [37], by ultracentrifugation, have observed that a plot of [Prot]/[CaProt] against $1/[Ca^{++}]$ is indeed linear in human serum at this pH. This, of course, does not necessarily mean that successive K' values are identical, but suggests that differences are not detectable at this pH and over the Ca^{++} range studied. The problem is further complicated by the fact that serum proteins other than albumin also bind calcium, presumably with different dissociation constants.

Figure 18 shows our results upon addition of calcium to normal serum. For each point in the figure, it was assumed that the molecular weight of albumin is 69,000 [61] and that 80 percent of the protein-bound calcium was bound to the albumin fraction. The reason for the latter figure will be apparent in Section VIII below. The relationship appeared to be quite linear, suggesting that the binding of calcium to serum proteins obeys the mass-law equation, at least over the range in total calcium observed in man.

From the intercept, a value of 8.4 negative sites per albumin molecule was obtained. This appears to be a very reasonable number. In his studies with collodion membrane electrodes, Carr [14] obtained a value of 7-8 sites per molecule for fractionated bovine albumin.

The pK' for the reaction, derived from the slope of the function, was 2.18. This is in close agreement with previous studies [9] and is almost the exact value obtained with the frog heart [4] and by ultracentrifugation studies [37]. If it had been assumed that all protein-bound calcium was bound to albumin, the value for n would have been 10.5 sites per molecule but K'_{CaAlb} would have been the same ($pK' = 2.18$).

From these data, we believe the calcium ion electrode provides a powerful new tool for the study of calcium-protein interaction. This will be illustrated further in Sections VII and VIII.

V. Distribution of Calcium Across the Blood-CSF Barrier

As an example of another type of physiologic problem, i.e., transport across biologic membranes, which can be readily studied with Ca^{++} electrodes, we will consider briefly the distribution of calcium across the blood-cerebrospinal fluid (CSF) barrier. These studies were made in collaboration with Dr. Andre Blum and have appeared in abstract form [62].

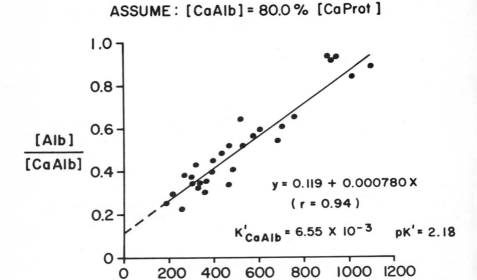

Figure 18. Dissociation constant of calcium-albuminate (K'_{CaAlb}) upon addition of $CaCl_2$-NaCl to pooled normal sera (6 studies) at 25 °C, pH 7.3-7.4 and $I \cong 0.16M$. Linearity of the function suggests that the binding of calcium by human serum albumin obeys the mass-law equation for a mono-ligand association and that successive negative sites on the protein molecule may be considered as identical and independent within limits of experimental error. For each point, it was assumed that 80 percent of the protein-bound calcium was bound to the albumin fraction. This figure was obtained from data presented in Section VIII.

A. PREVIOUS CONCEPTS

Table 5, excerpted from a current leading textbook of physiology [63], summarizes previous data for the distribution of certain ions between plasma and CSF. The "predicted" CSF/plasma concentration ratios for each ion are those expected if the ion were passively-distributed (*i.e.*, by simple diffusion), calculated by the Nernst equation for a 5 mV potential difference (CSF +) between plasma and CSF. The latter value has been observed experimentally in dog and goat by Held *et al.* [64] at normal serum pH.

The previously observed [Cl⁻] distribution ratio of 1.21 is almost exactly that predicted for a passive process. In contrast, neither Na⁺ nor K⁺ appear to be in electrochemical equilibrium. The observed CSF/plasma

Table 5. Distribution of certain ions between cerebrospinal fluid (CSF) and plasma.[a,b]

Ion	CFS/plasma ratio for passive distribution	Observed CSF/plasma ratio
Cl^-	1.20	1.21
Na^+	0.82	1.08
K^+	0.82	0.60
Ca^{++}	0.68	0.50

[a] Predicted CSF/plasma concentration ratios are those for a potential difference of 5 mV (CSF+), based on data of Held *et al.* [64]

[b] Observed ratios are those from the literature [63]; Ca^{++} refers to total, rather than ionized calcium, however.

[Na^+] ratio (1.08) is higher than that predicted for a passive distribution, suggesting an "active" or "facilitated" transport **into** CSF, while for K^+ the reverse is true, suggesting active or facilitated transport **out** of CSF. For Ca^{++}, the observed ratio of 0.50 is lower than that predicted for a passive distribution (0.68), suggesting that Ca^{++} is also actively transported from CSF to blood. This, however, refers to the distribution of **total calcium** and not Ca^{++} specifically. Since less than half of serum calcium is represented by Ca^{++}, it seemed to us that such a conclusion is not necessarily justified. The following studies were therefore performed.

B. Ca^{++} ELECTRODE STUDIES IN MAN AND DOG

Spinal fluid was obtained by lumbar puncture from 5 hospitalized patients without evidence of central nervous system disease, and by cisternal puncture in 5 healthy mongrel dogs. Venous blood was obtained simultaneously and serum separated under oil as described above. Total calcium (EDTA method), [Na], [K], [Cl] and pH were measured in each serum and CSF sample, while [Ca^{++}] was determined with the flow-through electrode.

Results are summarized in Figure 19. Our observed CSF/plasma concentration ratios were in very close agreement with previous studies. The observed ratio for total calcium (not shown) was 0.52 ± 0.01 (SE) in both

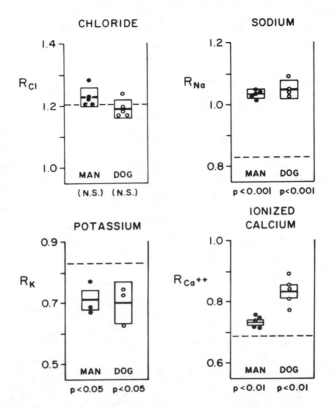

Figure 19.   Observed CSF/serum distribution ratios in man (lumbar fluid) and dog (cisternal fluid). Dashed lines for each ion represent theoretical passive-distribution ratios for
a 5 mV potential difference between CSF and blood. Note that Ca^{++} ratios, determined
with the flow-through electrode, were higher than that predicted for a passive-distribution
in both man and dog.

man and dog, almost exactly that noted previously (Table 5). In contrast,
the distribution of Ca^{++}, determined with the electrode, was significantly
higher in both man and dog than that predicted for a passive distribution:
0.73 ± 0.01 (man) and 0.83 ± 0.02 (dog). The latter value in the dog was
significantly ($p < 0.01$) higher than that in man. While this may represent
some species differences, it seems likely related to the more proximal
(cisternal) sampling site in dogs than in man (lumbar). Thus, after its entry
into CSF from the choroid plexus, $[Ca^{++}]$ may decrease progressively
down the spinal canal by back-diffusion into blood.

We conclude from these studies that $[Ca^{++}]$ in CSF is not in electrochemical equilibrium with plasma. In contrast to observed **total** calcium ratios, observed calcium ion ratios suggest that Ca^{++} is transported
from blood to CSF (presumably by an active or facilitated process) and
not from CSF to blood, as held previously.

VI. Studies of Hyperparathyroidism

Turning now to an entirely different problem, we [65] have recently had the opportunity of studying a 34 year old white female with hyper-parathyroidism and hereditary neurofibromatosis:

In June 1967, the patient noted numbness of the lips and face and was later admitted to a psychiatric hospital where a diagnosis of schizophrenia was made and a lump in the left neck noted. In early 1968, serum total calcium was repeatedly elevated. She was admitted to our Metabolic Research Unit in September 1968; her subsequent course is summarized in Figure 20.

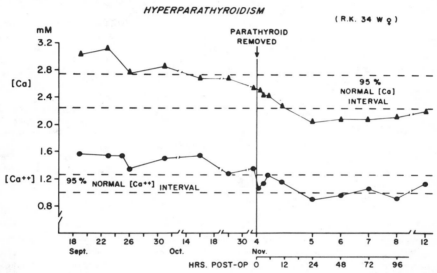

Figure 20.   Serum total and ionized calcium values in a patient with primary hyperpara-thyroidism. Note that total calcium values fell preoperatively to within the normal range, while ionized calcium values remained consistently elevated.

On admission, serum total calcium was 3.0mM (12 mg%) about 1 S.D. above our 95% normal confidence limit, indicated by the upper band in Figure 20. Serum ionized calcium was 1.6mM, some 4 S.D. above the upper normal limit, indicated by the lower band. Serum parathormone level, kindly determined by Dr. Armen Tashjian, was also elevated, as measured by radioimmunoassay [66].

In the following weeks, her serum total calcium slowly declined to within the normal range, in association with a reduction in serum albumin level. Serum ionized calcium, however, determined with the electrode, remained elevated. If she had been first seen at this time and only total calcium measured, the diagnosis of hyperparathyroidism might have been overlooked.

In an effort to stimulate the release of parathyroid hormone, an intravenous infusion of di-sodium EDTA was given in October 1968 and [Ca++] monitored with the flow-through electrode at 5-10 min intervals, using heparinized whole blood.

Results are shown in Figure 21. (To our knowledge, these data represent the first measurements of Ca++ upon administration of EDTA

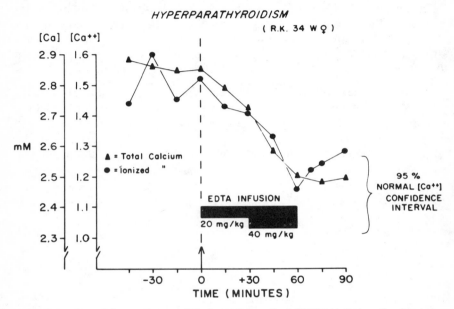

Figure 21.   Effect of intravenous infusion of di-sodium EDTA (ethylenediamine tetra-acetate) on serum total and ionized calcium concentrations in a patient with primary hyperparathyroidism. Vertical scales are adjusted to show the parallel and nearly identical decrease in total and ionized calcium. [Ca] values were determined by EDTA titration; [Ca] measured by atomic absorption spectroscopy (not shown) remained constant throughout the infusion.

in vivo.) The infusion consisted of 20-40 mg/kg/30 min of di-sodium EDTA in isotonic NaCl administered into one arm while blood was obtained from an indwelling catheter in the other arm. Within minutes, a decrease in blood [Ca++] was observed; [Ca++] similarly rose within minutes after stopping the infusion. The decrease in [Ca++] was accompanied by an identical decrease in total calcium as determined by the EDTA method (total calcium determined by atomic absorption spectroscopy, not shown in Figure 21, remained quite constant; the difference between the two methods reflected calcium chelated by administered EDTA).

On November 4, she underwent surgery and two large hyperplastic parathyroid glands were removed. Both total and ionized calcium were measured following induction of anesthesia and at intervals after removal of the parathyroids (Fig. 20). Within an hour, both total and ionized calcium had begun to fall. The change in ionized calcium was more abrupt, decreasing about 30 percent within 3 hours. Serum total calcium remained below normal for over a week. Ionized calcium was also below normal for several days and during this time she had mild tetany.

It is evident from these studies that the calcium ion electrode may provide an important new tool in clinical medicine, both in diagnosis and in evaluation of therapy.

VII. Studies of Serum Calcium in Cirrhosis [67]

In our studies of normal subjects (Section III, above) it was emphasized that no correlation was observed between ionized calcium and total calcium concentrations in normal serum. Increase in serum total calcium was almost quantitatively accounted for by an increase in protein-bound calcium; from this it was concluded that, in the normal, a serum total calcium measurement is an indirect measure of the serum albumin level. The basis for this statement will be developed more fully in the present section, in which another group of normal subjects is compared with patients with advanced cirrhosis of the liver.

Patients with cirrhosis are of particular interest for several reasons: 1) they often have a reduction in serum total calcium, 2) they frequently have reduced serum albumin levels (the major site of calcium-binding in normals), 3) with concomitant elevation of serum globulins, and 4) they frequently have respiratory and/or metabolic alkalosis, yet clinical tetany has not been recognized in over 1000 consecutive cirrhotic patients at the Shattuck Hospital during the past 13 years. This suggests that, unlike serum total calcium, serum ionized calcium may be relatively normal in this disease. Cirrhotic patients are thus of particular interest for the study of the binding of calcium to the serum proteins and the complex physiologic and physicochemical factors governing the level of Ca^{++} in human serum.

Studies were made in 42 hospitalized patients with advanced cirrhosis, 25 males and 17 females whose age ranged from 33 to 82 years (mean: 50.4 years). All patients admitted to at least moderate alcohol intake and the majority were considered to be chronic alcoholics. Diagnosis was established by liver biopsy in 27 patients and by clinical and laboratory findings in the remainder. Of the biopsied patients, 18 were considered to have "Laennec's cirrhosis", 4 "post-necrotic", and in 5 the cirrhosis was of questionable type. Of the non-biopsied patients, all were considered to have cirrhosis of the alcoholic. Marked ascites was present in 24 patients; 11 others had mild ascites. The majority were clinically stable at the time of study.

Studies were also made on 21 healthy volunteer hospital personnel, 6 males and 15 females whose ages ranged from 20 to 61 years (mean: 30.5 years). Eight of these subjects were included in the above studies of 60 normal subjects (Section III).

Venous blood was obtained under oil without anticoagulant, usually 2-3 hours after breakfast. Following centrifugation under oil, an aliquot of serum was removed for pH measurement; the remaining serum was again placed under oil without exposure to air. A heparinized blood sample was obtained simultaneously for determination of whole blood pH. Most [Ca^{++}] measurements in the cirrhotic patients (32 of 42) were made with static-type electrodes (Figs. 2, 3). In the normals, 8 subjects were studied with static electrodes and 13 with flow-through electrodes (Fig. 4), as described above.

A. CALCIUM FRACTIONS OF SERUM

As shown in Figure 22a, serum total calcium was significantly reduced in the cirrhotic patients. Mean serum [Ca] in the 21 normal subjects was 2.47 ± 0.08[3] mM as compared with 2.16 ± 0.08mM in cirrhotics (p < 0.001). In contrast, total ultrafiltrate (diffusible) calcium was significantly increased (p < 0.01) in the latter group. Mean values in normals and cirrhotics were 1.47 ± 0.06mM and 1.62 ± 0.6mM, respectively. Thus, of the total serum calcium, a significantly (p < 0.001) higher fraction was diffusible in the cirrhotic patients: in the normal, an average of 59.8 ± 2.8 percent was ultrafiltrable, while in the cirrhotics 75.5 ± 3.6 percent of the serum total calcium was represented by the diffusible [Ca^{++} + CaR] fractions. These data indicate a significant reduction in protein-bound calcium in the cirrhotics, as shown in Figure 22c. Mean [CaProt] in normals was 1.00 ± 0.09mM, almost twice the value of 0.54 ± 0.09mM in cirrhotics (p < 0.001).

In the absence of electrode data for ionized calcium, the observed increase in total diffusible calcium might be interpreted as suggesting that [Ca^{++}] is normal or increased in such patients or, alternatively, that if [Ca^{++}] were decreased, the increase in ultrafiltrable calcium would reflect an increase in diffusible complexes, [CaR].

That the latter is the case is shown in Figure 23. Serum ionized calcium was significantly reduced in the cirrhotic patients as compared with normals, with means of 1.09 ± 0.06mM and 1.16 ± 0.02mM, respectively (p < 0.02). While these mean values were "significantly" different, there was considerable variability in [Ca^{++}] in the cirrhotic group. As was the case with serum total calcium, about half of the cirrhotic patients were below the lowest value observed in the normals but, unlike total calcium, 5 of the 42 patients (12 percent) were above the highest normal value.

---

[3]These and all subsequent values refer to ± 2 SE of the mean.

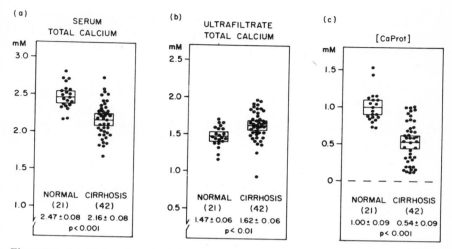

Figure 22.   (a) Observed total calcium concentrations [Ca] in sera from 21 normal subjects and 42 patients with cirrhosis. (b) Observed [Ca] concentrations in serum ultrafiltrates. (c) Calculated concentrations of protein-bound calcium [CaProt]. In this and subsequent figures, enclosed boxes represent mean values ± 2 standard errors.

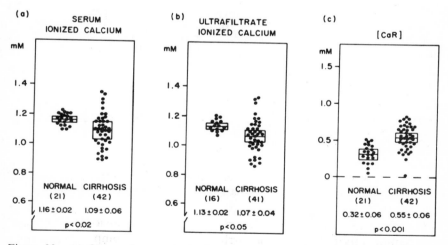

Figure 23.   (a) Observed serum ionized calcium concentrations in 21 normals and 42 cirrhotic patients. (b) Observed ultrafiltrate ionized calcium concentrations in 16 normals and 41 cirrhotics. (c) Calculated concentrations of diffusible calcium complexes [CaR] in sera from 21 normals and 42 cirrhotics.

Ultrafiltrate $[Ca^{++}]$ was almost identical to that in serum for the two groups. In each group the average difference between serum and ultrafiltrate $[Ca^{++}]$ was $0.02 - 0.03$ mM.

As expected from the significant increase in total diffusible calcium and decrease in serum [Ca^{++}] in cirrhotic patients, the concentration of diffusible calcium complexes, [CaR], was significantly increased in the cirrhotic group. Mean [CaR] was 0.55 ± 0.06mM, or 72 percent higher than the mean of 0.32 ± 0.06mM in normals (p < 0.001).

From Figures 22 and 23, it is concluded that in cirrhosis there is a significant: 1) decrease in serum [Ca] and [CaProt], 2) decrease in serum [Ca^{++}], 3) increase in [CaR], and 4) increase in total diffusible calcium.

The relative contributions, in percent, for each of the 3 calcium fractions for both normals and cirrhotics are shown on triangular coordinates in Figure 24. Cirrhotic patients tended to fall in that area of the triangle characterized by decreased [CaProt], increased [CaR] and normal or increased [Ca^{++}].

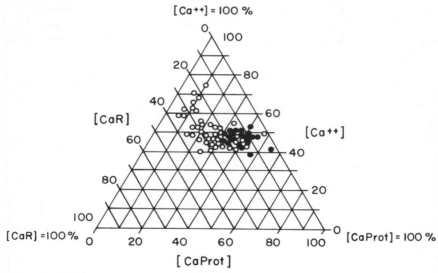

Figure 24.   Relative contribution, in percent, of each of the 3 calcium fractions of serum in 21 normals (closed circles) and 42 cirrhotics (open circles). Note that cirrhotics tended to fall in an area characterized by decreased [CaProt], increased [CaR] and normal or increased [Ca^{++}].

In the normal group, [Ca^{++}] constituted an average of 47.1 ± 1.7 percent of the serum total calcium, as compared with 50.9 ± 2.6 percent in cirrhotics. This difference was not significant. Thus, while [Ca^{++}] was significantly reduced in cirrhotics on an absolute scale, that **fraction** as [Ca^{++}] was somewhat increased. In the normal, [CaProt] averaged 40.2 ± 2.8 percent of the total calcium, which was significantly (p < 0.001) greater than the value 24.4 ± 3.6 percent in cirrhotics. [CaProt] was thus reduced on both absolute and percentage scales. [CaR] averaged 12.7 ± 2.2 percent of the total in normals, as compared with 24.6

± 2.4 percent in cirrhotics (p < 0.001). [CaR] was thus increased in both relative and absolute terms.

B. SERUM PROTEINS

Total protein, albumin and globulin levels in serum are given in Figure 25. In the normal group, mean total protein was 72.3 ± 2.2 g/l, which was significantly greater than the value 64.4 ± 3.3 g/l in cirrhotics (p < 0.01). In the latter, total protein was quite variable, ranging from 35 to 90 g/l.

The reduction in total protein in the cirrhotics was due to marked reduction in serum albumin concentration. Mean [Alb] in normals was 47.3 ± 2.2 g/l as compared with 29.3 ± 2.5 g/l in cirrhotics (p < 0.001). Serum [Glob] was significantly increased in the cirrhotic patients, with a mean of 35.6 ± 2.6 g/l as compared with 25.0 ± 2.0 g/l in normals (p < 0.001). There was no correlation in the cirrhotics (r = − 0.16) and only a slight correlation in normals (r = − 0.46) between serum [Alb] and [Glob].

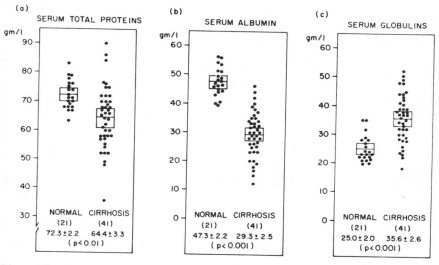

Figure 25. Serum total protein (a), albumin (b), and globulin (c) concentrations in 21 normal subjects and 41 patients with cirrhosis.

C. RELATION OF [Ca⁺⁺] TO TOTAL CALCIUM AND ALBUMIN

As shown in Figure 26a, there was no correlation between serum ionized calcium and serum total calcium in either normals or cirrhotics. Serum [Ca⁺⁺] was within a rather narrow range regardless of the total calcium level. Thus, measurement of total calcium did not provide an accurate index of serum ionized calcium in these patients, an observation

similar to that noted (Section III) in normal subjects. As noted above, the
95 percent confidence limit for ionized calcium in the normal was
1.01-1.26mM, indicated by the shaded area in Figure 26. Thus, in the 42
cirrhotics, there were 14 patients (33%) outside the 95 percent normal
confidence limit, 4 with elevated [Ca^{++}] levels and 10 with reduced
[Ca^{++}] values. As may be seen in Figure 26b, there was also no correlation between serum [Ca^{++}] and albumin levels in either normals or
cirrhotics.

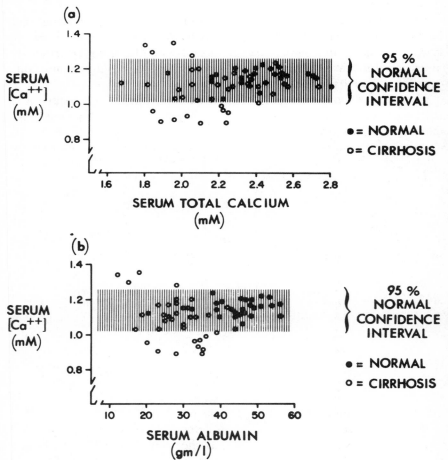

Figure 26.   (a) Relationship between serum ionized calcium and serum total calcium concentrations in 21 normals (closed circles) and 42 cirrhotics (open circles). (b) Relationship between serum ionized calcium and serum albumin concentrations in 21 normals
(closed circles) and 41 cirrhotics (open circles). The shaded areas represent the 95 percent confidence interval for serum [Ca^{++}] in normal subjects (Section III). Note the
complete lack of correlation; ionized calcium was within a rather narrow range, irrespective of total calcium and albumin concentrations.

D. Relation of [CaProt] to Serum Proteins

It is concluded from these data that, although [Ca^{++}] is significantly reduced and [CaR] significantly increased in cirrhotic patients, the overall reduction in serum total calcium is primarily due to marked reduction in protein-bound calcium, [CaProt]. Since albumin has long been recognized as the primary site of calcium-binding in serum, reduced [CaProt] might be expected to accompany significant reduction in serum albumin.

The relation between [CaProt] and [Alb] levels for both normals and cirrhotics is shown in Figure 27. Individual subject data are given in Figure 27a, while in Figure 27b, samples were pooled by 5 g/l increments in serum albumin. [CaProt] was linearly related to serum albumin concentration in both normals and cirrhotics.

There are two questions: 1) is calcium bound **entirely** to albumin, or is there also some binding to serum globulins and 2) does a biochemically diseased liver produce qualitatively abnormal albumin (*i.e.*, in terms of calcium-binding affinity) or is reduction in [CaProt] purely quantitatively related to reduction in [Alb]?

The first question relates primarily to the intercept(s) of the function(s) in Figure 27, while the second is primarily related to the slope(s) of the function(s). Both, of course, are mathematically and physicochemically interrelated.

The linear relationship between [CaProt] and [Alb] indicates that most (perhaps all) of protein-bound calcium is bound to albumin. (There was no relationship between [CaProt] and serum globulin levels in either normals or cirrhotics). That calcium is bound **entirely** to albumin in cirrhotics is suggested by the intercept on the horizontal axis in Figure 27b. If there were measurable binding to globulins, an intercept on the vertical axis would be expected, particularly in view of the significant elevation of serum globulins in these patients. Since, from the mass-law equation an intercept on the horizontal axis would make no physicochemical sense, it is likely that the true intercept of the function is zero in cirrhotics, in which case calcium may be considered to be quantitatively bound to albumin in these patients.[4]

It would appear that there were no detectable qualitative differences between normals and cirrhotics since, as shown in Figure 27b, the slopes of the calculated regressions for the two groups were almost identical, 0.0190mm$M$/g and 0.0197mm$M$/g respectively. If the molecular weight of albumin is 69,000 in both groups, this would correspond to 1.31

---

[4] The intercept on the horizontal axis may reflect the fact that ultrafiltrates were obtained at 25 °C rather than 37 °C. As noted in Section III.B., data of Loken *et al.*[37] indicate that [CaProt] is about 5-6% higher at 37 °C than at 25 °C.

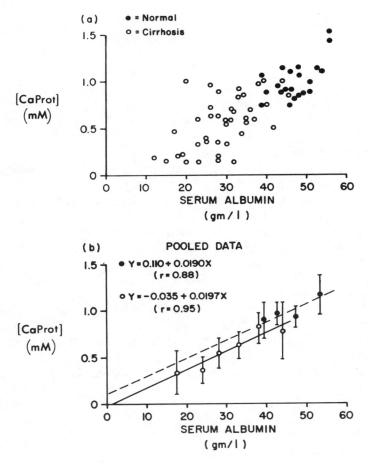

Figure 27.   Relationship between protein-bound calcium [CaProt] and serum albumin concentrations in 21 normals and 41 cirrhotics. Individual subject data are given in (a). In (b), data from normals and cirrhotics were each pooled by 5 g/l increments in serum albumin. Vertical bars represent ±2 SE. Note that the slopes of the calculated least-squares regressions in (b) were almost identical in the 2 groups. In normals, the calculated intercept was 0.11 mM while in cirrhotics, it was very nearly zero.

molecules of calcium per molecule of albumin in normals, and 1.36 in cirrhotics.

In normals (Fig. 27b), the calculated intercept of 0.11mM on the vertical axis suggests some binding to serum globulins. Since mean [CaProt] in the normal was 1.0mM (Fig. 22), the data suggest that about 11 percent of protein-bound calcium is in the globulin fraction. The extrapolation is quite long, however, and as will be shown in Section VIII, this problem is perhaps better studied by another type of mathematical analysis.

Mean K'_{CaAlb} values, calculated by Equation (10), were 7.43 ± 0.64 ($\times 10^{-3}$), ($pK' = 2.13$) in the normals and 10.06 ± 2.74 ($\times 10^{-3}$), ($pK' = 2.00$) in cirrhotics. While K' values in the majority of cirrhotics were within the normal range, some 15-25 percent of patients showed values 2-6 times those of normals. This suggests that the calcium-binding affinity of serum albumin may be decreased in some patients. These data should be viewed with extreme caution, however, owing to the uncertainties in K' calculations (Section IV.D.) and to variation in other factors, such as pH and complexing anions, which may affect calcium binding.

E. RELATION OF TOTAL CALCIUM TO [CaProt] AND [Alb]

As noted above, [CaProt] decreased linearly with decreasing albumin concentration. Although [Ca^{++}] was significantly decreased and [CaR] significantly increased in the cirrhotics, the resulting relationship between serum total calcium and [Alb] was also linear, as shown in Figure 28. Both normals and cirrhotics appeared to fall on the same regression. If the extrapolation is valid, the data suggest that at zero albumin concentration, serum [Ca] would be 1.61mM.

The slope of the function in Figure 28b (0.019mM/g) is identical to those in Figure 27b, indicating that reduction in serum [Ca] paralleled the reduction in [CaProt]. That this is the case is shown in Figure 29. The slope, 0.92 in both normals and cirrhotics, indicates that reduced [CaProt] accounted almost quantitatively for the reduction in serum total calcium. The extrapolated value for [Ca] at zero [CaProt] was 1.57mM in cirrhotics and 1.33mM in normals. (The displacement of the intercept on the horizontal axis in the cirrhotics reflected the increased [CaR] fraction in these patients.)

F. pH EFFECTS: NOMOGRAMS FOR [CaProt].

We will now consider the effect of pH on serum ionized calcium and protein-bound calcium. Nomograms will then be constructed for [CaProt] in both normals and cirrhotics for any given pH and albumin level.

In our static electrode studies of normal serum (Fig. 12, Section III.C.), it was noted that [Ca^{++}] decreased progressively and nearly linearly with increasing pH. The effect was accentuated upon concentration of the serum proteins. In the 52 normals so studied, the following data were obtained:

$$[Ca]_{\bar{x}} = 2.505 \text{mM}$$

$$[Ca^{++}]_{\bar{x}} = 1.36 \text{mM at pH } 6.8$$

$$[Ca^{++}]_{\bar{x}} = 0.94 \text{mM at pH } 7.8$$

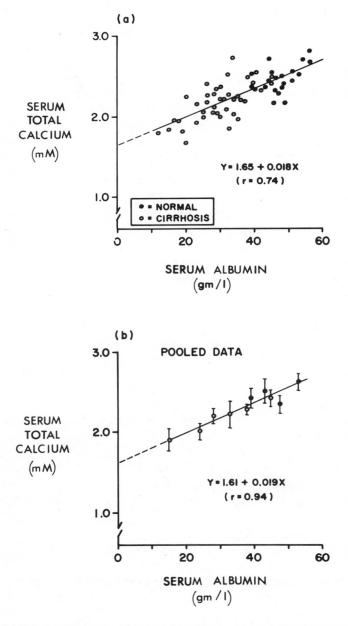

Figure 28.   Relationship between serum total calcium and serum albumin concentrations in 21 normals and 41 cirrhotics. In (b), the data were pooled by 5 g/l increments in serum albumin. Vertical bars represent ±2 SE. Note that both normals and cirrhotics appeared to fall on the same regression and that the slope of the function was very nearly identical to those in Figure 27b.

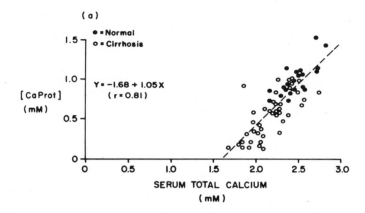

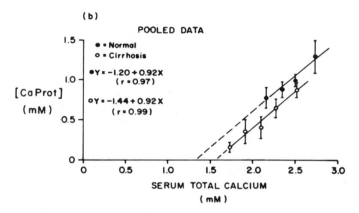

Figure 29.   Relationship between protein-bound calcium [CaProt] and serum total calcium concentrations in 21 normals and 42 cirrhotics. In (b), data were pooled by 5 g/l increments in serum albumin. Vertical bars represent ± 2 SE. Note that the slopes were identical in the 2 groups; the observed slope of 0.92 indicates that the change in serum total calcium was almost quantitatively accounted for by the change in the protein-bound fraction. The displacement of the curve to the right in cirrhotics reflected the increased [CaR] levels in these patients. Predicted [Ca] levels at zero [CaProt] concentration were 1.33 and 1.57mM in normals and cirrhotics, respectively.

Thus, at pH 6.8, an average of 54.3 percent (1.36/2.505) of the serum total calcium was ionized, while at pH 7.8 it was 37.5 percent. In other words, a 1 unit pH change resulted in a 16.8 percent (54.3-37.5) decrease in the ionized calcium fraction of normal serum. This is virtually identical to the change in free calcium of normal serum noted by Loken *et al.* [37], as determined by ultracentrifugation. From this, we may surmise that a pH-induced decrease in ionized calcium is accompanied by a corresponding increase in protein-bound calcium. (As noted in Section III.E. above, the common diffusible complexes of calcium in serum do not appear to be pH-dependent in this pH range.)

Stated another way, the average change in serum $[Ca^{++}]$ for a 1 unit pH change was 0.42mM. If we may apply this figure to the present group of 21 normal subjects in whom the serum proteins were also measured, the value 0.42mM thus represents that change in [CaProt] produced at an average serum albumin concentration of 47.3 g/l (Fig. 25) and average globulin concentration of 25.0 g/l (Fig. 25). The change in $[Ca^{++}]$ or [CaProt] would be expected to be proportionately greater at higher protein concentrations (Fig. 12) and proportionately less at lower protein concentrations. **In other words, the absolute change in [CaProt] induced by pH change would be expected to be proportional to existing protein levels, while the percentage change in [CaProt] would be expected to be constant.**

In the present series of 21 normal subjects, average [CaProt] was 1.00mM (Fig. 22) and average serum pH at the time of ultrafiltration was 7.42 ± 0.01 (2 SE). The following equation may therefore be written relating [CaProt] to [Albumin], [Globulin] and pH:

$$[CaProt] = [CaAlb] - [(0.42) \frac{[Alb]}{47.3} (7.42 - pH)]$$

$$+ [CaGlob] - [(0.42) \frac{[Glob]}{25.0} (7.42 - pH)] \quad (12)$$

where pH is that at the time of ultrafiltration.

We now need a way of estimating [CaAlb], *i.e.*, calcium bound to albumin, and [CaGlob], calcium bound to globulins. This can be obtained from the slope of the function in Figure 27:

$$[CaAlb] = 0.0190 [Alb] \quad (13)$$

Since the average [Alb] in the 21 subjects was 47.3 g/l:

$$[CaAlb] = (0.019)(47.3) = 0.899mM \quad (13a)$$

Since average [CaProt] was 1.00mM, the remainder (0.101mM) represents [CaGlob], at an average [Glob] level of 25.0 g/l. Thus:

$$[CaGlob] = 0.101 = (z)(25.0) \quad (14)$$

where $z = 0.004mM/g$. Equation (12) may thus be re-written in terms of known quantities:

$$[CaProt] = 0.019[Alb] - [(0.42) \left(\frac{[Alb]}{47.3}\right) (7.42 - pH)]$$

$$+ 0.004[Glob] - [(0.42) \left(\frac{[Glob]}{25.0}\right) (7.42 - pH)] \quad (15)$$

The correspondence between observed [CaProt] levels, determined by ultrafiltration, and those calculated by Equation (15) was rather close. Thus, in the 21 subjects, average calculated [CaProt] was 1.00mM, exactly that observed experimentally, while the average error (without regard to sign) was 0.135 ± 0.02 (SE)mM or 13.5 percent.

The constants 0.019 and 0.004 in Equation (15), *i.e.,* albumin and globulin binding constants, will be derived in a different manner in Section VIII below, and will be found to be 0.0167 and 0.0079, respectively. The use of these latter constants in Equation (15) yielded almost identical results, however. Thus, mean calculated [CaProt] was 0.99mM and average error was 0.131mM or 13.1 percent.

Our best estimate of [CaProt] from measured albumin, globulin and pH thus appears to yield an average error of about 13 percent in normals. While this is close enough for most clinical purposes, Equation (15) does not readily lend itself to a bedside solution. Clearly, a simple nomogram is desirable, but this is not easily done with 3 measured variables and a constant fractional amplification. A simple solution was obtained as follows:

If we assume that all protein-bound calcium is bound to albumin, then from observed mean values of:

$$[\text{Alb}]_{\bar{x}} = 47.3 \ \text{g/l} \tag{16}$$

$$[\text{CaProt}]_{\bar{x}} = 1.00 \ mM = [\text{CaAlb}]_{\bar{x}} \tag{17}$$

Neglecting the pH term:

$$[\text{CaAlb}] = 0.0211 \ [\text{Alb}] \tag{18}$$

and with the pH term:

$$[\text{CaAlb}] = 0.0211 [\text{Alb}] - [(0.42) \left(\frac{[\text{Alb}]}{47.3}\right) (7.42 - \text{pH})] \tag{19}$$

Equation (19), with only two measured variables, is readily expressed graphically as a nomogram. This is given in Figure 30. Using this nomogram, average calculated [CaProt] in the 21 subjects was 1.00mM, exactly that observed experimentally and the average error was 0.136mM or 13.6 percent. The reason for the close correspondence of values calculated by Equations (12), (15) and (19) is of course the small variations in albumin, globulin and pH. In fact, we would have done as well if the pH term in Equation (19) had been neglected altogether. Neglecting the pH term, mean [CaProt] was 1.00mM and the average error was 13.5 percent. pH is therefore included in the nomogram more for the sake of emphasis than for the sake of accuracy.

In cirrhosis the situation is already simplified since, from Figure 27, there was no detectable binding to globulins and there would therefore be

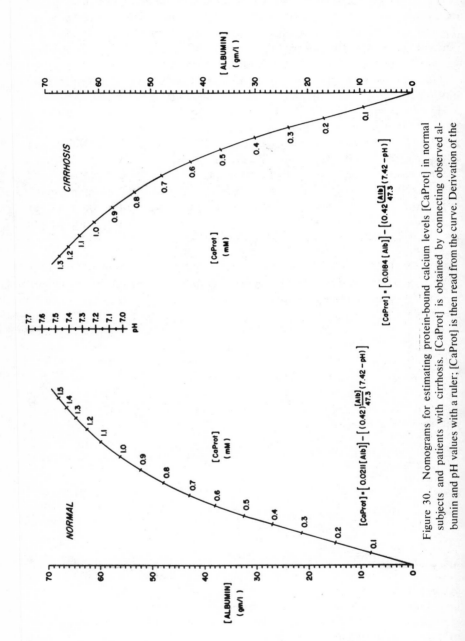

Figure 30. Nomograms for estimating protein-bound calcium levels [CaProt] in normal subjects and patients with cirrhosis. [CaProt] is obtained by connecting observed albumin and pH values with a ruler; [CaProt] is then read from the curve. Derivation of the

no globulin term in the equations. The faulty intercept on the horizontal axis in cirrhotics has already been noted, probably relating to a temperature effect as well as to analytical and regression analysis errors. The observed slope in cirrhotics, 0.0197 yielded calculated [CaProt] values about 15 percent too high. From observed mean [Alb] and [CaProt], values of 29.3 g/l and 0.54mM respectively, the correct slope may be estimated to be:

$$\frac{0.54}{29.3} = 0.0184 \text{ m}M/\text{g}$$

and estimated [CaProt] from existing albumin and pH levels would be:

$$[CaProt] = 0.0184 \ [Alb] - [(0.42)\left(\frac{[Alb]}{47.3}\right)(7.42 - pH)] \tag{20}$$

The resulting nomogram is given in Figure 30.

Mean calculated [CaProt] in the cirrhotics was 0.54mM, exactly that observed experimentally, and the average error was 0.193 ± 0.02mM. Since mean [CaProt] was only about half that in normal subjects, the overall percentage error was much larger than in normals, 35.7 percent. While this may largely reflect analytical errors at low albumin and [CaProt] concentrations, it is possible that other variables affecting protein-binding of calcium should also be considered. In particular, one wonders about the elevated [CaR] levels in these patients; we do not yet know what these complexing anion(s) are, although it would not appear to be phosphate.

As in normals, the accuracy of estimated [CaProt] levels in cirrhotics [Eq. (20)] was not improved by the pH term. In fact, the error was somewhat less without it. Thus, neglecting the pH term, average [CaProt] was 0.54mM and the average error was 0.188mM or 34.8 percent. The reason for this rather surprising result is undoubtedly related, in part at least, to the fact that those patients with large deviations in blood pH also tended to have the lowest albumin levels, i.e., these were the most severely ill patients. Since the absolute change in [CaProt] induced by pH change is related to the albumin level, the overall pH effect was quite small. For example, the lowest blood pH observed was 7.09, obtained a few minutes before demise, while [Alb] was also the lowest observed, 12 g/l. Observed [CaProt], determined by ultrafiltration, was 0.18mM, while that calculated by Equation (20) was 0.188mM. Without the pH term, calculated [CaProt] was 0.22mM, or only 0.04mM error. Thus, while pH must be considered an important theoretical factor in these patients, the overall effect is quite small and, as in normals, is included in the nomogram more for the sake of emphasis than for the sake of accuracy.

Finally, it should be noted that the nomograms were constructed for data obtained at 25 °C. From data of Loken *et al.* [37], corresponding values *in vivo* would be about 5 percent higher.

G. SUMMARY

The data from cirrhotics are summarized in Figure 31, in which serum total calcium and each of the 3 calcium fractions are given as a function of serum albumin concentration. Note that mean serum $[Ca^{++}]$ remained unchanged with decreasing albumin concentration. $[CaR]$ was significantly elevated above normal and increased slightly with decreasing albumin concentration.

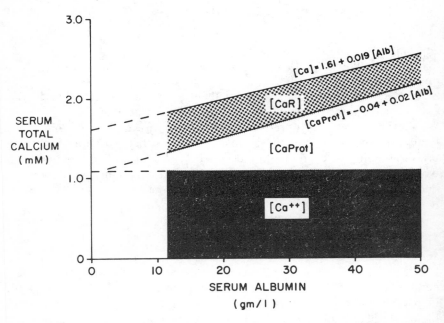

Figure 31.   Summary figure for the relationship of serum total calcium concentration (upper line) and each of the 3 calcium fractions of serum (shaded areas) to serum albumin concentration (Fig. 26). Decrease in serum total calcium was virtually quantitatively accounted for by decrease in protein-bound calcium. At zero albumin concentration, the extrapolated value for serum total calcium was 1.61 mM (Fig. 28).

In cirrhotics, as well as in normals, change in serum total calcium was almost quantitatively accounted for by a corresponding change in protein-bound calcium. The latter, in turn, reflected the serum albumin level. In contrast to normals, there was no detectable binding to serum globulins in the cirrhotics.

While cirrhotics are a heterogeneous population, with several variables affecting serum calcium, the overriding consideration is the serum albumin level, as shown in this model.

VIII. Studies of the Hypercalcemia of Cancer[5]

In both normals and patients with cirrhosis, it was emphasized that serum ionized calcium concentrations were within a rather narrow range, independent of serum total calcium and albumin concentrations. In both groups, variation in serum total calcium was almost totally accounted for by variation in protein-bound calcium, mainly to serum albumin.

Hypercalcemia is a common and often distressing complication in patients with certain types of malignancy. As a final example of the usefulness of calcium electrodes in biomedical research and clinical medicine, we will now consider some results of 30 studies recently performed in 24 patients with cancer and hypercalcemia. Comparison will be made with the 21 normal subjects presented in Section VII. It will be shown that, although serum protein abnormalities are comparable to those in cirrhosis, there are striking differences in serum ionized calcium and in the protein-binding of calcium in these patients. As was given for cirrhotics, a model will be developed for total calcium and each of the 3 calcium fractions of serum in normals and in the hypercalcemia of malignancy.

A. Calcium Fractions of Serum

1. Total Calcium, Ultrafiltrable Calcium and [CaProt]

Patients were selected for study on the basis of hypercalcemia, *i.e.,* elevation in serum total calcium. As shown in Figure 32a, this elevation was significant ($p < 0.001$); mean [Ca] in the 30 studies (24 patients) was 3.35 ± 0.18 (2 SE)mM, as compared with 2.47 ± 0.08mM in the 21 normals.

Total diffusible calcium was also increased (Fig. 32b), with means of 2.17 ± 0.13mM and 1.47 ± 0.06mM in the cancer patients and normals, respectively ($p < 0.001$). Of the serum total calcium, 64.8 percent was thus ultrafiltrable, as compared with 59.8 percent in normals. In contrast to cirrhotics (Section VII), this difference was not significant.

As seen in Figure 32c, average [CaProt] was significantly ($p < 0.02$) increased in the cancer patients, with means of 1.18 ± 0.10mM and 1.00 ± 0.09mM in cancer and normals, respectively. This finding is also in sharp contrast to that observed in cirrhotics (Fig. 22).

[5]The collaboration of Dr. Carlos Guzzo and the Oncology Division of the Medical Services in these studies is gratefully acknowledged.

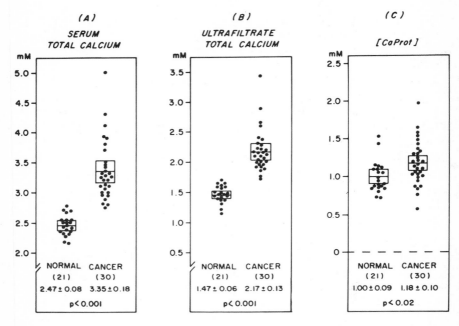

Figure 32.   (a) Total calcium concentrations (EDTA method) in sera from 21 normal subjects and 24 patients with malignancy (30 studies). (b) Total calcium concentrations in serum ultrafiltrates. (c) Calculated concentrations of protein-bound calcium [CaProt]. In this and subsequent figures, enclosed boxes represent mean values ±2 standard errors.

2.   [Ca⁺⁺] and [CaR]

Serum ionized calcium was also significantly (p < 0.001) elevated in the cancer patients, with a mean value of 1.51 ± 0.10 mM as compared with 1.16 ± 0.02 mM in normals (Fig. 33). Variability in [Ca⁺⁺] was great, however, ranging from 1.13 to 2.14mM; in 7 studies (6 patients), serum [Ca⁺⁺] values were within the normal range. On the average, the percentage increase (30 percent) in [Ca⁺⁺] was similar to that for total calcium (36 percent).

Mean [CaR], shown in Figure 33b, was also significantly increased in the cancer patients, to about twice the normal value: 0.66 ± 0.10 mM and 0.32 ± 0.06 mM, respectively (p < 0.001).

3.   Relative Values for [Ca⁺⁺], [CaProt] and [CaR]

The relative contribution, in percent, for each of the 3 calcium fractions for both normals and cancer patients are shown on triangular coordinates in Figure 34. In the latter group, [Ca⁺⁺] constituted, on the average, 45.1 ± 2.0 percent of the total calcium, similar to the value 47.1 ± 1.7 percent

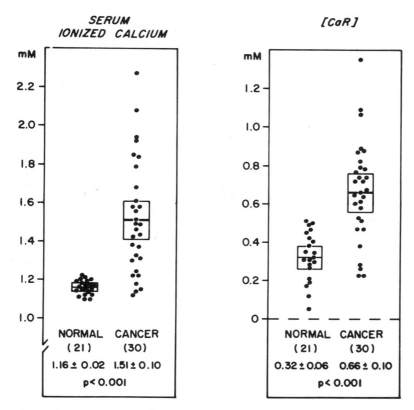

Figure 33.   (a) Serum ionized calcium concentrations [Ca^{++}] in 21 normal subjects and 24 patients (30 studies) with cancer and hypercalcemia. (b) Diffusible calcium complex concentrations [CaR], calculated as the difference in ultrafiltrate total calcium (EDTA method) and ultrafiltrate ionized calcium concentrations.

in normals. Thus, while [Ca^{++}] was significantly increased on the absolute scale, that **fraction** as [Ca^{++}] was normal. In the cancer patients, [CaProt] average 35.0 ± 2.2 percent of the total, significantly ($p < 0.01$) less than the value 40.2 ± 2.8 percent in normals. Thus, although mean [CaProt] was increased on an absolute scale in the cancer patients, its fractional contribution to the total was significantly reduced. [CaR] averaged 20.0 ± 2.8 percent of the total calcium in cancer, significantly ($p < 0.001$) higher than that (12.7 ± 2.2 percent) in normals. Mean [CaR] was thus increased in relative as well as absolute terms.

B. Serum Proteins

Serum total protein, albumin and globulin levels are shown in Figure 35. As may be seen by comparison with Figure 25, mean values for the

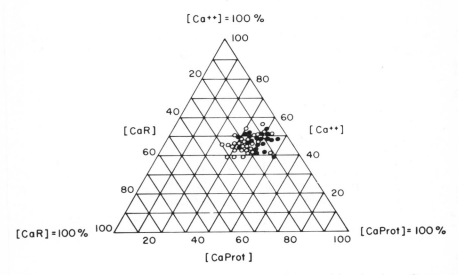

Figure 34. Relative contribution, in percent, of each of the 3 calcium fractions of serum in 21 normal subjects (closed circles) and 24 patients (30 studies) with cancer and hypercalcemia (open circles).

cancer patients were almost identical to those observed previously in cirrhotics. Mean total protein was 65.2 ± 3.8 g/l, significantly less than the value of 72.3 ± 2.2 g/l in normals (p < 0.01). Reduction in total protein

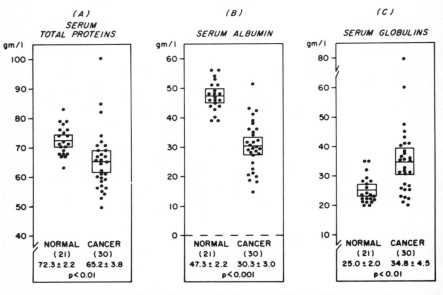

Figure 35. Serum total protein (A), albumin (B), and globulin (C) concentrations in 21 normal subjects and 24 patients (30 studies) with cancer and hypercalcemia.

was due to marked reduction in serum albumin, with means of 47.3 ±
2.2 g/l and 30.3 ± 3.0 g/l in normals and cancer patients, respectively (p <
0.001). As in cirrhotics, mean serum globulin level was significantly (p <
0.01) increased, with respective values of 25.0 ± 2.0 g/l and 34.8 ± 4.5 g/l
in normal and cancer.

C. Relation of [Ca^{++}] to Serum [Alb] and [Ca]

As may be seen in Figure 36, there was no apparent relation between
serum ionized calcium concentration and serum albumin level in the
cancer patients. This finding was similar to that observed in both normals
and patients with cirrhosis (Fig. 26b).

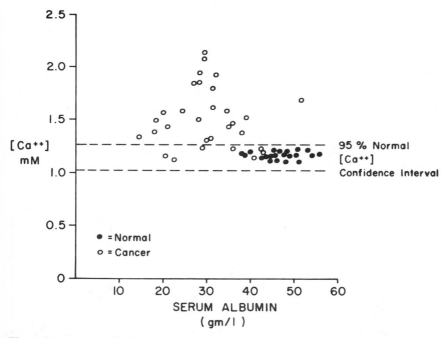

Figure 36.   Relationship between serum ionized calcium and albumin concentration in 21
normal subjects and 24 patients (30 studies) with hypercalcemia of malignancy.

In contrast to both normals and cirrhotics, who showed no relation
between serum ionized and total calcium concentrations, we find a striking difference in the hypercalcemia of malignancy. As shown in the upper
half of Figure 37, [Ca^{++}] was linearly related to [Ca]; the slope of the
function was 0.45 and the intercept was nearly zero. This is remarkably
similar to the observed relation between [Ca^{++}] and [Ca] seen upon dilution or addition of calcium to normal serum *in vitro* (Section IV). The
latter data are shown for comparison in the lower half of Figure 37.

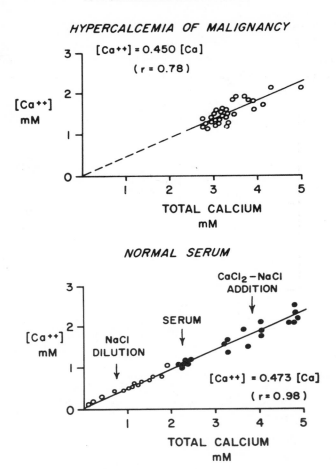

Figure 37.   (a) Relation of serum ionized calcium [Ca^{++}] and total calcium [Ca] concentrations in 30 studies of 24 patients with cancer and hypercalcemia. (b) Relation of serum ionized and total calcium concentrations upon dilution of normal serum *in vitro* with NaCl or addition of CaCl$_2$-NaCl, over the same [Ca] concentration range encountered in the cancer patients. pH, temperature and ionic strength are constant as described in Section IV.

Note particularly the slope of 0.47. **In other words, the ionized calcium values observed in the cancer patients were almost exactly those expected if we had simply added calcium to normal serum in a test tube.** The presumed significance of this will be noted below.

D. RELATION OF TOTAL CALCIUM TO [Alb] AND [CaProt]

The relation between serum total calcium and albumin levels in the hypercalcemia of malignancy is shown in Figure 38. Data from normal

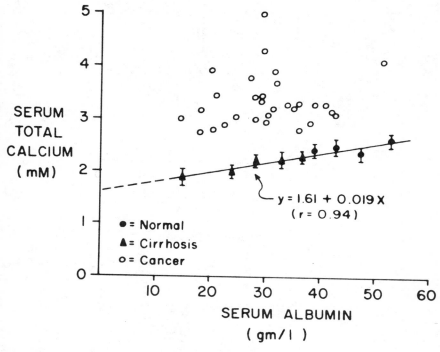

Figure 38.   Relationship between serum total calcium and albumin concentrations in 30 studies of 24 patients with cancer and hypercalcemia. Note that there is no strong correlation, in contrast to findings in normals and patients with cirrhosis. Data for the latter 2 groups are from Figure 28.

subjects and patients with cirrhosis (Fig. 28) are also shown for comparison. In contrast to the latter groups, there was no strong correlation between [Ca] and [Alb]. This, in itself, suggests the possibility of significant binding to serum globulins in cancer.

Another striking difference in these patients was the relation of protein-bound calcium to serum albumin level. As noted in Figures 32 and 35, serum total calcium was significantly increased while serum albumin was significantly reduced in the cancer patients. Thus, it was not surprising to find that, in comparison with normals, a given [CaProt] level in cancer was achieved at a higher total calcium level. This is indicated in Figure 39, in which the curve for cancer patients was displaced to the right. Also, it is evident from Figure 39 that, in contrast with normals and also cirrhotics (Fig. 29), change in serum total calcium was not accounted for by corresponding change in [CaProt]. The lower slope (0.44) for cancer patients in Figure 39 reflects the fact that there was also a proportionate increase in ionized calcium (Fig. 37). Clearly, we are dealing with a problem quite different from that in cirrhotics.

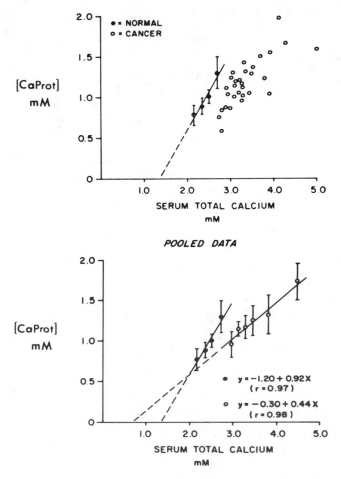

Figure 39. Relationship between protein-bound calcium [CaProt] and serum [Ca] concentrations in 21 normal subjects and 30 studies of 24 patients with cancer and hypercalcemia. The pooled data for normals are from Figure 29. Note that the curve for hypercalcemia cancer patients, with reduced serum albumin levels, is displaced to the right with a slope less than half that observed in normals.

E. FRACTIONATION OF [CaProt]

This difference is further illustrated in Figure 40, in which [CaProt] is given as a function of serum albumin. The previous data from normal subjects are shown again for comparison. In contrast to cirrhotics, in whom there was a strong linear relationship with an intercept of about zero and a slope nearly identical to that in normals (Fig. 27), we find no strong correlation in the cancer patients. The slope was apparently less than normal and there was a sizable intercept on the vertical axis, suggesting that these patients may have a substantial fraction of protein-bound calcium in the globulin fraction. If this were the case, the slope of the function would not tell us anything about that fraction bound to albumin because, as it so happens, serum albumin and globulin were inversely related in these patients.

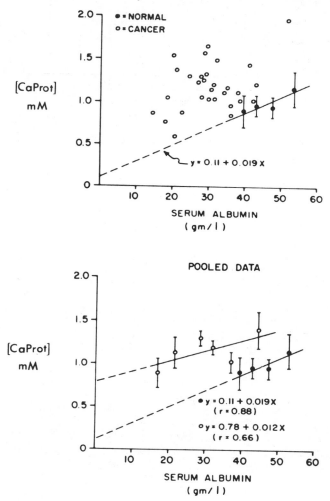

Figure 40. Relationship between protein-bound calcium [CaProt] and serum albumin concentrations in 30 studies of 24 patients with cancer and hypercalcemia. Normal data from Figure 27 are shown for comparison. Note the lack of a strong correlation among the cancer patients. The pooled-data function below suggests that a significant fraction of protein-bound calcium is in the globulin fraction.

How, then, can one tell how much is bound to albumin and how much to globulin? Studies in the past [22] with fractionated serum proteins have suggested that albumin normally accounts for about 80% of the protein-bound calcium, while globulins account for the remaining 20%. But is this the case *in vivo* and particularly in cancer patients? (As noted above, Figure 28, our data in normals would suggest that about 11 percent of [CaProt] is in the globulin fraction).

An estimate of the relative binding to albumin and globulin was obtained as follows: Let the observed [CaProt] concentration at any given total calcium and albumin level represent the sum of calcium albuminate and calcium globulinate:

$$[CaProt] = [CaAlb] + [CaGlob] \tag{21}$$

Both [CaAlb] and [CaGlob] are unknown. Albumin and globulin levels are known, however, and at any given calcium level Equation (21) may be rewritten with two new unknowns, x and z:

$$[CaProt] = x[Alb] + z[Glob] \tag{22}$$

where [Alb] and [Glob] are in g/l and:

$$x = \frac{[CaAlb]}{[Alb]} \; (mM/g) \tag{23a}$$

$$z = \frac{[CaGlob]}{[Glob]} \; (mM/g) \tag{23b}$$

Rearrangement of Equation (22) yields:

$$\frac{[CaProt]}{[Alb]} = x + z\frac{[Glob]}{[Alb]} \tag{24}$$

If x and z are constant, a plot of $\dfrac{[CaProt]}{[Alb]}$ against $\dfrac{[Glob]}{[Alb]}$ should yield a straight line with intercept and slope equal to the albumin (x) and globulin (z) binding constants, respectively.

The observed relationship was indeed linear, as shown in Figure 41. Individual data are shown on the top; on the bottom the data were pooled by increments in the [Glob]/[Alb] ratio in an effort to obtain the best estimates of the functions.

In normals, the intercept indicated that, on the average, 0.0167mM calcium was bound to each gram of albumin, while the slope indicated that less than half as much was bound to each gram of globulin, 0.0079mM/g. In cancer patients, at higher total and ionized calcium levels, the respective constants were 0.0256mM/g and 0.0133mM/g, respectively. Comparison of respective intercept and slope values for the two groups sug-

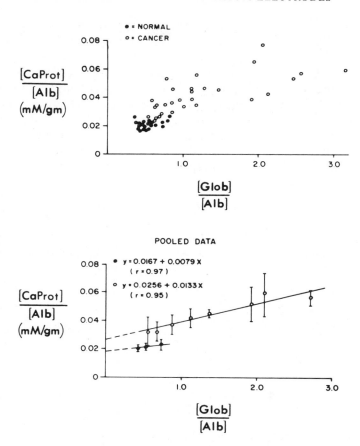

Figure 41.   Plots of Equation (24) for estimation of albumin and globulin binding-constants as described in the text. Intercept values on the bottom indicate that in normals and cancer patients, respectively, an average of 0.0167mM and 0.0256mM calcium were bound to each gram of albumin. Slope values indicate that in normals and cancer patients, respectively, an average of 0.0079mM and 0.0133mM calcium were bound to each gram of globulin.

gests that the values in the cancer patients are about those predicted from the mass-law equation at the higher Ca^{++} levels present in these patients.

Having obtained the necessary constants, and knowing the albumin and globulin levels in each subject, the relative binding of albumin and globulin is readily calculated. Thus, in normals:

$$[CaAlb] = 0.0167 \ [Alb] \qquad [CaGlob] = 0.0079 \ [Glob] \qquad (25a)$$

$$[Alb]_{\bar{x}} = 47.3 \ g/l \qquad [Glob]_{\bar{x}} = 25.0 \ g/l \qquad (25b)$$

$$[CaAlb]_{\bar{x}} = 0.79 \ mM \qquad [CaGlob]_{\bar{x}} = 0.20 \ mM \qquad (25c)$$

and calculated mean [CaProt] was: $(0.79 + 0.20) = 0.99$mM. The latter value is in close agreement with the observed mean [CaProt] value of 1.00mM (Fig. 32).

Similar calculations in the cancer patients, in whom there was significant reduction in albumin and significant increase in globulin concentrations (Fig. 35), yielded mean [CaAlb] and [CaGlob] levels of 0.78mM and 0.44mM respectively. Their sum, 1.22mM, was also close to the mean observed [CaProt] concentration of 1.18mM (Fig. 32).

As summarized in Figure 42, our data in normals indicate that about 81 percent, calculated for each individual subject, of protein-bound calcium is bound to albumin and about 19 percent to globulins. These values are very close to those estimated by Neuman and Neuman [22], and are the reason that [CaAlb] was assumed to equal 80 percent of [CaProt] in Section IV above.

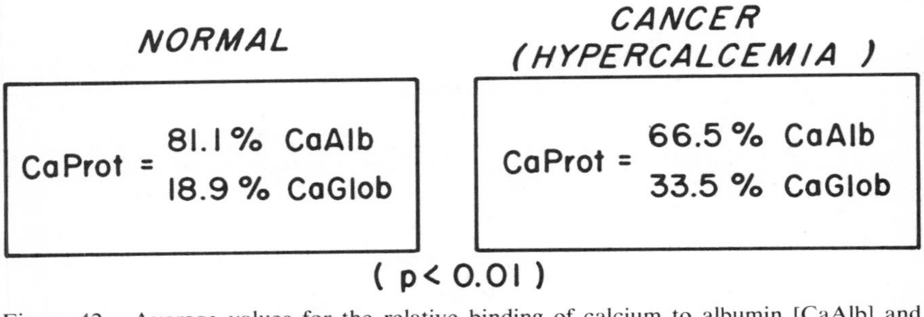

NORMAL

$$CaProt = \frac{81.1\% \ CaAlb}{18.9\% \ CaGlob}$$

CANCER (HYPERCALCEMIA)

$$CaProt = \frac{66.5\% \ CaAlb}{33.5\% \ CaGlob}$$

(p< 0.01)

Figure 42.   Average values for the relative binding of calcium to albumin [CaAlb] and globulin [CaGlob] in 21 normal subjects and 30 studies of 24 patients with cancer and hypercalcemia. Values were derived from data obtained in Figure 41.

In the cancer patients, the calculated percentage for calcium albuminate was 66.5 percent, significantly ($p < 0.01$) less than in normals, while calcium globulinate accounted for 33.5 percent of [CaProt], significantly higher than in normals ($p < 0.01$). These values for cancer patients are in sharp contrast to the findings in cirrhotics. Thus, while both groups of patients had almost identical albumin and globulin levels (Figs. 25 and 35), cirrhotic patients showed no detectable binding of calcium to serum globulins (Fig. 27). It would therefore appear that there are important qualitative differences in the serum globulins of these two groups of patients. This problem is still under study.

Since the above calculations in normals were based on a regression consisting of only 3 points (Fig. 41), an effort was made to check on the validity of the calculated [CaAlb] value [0.79mM, Eq. (25c)]: mean K'_{CaAlb} for the normals was calculated from Equation (10):

$$K'_{CaAlb} = \frac{[Ca^{++}](n[Alb] - [CaAlb])}{[CaAlb]} \tag{10}$$

Assuming that the molecular weight of albumin is 69,000 and n = 8.4 (Fig. 18), substitution of:

$$[Ca^{++}]_{\bar{x}} = 1.16mM \qquad \text{(Figs. 23 and 33)}$$

$$[Alb]_{\bar{x}} = 47.3 \, g/l \qquad \text{(Fig. 35)}$$

$$[CaAlb]_{\bar{x}} = 0.79mM \qquad \text{(Eq. 25c)}$$

for the 21 normal subjects yielded a mean K'_{CaAlb} value of 7.29×10^{-3} (p$K = 2.14$). This is in close agreement with the value (p$K' = 2.18$) obtained in Figure 18 upon addition of calcium to normal serum *in vitro*, suggesting that the values obtained in Figure 41 for normals are reasonably accurate.

F. SUMMARY

From these data, a model (Fig. 43) has been constructed for serum total calcium and each of the three calcium fractions: $[Ca^{++}]$, $[CaProt]$ and $[CaR]$ for both normals and patients with malignancy and hypercalcemia.

In normals, serum total calcium varied from about 2.25-2.75mM (95% confidence interval). Regardless of the serum total calcium, serum ionized calcium was maintained at about 1.16mM. Mean $[CaR]$ was also essentially constant at about 0.3mM. Variation in total calcium was almost entirely accounted for by corresponding variation in protein-bound calcium. Of this, about 80 percent was bound to albumin and 20 percent to globulins.

In sharp contrast, in patients with malignancy and hypercalcemia, increase in serum total calcium was accompanied by a progressive rise in ionized calcium at a constant fractional rate representing 45 percent of the total. This fraction was similar to that observed in normal subjects *in vivo* (Fig. 12) and upon addition of calcium to normal serum *in vitro* (Fig. 37). Both $[CaProt]$ and $[CaR]$ were significantly increased in absolute terms. $[CaProt]$ increased with increasing total calcium at a constant fractional rate of about 44 percent (Fig. 39). Of the $[CaProt]$, that fraction bound to globulin was increased in both absolute and relative terms, while the relative binding to albumin was significantly reduced to about 66 percent of the $[CaProt]$ level. The latter finding is in marked contrast to cirrhotic patients with comparable levels of albumin and globulin.

In these cancer patients, it would appear that the circulation has been presented with an excessive calcium load and that the resulting distribution in serum is that predicted physicochemically. Since the distribution of calcium in serum is subject to several variables, it may prove rather difficult to extrapolate from the regressions established for the group to the individual patient. Nevertheless, our data appear compatible with the be-

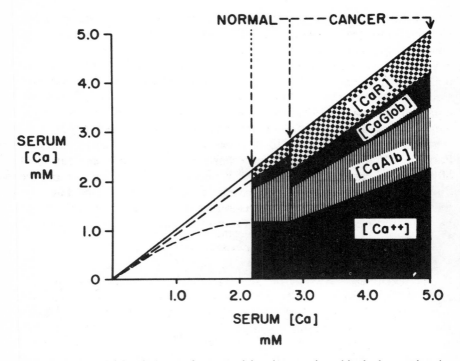

Figure 43.   A model for the state of serum calcium in normals and in the hypercalcemia
of malignancy.

lief [68] that the hypercalcemia may be the result of excessive parathor-
mone-like material in at least some of these patients.

IX. Summary

An attempt has been made in this chapter to summarize some of our
studies with ion-exchange calcium electrodes and to develop a reasonably
coherent thesis concerning some of the complex physicochemical factors
governing serum calcium in man. From data obtained in various aqueous
salt solutions, in sera and in ultrafiltrates, models have been developed for
the state of serum calcium in normals, in patients with cirrhosis, and in the
hypercalcemia of malignancy. The binding of calcium to the serum
proteins has been found to obey the mass-law equation and a dissection
of the relative contributions of albumin and globulin has been achieved by
a simple regression analysis apparently not recognized previously.

There is no doubt that these electrodes can provide very high quality
data in many biologic systems. Space has not permitted a discussion of all
the types of studies which have been made. The development of a Ca^{++}
activity scale by Bates (Chapter 6) is an important advance in the applica-

tion of these electrodes to many biological problems. It is anticipated that meaningful thermodynamic data will soon be forthcoming concerning calcium transport across various biologic membranes.

While these electrodes are by no means perfected—they can be quite frustrating at times—it should be remembered that ion-exchange electrode technology is still in its infancy. Further improvements will undoubtedly enhance their general usefulness. On-line monitoring, for example, is quite feasible today and telemetering cannot be far behind.

Should it prove possible to develop suitable Ca^{++} microelectrodes, Pandora's Box will become so large that physiologists may not come out of it in this century. In any case, it seems clear that we are on the threshold of a bright new era in the field of calcium metabolism. The electrode, coupled with recent advances in peptide chemistry and immunology, will greatly enhance our present understanding of calcium metabolism.

X. Acknowledgment

This work was supported by U. S. Public Health Service research grants AM-07417, AM-10307 and AM-13357, by Training Grant No. AM-05424, National Institute of Arthritis and Metabolic Diseases, and by Research Career Development Award K3-GM-11-386, National Institute of General Medical Sciences, U.S. Public Health Service. The author is indebted to Dr. James W. Ross, Jr., for his assistance in electrode fabrication and many helpful suggestions, to I. Rasmusen, L. Anderson, S. Lee, S. Sullivan and D. Alvarez for their able technical assistance, to Mr. B. T. O'Neil for his assistance with the illustrations, and to Miss C. Benjamin for her able secretarial assistance. The efforts of several colleagues who participated in some of these studies are also gratefully acknowledged: Dr. Joel Jacknow, Dr. Andre Blum, Dr. Carlos Guzzo and Dr. Roger Dawkins.

XI. References

[1] Moore, E. W., in Glass Electrodes for Hydrogen and Other Cations: Principles and Practice, G. Eisenman, Ed., Marcel Dekker, New York, 1967, p. 412.
[2] Moore, E. W., in Bioelectrodes, W. Feder, Ed., Ann. N. Y. Acad. Sci. 148: Art. 1, 93 (1968).
[3] McLean, F. C. and Hastings, A. B., J. Biol. Chem. 107, 337 (1934).
[4] McLean, F. C. and Hastings, A. B., J. Biol. Chem. 108, 285 (1935).
[5] McLean, F. C. and Hastings, A. B., Amer. J. Med. Sci. 189, 601 (1935).
[6] Ross, J. W., Jr., Science 156, 1378 (1967).
[7] Fosbinder, R. I., J. Amer. Chem. Soc. 51, 1345 (1929).
[8] Joseph, N. R., J. Biol. Chem. 126, 389 (1938).
[9] Greenberg, D. M., in Advances in Protein Chemistry, Vol. I, M. L. Anson and J. T. Esdall, Eds., Academic Press, New York, 1944, p. 121.
[10] Sollner, K., J. Amer. Chem. Soc. 65, 2260 (1943).
[11] Abrams, I. M. and Sollner, K., J. Gen. Physiol. 26, 369 (1943).
[12] Sollner, K. and Neihof, R. A., Arch. Biochem. Biophys 33, 166 (1951).

[13] Gregor, H. P. and Sollner, K., J. Amer. Chem. Soc. **58**, 409 (1954).
[14] Carr, C. W., in Electrochemistry in Biology and Medicine, T. Shedlovsky, Ed., John Wiley and Sons, New York, 1955, p. 266.
[15] Gregor, H. P. and Schonhorn, H., J. Amer. Chem. Soc. **79**, 1507 (1957); ibid., **81**, 3911 (1959); ibid., **83**, 3576 (1961).
[16] Eisenman, G., Rudin, D.O., and Casby, J. U., Science **126**, 831 (1957).
[17] Truesdell, A. H. and Christ, C. L., in Glass Electrodes for Hydrogen and Other Cations: Principles and Practice, G. Eisenman, Ed., Marcel Dekker, New York, 1967, p. 293.
[18] Raaflaub, J., Z. Physiol. Chem. Hoppe-Seylers **288**, 228 (1951).
[19] Rose, G. A., Clin. Chim. Acta **2**, 227 (1957).
[20] Walser, M., Anal. Chem. **32**, 711 (1960).
[21] Walser, M., J. Clin. Invest. **40**, 723 (1961).
[22] Neuman, W. F. and Neuman, M. W., The Chemical Dynamics of Bone Mineral, Univ. of Chicago Press, Chicago, 1958, p. 12, pp. 1-38.
[23] Copp, H. D., in Advances in Internal Medicine, Vol. XIV, I. Snapper and G. H. Stollerman, Eds., Year Book Medical Publishers, Chicago, 1968, p. 55.
[24] Albright, F. and Reifenstein, E. C., The Parathyroid Glands and Metabolic Bone Disease, Williams and Wilkins, Baltimore, 1948.
[25] Nordin, B. E. C. and Smith, D. A., Diagnostic Procedures in Disorders of Calcium Metabolism, Little, Brown, Boston, 1965.
[26] Fourman, P. and Royer, P., Calcium Metabolism and The Bone, Blackwell Scientific Publications, Oxford, 1968.
[27] Rona, P. and Takahashi, D., Biochem. Z. **31**, 336 (1911).
[28] Marrack, J. and Thacker, G., Biochem. J. **20**, 580 (1926).
[29] Watchorn, E. and McCance, R. A., Biochem. J. **26**, 54 (1932).
[30] Greenberg, D. M. and Gunther, L., J. Biol. Chem. **85**, 491 (1930).
[31] Nicholas, H. O., J. Biol. Chem. **97**, 457 (1932).
[32] Dillman, L. M. and Visscher, M. B., J. Biol. Chem. **103**, 791 (1933).
[33] Morison, R. S., McLean, R., and Jackson, E. B., J. Biol. Chem. **122**, 439 (1937).
[34] Hopkins, T., Howard, J. E., and Eisenberg, H., Bull. Johns Hopkins Hosp. **91**, 1 (1952).
[35] Toribara, T. Y., Terepka, A. R., and Dewey, P. A., J. Clin. Invest. **36**, 738 (1957).
[36] Walser, M., J. Cell. Comp. Physiol. **55**, 245 (1960).
[37] Loken, H. F., Havel, R. J., Gordan, G. S., and Whittington, S. L., J. Biol. Chem. **235**, 3654 (1960).
[38] Prasad, A. S. and Flink, E. B., J. Lab. Clin. Med. **51**, 345 (1958).
[39] Prasad, A. S., A.M.A. Arch. Int. Med. **105**, 560 (1960).
[40] Breen, M. and Freeman, S., Clin. Chim. Acta **6**, 181(1961).
[41] Moore, E. W. and Makhlouf, G. M., Gastroenterology **55**, 465 (1968).
[42] Moore, E. W. and Ross, J. W., Jr., J. Appl. Physiol. **20**, 1332 (1965).
[43] Harned, H. S. and Owen, B. B., The Physical Chemistry of Electrolytic Solutions, Reinhold, New York, 1963, p. 595.
[44] Klotz, I. M., Chemical Thermodynamics, Prentice-Hall, Englewood Cliffs, N. J., 1950, p. 329.
[45] Robinson, R. A. and Stokes, R. H., Electrolyte Solutions, Butterworth, London, 1959, p. 438.
[46] Bachra, B. N., Dauer, A., and Sobel, A. E., Clin. Chem. **4**, 107(1958).
[47] Gornall, A. C., Bardavill, C. J., and David, M. M., J. Biol. Chem. **177**, 751 (1949).
[48] Moore, E. W., J. Clin. Invest. **45**, 1047 (1966) (Abstract).
[49] Sillén, L. G. and Martell, A. E., Stability Constants of Metal-Ion Complexes, Special Publication No. 17, The Chemical Society, London, 1964, p. 478.

[50] Fanconi, A. and Rose, G. A., Quart. J. Med. **27**, 463 (1958).
[51] Nakayama, F. S. and Rasnick, B. A., Anal. Chem. **39**, 1022 (1967).
[52] Garrels, R. M., in Glass Electrodes for Hydrogen and Other Cations:Principles and Practice, G. Eisenman, Ed., Marcel Dekker, New York, 1967, p. 349.
[53] Bates, R. G., Determination of pH, John Wiley and Sons, New York, 1964, p. 275.
[54] Moore, E. W. and Wilson, D. W., J. Clin. Invest. **42**, 293 (1963).
[55] Yendt, E. R., Connor, T. B., and Howard, J. E., Bull. Johns Hopkins Hosp. **96**, 1 (1955).
[56] Ettori, J. and Scoggan, S. M., Nature **184**, 1315 (1959).
[57] Scatchard, G., Ann. N. Y. Acad. Sci. **51**, 660 (1949).
[58] Klotz, I. M., Arch. Biochem. **9**, 109 (1946).
[59] Katz, S. and Klotz, I. M., Arch. Biochem. **44**, 351 (1953).
[60] Tanford, C., Physical Chemistry of Macromolecules, John Wiley and Sons, New York, 1961, pp. 526-586.
[61] Schultze, H. E. and Heremans, J. F., Molecular Biology of Human Proteins, Elsevier, Amsterdam, 1966, p. 182.
[62] Moore, E. W. and Blum, A. L., J. Clin. Invest. **47**, 70a (1968) (Abstract).
[63] Ruch, T. C. and Patton, H. D., Physiology and Biophysics, W. B. Saunders, Philadelphia, 1965, p. 943.
[64] Held, D., Fencl, V., and Pappenheimer, J. R., Fed. Proc. **22**, 332 (1963)(Abstract).
[65] Dawkins, R. L. and Moore, E. W., Clin. Res. **17**, 283 (1969) (Abstract).
[66] Tashjian, A. H., Jr., Levine, L., and Munson, P. L., Endocrinology **74**, 244 (1964).
[67] Moore, E. W., presented in part before The Gastroenterological Research Forum, American Gastroenterological Association, Washington, D. C., May 1969; (Abstract), Gastroenterology (in press).
[68] Bower, B. F. and Gordan, G. S., Ann. Rev. of Medicine **16**, 83 (1965).

CHAPTER 8

ION-SELECTIVE ELECTRODES IN BIOMEDICAL RESEARCH

Raja N. Khuri

Department of Physiology
American University of Beirut
Beirut, Lebanon

I. Potentiometry in Biological Systems

Potentiometry consists of the measurement of the electromotive force of a galvanic cell (composed of two half-cells). Direct analytical potentiometry has been widely applied in the measurement of ionic activities of many ionic species of a wide variety of biological systems. The determination of ion activity by the electrometric method offers some special advantages over such methods as colorimetric analysis, flame photometric analysis, compleximetric and other chemical methods in the measurement of ions in biological systems.

The indicator half-cell consists of an ion-selective electrode predominantly sensitive to a specific ion species, the so-called primary ion in question. The fact that ion-selective electrodes measure ion activities rather than concentrations is not a disadvantage in biological work, since biological phenomena are functions of ionic activities rather than concentrations. The measurement of ionic activity is all the more significant because ion-complexing and ion-association phenomena are common in biological systems. Ion-sensitive electrodes can be adapted for continuous *in situ* measurements [1,2] which is superior to the intermittent sampling techniques that the other methods employ. The most unique advantage of ion-sensitive electrodes is their ability to perform a direct measurement of ionic activity in a biological system *in situ*. This applies to both the macro and microscales. The latter, microelectrode analysis, is a field of great importance in fundamental biological research.

Biological systems are quite complex. Although water is the principal biological solvent, the aqueous media of living systems are mixed electrolyte solutions that often contain colloidal polyelectrolytes. Even the microscopic units of structure and function, the single cells, are not homogeneous and consist of several distinct phases.

A. MIXED ELECTROLYTE SOLUTIONS

Biologic aqueous solutions are not simple solutions but usually consist of a mixture of several salts. Mixed ionic solutions require highly selec-

287

tive electrodes to measure a specific ion in question in the presence of all other ions. Only electrodes of pH-sensitive glasses fully meet this requirement.

Sodium and potassium are two prevalent cations in many biologic solutions. The potential of a cell incorporating Na^+-sensitive glass electrode NAS_{11-18} may be described by the following equation:

$$E_{Na} = E^\circ_{Na} + RT/F \ln \left[(Na^+) + k_{Na-H}(H^+) + k_{Na-K}(K^+) \right] \qquad (1)$$

where R, T and F are the gas constant per mole, the temperature in degree Kelvin, and the Faraday constant, respectively. E_{Na} is the measured potential and E°_{Na} the standard potential of the sodium electrode. (Na^+) is the activity of the sodium ion. The selectivity constants of the glass electrode to H^+ and K^+ ions relative to Na^+ ion are k_{Na-H} and k_{Na-K}. Electrodes of NAS_{11-18} glass yield values of $k_{Na-H} \approx 10$ and k_{Na-K} of 0.01-0.001. Thus, in neutral mammalian extracellular fluid with a K^+ concentration of $5 \times 10^{-3}M$ the sodium glass electrode is essentially sensitive to the Na^+ ion only and Equation (1) reduces to:

$$E_{Na} = E^\circ_{Na} + RT/F \ln (Na^+) \qquad (2)$$

The so-called "cation-sensitive" glasses are characterized by a selectivity order:

$$H^+ > K^+ > Na^+ \text{--------} >> Ca^{++}$$

In neutral biologic fluids electrodes of these glasses have a predominant selectivity for the K^+ ion and the electrode potential may be described by the following equation:

$$E_K = E^\circ_K + RT/F \ln \left[(K^+) + k_{K-Na}(Na^+) \right] \qquad (3)$$

Such an electrode is sensitive to both K^+ and Na^+ ions. When a "cation-sensitive" electrode is paired with a sodium-sensitive electrode. the potential of the galvanic cell composed of the two glass electrodes is obtained by subtracting the half-cell Equation (2) from (3):

$$E_{K-Na} = E^\circ_{K-Na} + RT/F \ln \left[\frac{(K^+) + k_{K-Na}(Na^+)}{(Na^+)} \right] \qquad (4)$$

The two-glass electrode cell described by Equation (4) measures a concentration ratio since the activity coefficients cancel out in the ratio. Garrels [3] used the K-Na glass electrode cell for measuring these cations in sea water. Friedman, et al. [1] used the all-glass cell to monitor the cations in blood. Khuri, et al. [4,5] and Lev [6,7] used the pair of Na and K-glass microelectrodes in biological research. The all-glass cell employed by Khuri, *et al.* is shown in Figure 1. The use of a pair of two glass electrodes with different selectivity constants is a useful technique in

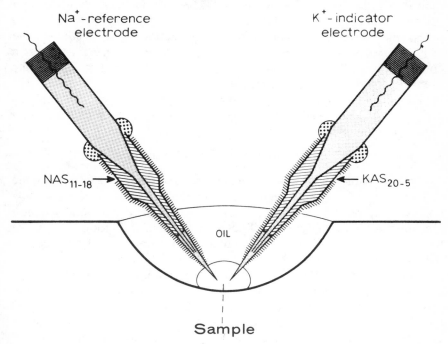

Figure 1.   K+ microelectrode – Na+ microelectrode cell (for K/Na measurement).

studies of mixed electrolytes. It is a cell without a liquid-liquid junction. There is no leakage of salt-bridge electrolyte into the test sample, and as stated above, the method may be independent of activity coefficients. In solutions of mixed salts, one can under certain conditions speak of "mixed" activity coefficient for a mixture of two salts with a common anion. The concentration of uni-univalent salts in mammalian body fluids is about 150 mM, a value which is well above what is generally regarded as dilute solutions. This is one of the factors that contributes to the differences between ionic activities and concentrations in biologic solutions.

B. COLLOIDAL SOLUTIONS

Biologic solutions contain variable but significant amounts of colloidal polyelectrolytes. Protein constitutes the major organic polyelectrolyte. Mammalian plasma has 6-7 g protein/100 ml (referred to as g%), while the intracellular protein varies over a wide range (8-36 g%). The intracellular protein is in the form of a colloidal suspension. At the physiologic pH of their respective media, both the intracellular and the extracellular proteins are anionic and may potentially possess cation exchange properties. The cation exchange properties of protoplasmic polyelectrolytes and their role in the distribution of Na^+ and K^+ across cell membranes has not been elucidated.

Ion-selective electrodes are useful analytical tools for the study of the protein binding of ions. However, protein poisoning of electrodes is a common problem which is particularly serious in the case of the metallic electrodes and the oxidation-reduction electrodes. Glass electrodes are in general less susceptible to protein poisoning, but to avoid developing a protein coat on the electrode it is advisable to rinse the probe promptly with a buffer standard.

C. THE LIQUID JUNCTION POTENTIAL

The liquid junction potential exists at the junction of two different ionic solutions. A junction between two dissimilar electrolyte solutions is made up of a mixture of ions in the process of traversing the boundary. If the ions migrate with different mobilities, a spatial ionic separation results. In the steady-state this chemical gradient across the boundary is balanced by the liquid junction potential.

In practical potentiometric analysis, the liquid junction exists between the salt bridge component of the reference half-cell and the calibrating standard or test sample. Bates [8] emphasized that it is the "residual liquid junction potential" which is significant. This is the difference between the potential at the salt bridge — standard junction and the potential at the salt bridge — test solution junction. The magnitude of the liquid junction potential is often very difficult or even impossible to determine. Thus it is a major uncertainty in potentiometric analysis since the value of the residual liquid junction contributes to the apparent ionic activity of the species in question.

There are several factors which affect the liquid junction potential. The first is the geometry of the junction itself. In biological work the most widely used reference half-cell is one that incorporates a KCl-filled Ling and Gerard [9] micropipette for a salt bridge. Although KCl will diffuse into the tissue or test sample, the flow of salt bridge electrolyte is highly restricted by the very small caliber of the tip of the micropipette. To prevent the flow of concentrated KCl resulting from hydrostatic forces, one of several approaches may be undertaken. The simplest would be to maintain the salt bridge micropipette in the horizontal position. Another would be to dissolve the KCl in 1-2% agar and fill the micropipette with the hot agar. This serves both to eliminate the hydrostatic forces on the aqueous phase as well as to impede the diffusion of KCl in the viscous agar. A third technique consists of dipping an already filled internal capillary microelectrode in the salt bridge solution in the same manner as the

Radiometer pH cell reported by Siggaard-Andersen [10]. The tip of the KCl-filled micropipette often picks up organic matter following tissue penetration. This may alter the tip potential and necessitates recalibration of the cell. The author [11] mounts the reference micropipette into a holder shown in Figure 2 after the design of Grundfest, *et al.* [12]. This micropipette holder allows the injection of KCl solution through the tip following each tissue penetration. Thus a stable potential may be maintained at the tip, a fresh junction being reformed each time by the KCl injection.

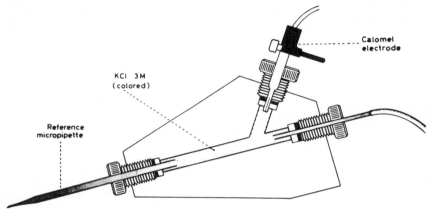

Figure 2.   Reference micropipette holder with injecting mechanism.

Of the factors that affect the residual liquid junction potential, a radical change in ionic strength or pH of the solutions should be avoided. In biological work these may be avoided by maintaining the pH and the ionic strength of the standards close to the values of the unknowns in question.

The salt bridge solution itself certainly affects the potential that arises at the junction between itself and the buffered standards or the unknown solution. Concentrated KCl, $3M$ or saturated ($4.2M$), is the most widely used. The choice of KCl is based on the fact that the ionic mobilities of potassium and chloride are practically identical, thus minimizing the liquid junction potential. In addition, a small junction potential is favored by maintaining a salt bridge of high concentration in contact with the test sample. For $3M$ KCl the concentration ratio of the salt bridge/mammalian extracellular fluid is about 200. Biological investigators have substituted other salt bridges for the conventional concentrated KCl in order to avoid contamination with KCl or the effect of KCl on proteins. Semple [13] using a $0.152M$ NaCl salt bridge, found that it yielded a blood pH which was on the average 0.11 pH units lower than the pH obtained with a cell incorporating a concentrated KCl bridge. This difference probably represents a significant residual liquid junction potential that arises on substituting NaCl for the equitransferent KCl. Khuri, *et al.* [14] used an equilibrium diffusate of plasma as a salt bridge for blood pH determinations. Except for the Donnan effect, the boundary that the colloid-free plasma salt bridge forms with its own plasma is probably characterized by equivalent ion migration in both directions.

In an attempt to eliminate the liquid junction potential, Khuri and Merril [15] performed a potentiometric study and found the blood pH measured by a cell, which utilizes a sodium glass electrode as a reference to the pH glass electrode (does not incorporate a liquid-liquid junction), to be identical with the pH measured with a saturated KCl salt bridge. This suggests that concentrated KCl minimizes the liquid junction potential in blood as in simple solutions.

D. BIOLOGIC STANDARDS

It is often advisable that biomedical workers prepare their own standards for potentiometric analyses. In general, the standards used for calibrating the galvanic cell are prepared by reliable gravimetric and volumetric methods. Ideally, a measurement by a non-potentiometric method is both useful and of some comparative value.

For the calibration of pH-sensitive electrodes, for blood pH determinations, Khuri and Merril [15] used buffer standards containing 140 mM NaCl in 5 mM Tris(hydroxymethyl-amino-methane) titrated with HCl to various pH values around neutrality. These buffers were initially and repeatedly calibrated against three National Bureau of Standards buffers whose pH values at 25 °C are 4.008, 6.865 and 7.413. The saline buffers have an ionic strength, a composition, and pH values that are not very dissimilar from the plasma being measured. By bracketing the biologic unknown samples with such biologic standards, the residual liquid junction potential may be minimized and the response time in going from standard to unknown may be favorably reduced.

Standards for the calibration of ion-selective electrodes should be buffered to a constant and neutral pH. This is particularly important in the case of Na-glass and K-glass electrodes which are more sensitive to H$^+$ than to either Na$^+$ or K$^+$ ions.

The performance of several types of electrodes may be improved by storage or conditioning in calibrating standards or dilute solutions of their primary ion. Following the exposure of ion-selective electrodes to solutions rich in protein or after their use *in vivo*, the electrodes should be promptly rinsed and washed with appropriate calibrating standards.

The entire electrode cell assembly should be maintained at constant temperature. Also, the measurements of standards and unknowns should be carried out at the same temperature. For *in vitro* studies, all measurements could be carried out at room temperature or any arbitrary temperature which does not undergo significant fluctuations. But when undertaking potentiometric work *in vivo*, where body temperature is maintained at a constant value (37-38 °C in warm-blooded animals), the electrometric cell and the calibrating standards must be maintained at body temperature.

E. "BIOELECTRODES"

Cellular membranes made up of anionic lipo-proteins often exhibit cation exchange properties. Mueller and Rudin [16] studied the cation exchange properties of the valinomycin membrane, a bimolecular phospholipid membrane, and found it to be predominantly selective for K^+ among the group Ia cations.

In studies of the electrical potential of biological membranes and their passive permeabilities to the cations, Ussing [17] concluded that the outward-facing membrane of the frog skin has a greater passive permeability for Na^+ than for K^+. The inside membrane of the frog skin behaved as a potassium electrode, *i.e.*, the membrane electrical potential difference was solely determined by the K^+ ion concentration bathing it. Similarly, the outside membrane behaved as a sodium electrode. The transepithelial electrical potential difference may be simulated to two cation electrodes in series. In contrast, Giebisch [18] found that both the luminal and peritubular cell boundaries of the proximal tubular epithelium of Necturus kidney are depolarized by elevation of the K^+ ion concentration. A slope in excess of 50 mV for a decade change in potassium concentration was observed. Thus in the renal epithelium, both boundaries exhibit high K^+ selectivity and behave as potassium electrodes. Hodgkin, *et al.* [19,20] have shown that the resting potential across single muscle and nerve fibers when plotted against the external concentration of potassium exhibit a Nernstian response over a significant range of K^+ concentration. Thus, the plasma membrane of single muscle and nerve fibers exhibit potassium electrode behavior.

II. *In Vitro vs. In Vivo*

Ion-selective electrodes have been widely used to measure ion activities in biologic media both *in vitro* and *in vivo*. Both applications have utilized the full spectrum of electrode size from the macro to the ultramicro. The demarcation between the macro and the microscales is quite arbitrary. For our purposes, we shall define the upper limit of the microscale by the volume of an average aqueous drop, 50 μl or an even smaller volume of 10 μl may be chosen.

Potentiometric analysis at the microscale brings up special problems and requires special precautions. The field of ion-selective microelectrodes has been reviewed by several workers [21,23].

A. POTENTIOMETRIC MEASUREMENTS *In Vitro*

Innumerable studies have been performed using macro and micro ion-selective electrodes *in vitro*. Microelectrode analysis *in vitro* is advantageous over other methods in that it does not require the measurement of a micro volume and its subsequent dilution, both of which are potential sources of error. One potential source of error is the contamination of a small test sample by the leakage of salt bridge solution. This may be minimized by using a conventional micropipette reference with a tip diameter of less than 1 micrometer (μm). However, the tip potential and resistance of micropipettes with tips less than 1 μm in diameter may be high.

The Radiometer thermostated pH capillary glass electrode reported by Siggaard-Andersen [10] is widely used in biomedical laboratories for pH measurement of biologic samples. The cell measures pH on a 25 μl sample of capillary blood with a standard deviation of $\pm$ 0.006 pH units.

Intracellular protein extracts and desoxyribonucleic acids have been studied for their cation binding properties *in vitro* using Na^+ selective and K^+ selective glass electrodes. A variety of biologic solutions and tissues have been studied with various types of ion-selective electrodes to measure ion species of physiologic or clinical interest. Innumerable potentiometric measurements were made on plasma and serum to determine the ionic activities of H^+, Na^+, K^+, Ca^{++}, F^- and I^-. Measurements have been made on cerebrospinal fluid and urine for H^+, Na^+, K^+, and Ca^{++} ionic activities. Gastric juice has been analyzed for H^+, Cl^- and more recently Ca^{++} ions. Recently, both saliva and mineralized tissues have been studied with calcium and fluoride electrodes. The above-listed applications will be discussed individually in Section III.

B. POTENTIOMETRIC MEASUREMENTS *In Vivo*

Ion-selective electrodes have been adapted to biological measurements *in vivo* on both a macro and a microscale. Perhaps the most unique advantage of ion-selective electrodes is their capacity to monitor ion activities *in vivo* or *in situ*.

Biological systems, even at the microscopic level, are quite complex and heterogeneous. The geometry is usually not simple; the architecture quite intricate. The colloidal polyelectrolytes and the enzymes of tissues may occupy rather fixed sites. Our knowledge of the *in situ* intracellular ionic strength, osmotic pressure and the state of water itself is both scanty and very uncertain. Without a reliable knowledge of the *in situ* pH, the charge on the organic polyelectrolytes cannot be ascertained. Ion-binding by the colloidal polyelectrolytes is pH dependent. The local *in situ* carbon dioxide pressure is another element of uncertainty. The latter is one of the factors that determine the local pH.

Although several uncertainties are involved in the *in vitro* determinations of ionic activities of biological systems in general, these uncertainties become even more serious in the case of pH measurement. This is due to the fact that a major biologic buffer has a gaseous component, *i.e.*, CO_2. The measurement of pH *in situ* is advantageous in that it eliminates the uncertainty involved in the arbitrary choice of a CO_2 pressure with which to equilibrate the test samples. It also avoids the loss of CO_2 to the ambient air.

1. Extracellular Analyses

Friedman [24] has classified biologic systems into flowing and non-flowing systems depending on whether or not the medium is static or exhibits hydrodynamic flow.

In extracellular potentiometric analyses of non-flowing biologic systems, the shape of the indicator ion-selective electrode may be tailored to its mode of use *in situ*. For surface measurements, the electrode may have a flat, convex or concave surface depending on the curvature of the tissue under study. The spear shape is naturally suited for depth penetration. An important consideration in extracellular ion monitoring *in situ* is the response time of the ion-selective electrode. The electrode response time should be short so that changes due to metabolic alterations may be picked up promptly.

In situ monitoring of extracellular ionic activities has been applied to a number of non-flowing biologic systems. The ionic activities of H^+, Na^+, K^+, Ca^{++}, Cl^- and F^- have been measured with ion-sensitive electrodes. Extracellular measurements *in situ* were performed in cerebrospinal fluid and on the brain surface, skeletal muscle, aqueous humor, the lumen of the stomach and gall bladder.

In potentiometric analyses of flowing extracellular biologic systems, the pioneering work was done by Friedman, *et al.* [1-2,24,25]. Although it is elegant to monitor continuously the activity of various ions in a circulating fluid, the method should be carefully screened for artifacts arising from streaming potentials and electrode response time. In this case the streaming potential is the change in the electrode potential attributed to the flow of the electrolyte solution. Friedman, *et al.* [1] attributed the changing streaming potential to a change in the composition of the liquid junction of the salt bridge of the reference half-cell. They advise the maintenance of a constant flow rate to avoid these fluctuations. Friedman and coworkers used flow-through or cannula electrodes of sodium and potassium glasses to measure the cationic activities in flowing arterial blood of the rat [26] and the dog [27]. Rechnitz [28] has emphasized the critical importance of the electrode response time in ion monitoring in flowing systems. Certainly the electrode response time must be fast enough and should not itself be the rate-limiting step of the system.

In the nephrons of the kidney, the pre-urine flows through tubules of microscopic caliber. Several authors [4,11,29-31] have measured the pH or cation activities of the luminal fluid of single proximal tubules *in situ*. Figure 3 shows an indicator and a reference microelectrode localized

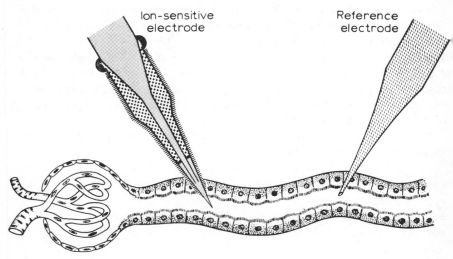

Figure 3.   An indicator and a reference microelectrode in the lumen of proximal tubule.

within the lumen of a kidney tubule. Vieira and Malnic [31] used an antimony microelectrode to measure the pH of tubular fluid *in situ*. The other workers [11,29,30] used pH glass microelectrodes. Khuri, *et al.* [4], used microelectrodes of the Na⁺-sensitive glass NAS_{11-18} to measure Na⁺ activity *in situ* in the circulating blood, glomerular fluid and proximal tubular fluid of the Necturus kidney. The reference micropipette was filled with $3M$ RbCl. The latter was selected as a salt bridge instead of the usual KCl because of the extremely low sensitivity of Na-glass to Rb⁺ ion.

2.   Intracellular Analyses

There has been a growing interest in intracellular ion analyses *in situ* with microelectrodes ever since the pioneering work of Caldwell [32,33]. Hinke [34,35] was the first to use sodium and potassium sensitive glass microelectrodes to measure intracellular ionic activities. Following these two investigators, there were several studies reported in which H⁺, Na⁺, K⁺, Cl⁻ were measured in the protoplasm of single fibers of nerve, muscle and the alga Nitella.

Knowledge of intracellular ion activities is vital to our understanding of many of the important phenomena in cellular physiology. The determination of intracellular ionic activity by means of an ion-selective microelectrode, if coupled with a separate determination of the total amount of the ion species in question, could yield useful information about ion-binding by the organic polyelectrolytes. Hinke and McLaughlin [36] found that, whereas K was essentially free in the myoplasm, a significant part of intracellular Na is bound. Lev [37] found that 70% of the intracellular Na content of the amphibian skeletal muscle is bound. In the squid axon, Hinke [35] concluded that 25% of the intracellular Na is bound whereas the K is essentially free. The Na and K activity gradients across the membrane of the squid axon as determined by cation-selective glass microelectrodes by Hinke [35] are compatible with the generally accepted theory of active and resting membrane potentials.

Intracellular pH has been measured in different cells by several authors using pH glass microelectrodes. Intracellular pH was measured by Caldwell [32,33] in crab muscle and the giant axon of the squid, by Kostyuk and Sorokina [38] in frog sartorius muscle, by Lavallee [39] in cardiac muscle, and Carter [40] in rat voluntary muscle. The intracellular pH observed ranged from 6.8-7.1, a value which is not compatible with a Donnan equilibrium distribution of H^+ across cell membranes. The observed values of intracellular pH by the above workers suggests that there is an independent mechanism within the cells which regulates the intracellular pH and maintains its stability at a level of H^+ ion activity which is lower than would be predicted from the Donnan equilibrium. But more recently, Carter, et al. [41] have found an intracellular pH of 6.0 in the skeletal muscle of rats and they concluded that the H^+ gradient across the cell membrane was in electrochemical equilibrium at all levels of the membrane potential.

There are a number of difficulties that plague intracellular analyses using ion-selective microelectrodes. The first relates to the indicator microelectrode and the major problem there is one of effective insulation of all the probe except for the highly restricted sensitive tip. Paint insulation and glass insulation are the two major insulation techniques generally used.

Technically, one has a choice between having two separate microelectrode half-cells or combining the ion-selective microelectrode and its reference into one physical unit. Having the cell as a single unit, although technically more difficult, is advantageous in intracellular ion analyses. The cell membrane is impaled at a single point and thus leakage is minimized. Also, the electrical potential difference across the cell membrane can be measured simultaneously and in the same cell whose intracellular ionic activity is being measured. Thus one can simultaneously correlate trans-membrane ionic activity gradients with the trans-membrane electrical potential difference. The latter may be obtained by recording the potential difference between an intracellular reference half-cell and a similar half-cell located in the extracellular space. If the potential of a cell is measured when the reference half-cell is in an extracellular location, one should subtract from the above the value of the membrane potential in order to get the potential which is a measure of intracellular ion activity.

The Ling and Gerard [9] KCl-filled micropipette represents a miniaturized salt bridge component of the reference half-cell. A source of great uncertainty is the liquid junction potential between the KCl-filled micropipette tip and the intracellular medium. In the first place, our knowledge of intracellular ionic activities and ionic strength is quite scanty and uncertain. Secondly, the anionic intracellular polyelectrolytes may selectively alter the ionic mobilities of the normally equitransferent KCl bridge electrolyte. Thus the residual liquid junction potential, *i.e.*, the difference between its value in extracellular and intracellular media, is unknown and may well be significant. In the latter case, the magnitude of the residual liquid junction potential is incorporated in the value of the intracellular ion activity or the membrane potential we measure.

III. Biomedical Applications

A. Glass Electrodes

Glass electrodes for hydrogen and other cations constitute a potent analytical tool for cation analyses in biological systems. For an extensive review of the subject the reader is advised to consult references [21,22,24]. The pH function of some glasses was discovered quite early in this century. But it was only a decade ago that Eisenman [42-44] began his pioneering studies that resulted in the development of glass electrodes sensitive to ions of the group Ia cation series.

The special advantages of the glass membrane in direct potentiometric analyses in living systems is that it is insensitive to oxidation-reduction reactions, not greatly affected by proteins, and as such indifferent to anions in general. Glass is a highly workable material. Glass gradually and continuously softens (decreasing viscosity) under progressive heating. This accounts for the easy workability of the glassy material into a wide variety of shapes, forms and sizes.

Ion-sensitive glass membranes are anionic and function as cation exchangers. The sensitive portion of the indicator glass electrode is normally a continuous membrane bathed internally by a stable reference solution. The external or measuring surface of the glass electrode is the critical variable of the system whose cation exchange reactions with standard and unknown solutions determine the change in the measured potential. The ion-sensitive glass membrane must be optimally hydrated to give a Nernstian response. Dryness results in poor electrode function while overhydration may dissolve a thin glass membrane. Glass electrodes may undergo hysteresis when immersed successively in solutions of widely varying composition. For that, it is advisable to frequently calibrate ion-sensitive glass electrodes with standards that are not too dissimilar from the unknown with respect to ionic strength, composition and pH values.

Although the ion-sensitive membrane of the glass electrode must be a continuous and sealed structure, there has recently been several reports of so-called incompletely sealed micropipette electrodes exhibiting ionic selectivity and Nernstian response. Lavallee [39] found that open-tip micropipettes (tip diameter <1 μm) of Corning code 0150 glass had a pH sensitivity of about 30 mV/pH unit when used against similarly filled Pyrex micropipettes. These cells yielded an intracellular pH of 6.9 in isolated rat atria. Lev [45] studied the electrochemical characteristics of the incompletely sealed cation sensitive microelectrodes. He observed that irrespective of whether the glass is primarily Na^+-sensitive or K^+-sensitive, the resulting incompletely sealed micropipette is K^+-sensitive. This he attributed to a K^+-selective anionic pore at the micropipette tip. These microelectrodes were 8-9 times more selective to K^+ as compared to Na^+ ions and had a sensitivity of about 57 mV/pK unit.

Ling [46], by coating Corning code 0150 glass with collodion, obtained electrodes of different selectivity orders depending on the manner in which collodion was treated. Gotoh, et al. [47] used a K^+-selective collodion-coated glass to measure ion activity from the surface of the brain in situ.

Glass electrodes sensitive to the divalent cations Ca^{++} and Mg^{++} were described by Garrels, et al. [48] but have not been applied, to our knowledge, in biomedical work. This is partly due to their not being sufficiently selective to Ca^{++} over the other divalent cations (Mg^{++}) and the monovalent cations (Na^+).

The three types of glass electrodes that have been used in biomedical work are those for hydrogen (pH), sodium, and potassium ions.

1. Hydrogen Glass Electrodes

Among ion-selective glass electrodes, the pH glasses are sufficiently selective to H^+ ion relative to the other cations that they can be regarded as pure and ideal electrodes. Both Na^+ and K^+ glass electrodes are essentially "mixed" electrodes. Measurements of pH in situ are to be preferred whenever feasible. This will avoid CO_2 loss to the ambient air. For measurement of pH in biological systems pH glass electrodes are favored over metallic or quinhydrone electrodes since the latter are sensitive to oxidation-reduction reactions and readily poisoned by proteins. For in *situ* pH measurement, the probe must be made as small as possible since tissue damage may increase the local acidity. Two general configurations of pH glass electrodes are used: (1) the external probe (spear-shaped, bulb), (2) the internal capillary. In the internal capillary configuration, the sample or standard is taken up into the capillary lumen while the external surface serves as the reference side. For pH determinations the internal capillary geometry is preferred since the internal location of the sample guards against gaseous (CO_2) exchanges with the environment.

Dubuisson [49-51] used a flat membrane pH glass electrode *in situ* to monitor the extracellular pH changes during contraction and relaxation of skeletal muscle. A ring device served to isolate only a film of extracellular fluid between the electrode membrane and the muscle surface. This film was assumed to be in equilibrium with the underlying muscle. Following contraction pH changes, probably mediated by CO_2 exchanges, occurred in less than a second. These changes could be picked up since the electrode response time was only a fraction of a second [51]. Sonnenschein, *et al.* [52] constructed and used spear-shaped pH electrodes for depth measurements of the pH of the brain *in situ*. More recently, Meyer, *et al.* [53,54] introduced small pH probes into the brain of cats and monkeys and monitored pH changes of the brain under different metabolic conditions. Intracellular pH studies [32,33,38-41] were discussed in Section II-B-2.

The kidney plays an important role in the acid-base balance of the living organism. Normally, the kidney excretes the excess acids of metabolism in order to regulate and maintain a constant pH in blood and other body fluids. To study the renal handling of H^+, it is important to measure the *in vivo* pH in single renal nephrons (see Fig. 3).

Figure 4 shows a micropipette type of pH glass electrode (Corning code 0150) which is insulated by mineral oil internally and by polystyrene

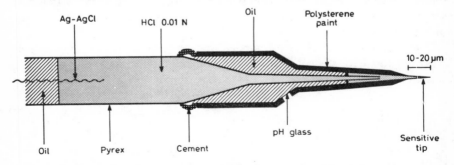

Figure 4.   pH glass microelectrode with external insulation.

paint externally. This indicator electrode was used against the reference with the injecting mechanism (Fig. 2) in the manner represented by Figure 3 to measure the *in vivo* intraluminal pH in the proximal tubule of the rat kidney [11]. A mean intraluminal pH of 7.22 ± 0.03 (standard error) was obtained. Rector, *et al.* [30] using glaze-insulated pH glass microelectrodes found in the proximal tubule of the rat kidney a mean intraluminal pH of 6.82 ± 0.13.

As mentioned earlier, the internal capillary configuration of glass electrodes has some distinct advantages particularly for pH determination. Other factors which contribute to the superior electrode function of the internal capillary configuration are the large area-to-volume ratio, the small asymmetry potential and the probability that in the drawing process the inner surface of a fine capillary is less subject to direct flame exposure than the outer surface.

Figure 5 shows an internal capillary pH microelectrode in combination with the reference half-cell to form a single unit. This cell, developed by

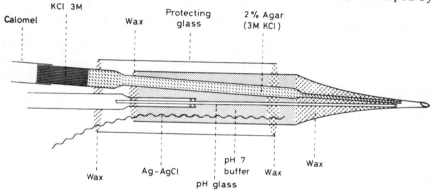

Figure 5. Single unit pH glass ultra-microelectrode.

Khuri, *et al.* [55], measures the pH of a sample of less than 0.05 μl in volume and is particularly suited for *in vivo* applications [29]. In Figure 6 [56] the internal pH glass capillary (C-0150) was fused to a micropipette of an inert glass (C-0120) by means of a glass-to-glass seal. In view of their similar softening points and thermal expansion coefficients, the ion-sensitive and insensitive glasses fuse readily. The electrode shown in Figure 6 can measure the pH of samples of fluid as small as 0.01 μl in volume. The internal capillary pH microelectrodes shown in Figures 5 and 6 were used by Khuri, *et al.* [29] to measure the intraluminal pH at different points along the length of the proximal tubules of rat kidneys *in vivo*. The results revealed that the intraluminal pH falls as the tubular fluid flows down the length of the proximal convoluted tubule. A significant inverse relationship was indicated by a correlation coefficient, $R = -0.92$.

To study the bicarbonate ion profile in the proximal tubule, Khuri, *et al.* [29] used the pH glass capillary microelectrode (Fig. 6) in the

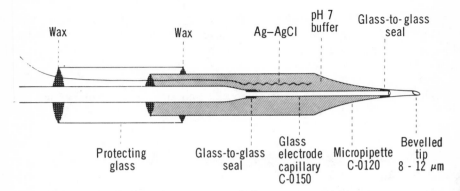

Figure 6. Glass ultra-microelectrodes, internal capillary type, glass-to-glass seal, for measurement of pH.

gas-equilibration chamber (Fig. 7) to measure samples of tubular fluid *in vitro*. The covering oil is equilibrated with a gas mixture having a known percentage of CO_2. At the time when the pH of an equilibrated sample of tubular fluid is measured, the partial pressure of CO_2 (pCO_2) of the equilibrated oil is determined by a Severinghaus CO_2 electrode. From these data one can readily calculate the bicarbonate concentration of tu-

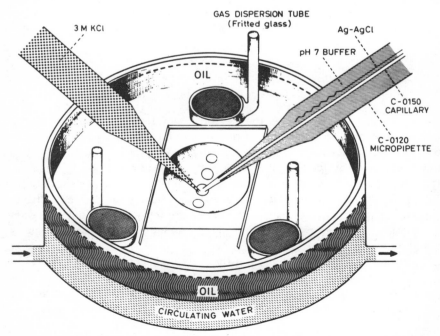

Figure 7. Lucite chamber for bicarbonate measurement of micro-samples with thermal and gas equilibrating mechanisms.

bular fluid. As with the pH studies, there was a definite tendency for the bicarbonate concentration to fall as the fluid moved distally along the length of the proximal tubule. The above illustrates that in dealing with a solution whose major buffer is the bicarbonate-carbonic acid buffer, if the CO_2 pressure is known and constant, then pH glass electrodes could be used *in vitro* to measure the bicarbonate ion concentration.

2. Sodium Glass Electrodes

The sodium alumino-silicate glass NAS_{11-18} of Eisenman [42] has been widely used for making Na^+-selective electrodes. The sodium electrode glasses have the following selectivity order: $Ag^+ > H^+ > Na^+ >> K^+$, Li^+, $--- >> Ca^{++}$. Although Na^+-selective electrodes are mixed electrodes, in the neutral, high sodium, low potassium biological systems like plasma, the electrode responds essentially to Na^+. The NAS_{11-18} sodium glass has selectivity ratios $k_{Na-K} \approx 0.005$, $k_{Na-H} \approx 10$. It is not sensitive to a change in pH above a pH of 5.5. Still, it is a good practice to maintain a constant pH in the sodium standards with buffers.

Gotoh, *et al.* [47] used Na^+-sensitive electrodes (NAS_{11-18}) to monitor Na^+ activity of the monkey's brain and blood *in vivo* simultaneously. They observed changes in the extracellular Na^+ activities of the brain which correlated with changes of the metabolic activity of the cortex. Portnoy, *et al.* [57] carried out similar studies on the brain of the cat *in situ*. Moore and Wilson [58] by determining sodium in human serum with both sodium electrodes and flame photometry, found no evidence for sodium binding in normal human serum. In a similar study of the state of sodium in bile, Moore and Dietschy [59] concluded that sodium is bound to the micelle structures. Sekelj and Goldbloom [60] applied Na glass electrodes to the skin as a rapid screening and diagnostic test for cystic fibrosis of the pancreas, a disease appearing at birth and characterized by an elevated Na^+ and Cl^- concentrations in sweat. In studies with Na^+ glass microelectrodes, Hinke [35] concluded that 25% of the intracellular Na of the squid axon is bound while Lev [37] found 70% of the intracellular Na of muscle to be bound.

The concentric cation glass microelectrode in Figure 8 was constructed by Khuri, *et al.* [4,5] of either the Na^+-glass NAS_{11-18} or the K^+-glass KAS_{20-5}. It is insulated internally with mineral oil and externally with polystyrene. When it was used *in vitro*, as shown in Figure 9, only the sensitive area of the cation electrode was introduced into the aqueous droplet. This afforded further external insulation of the shank by the mineral oil of the lucite well. RbCl ($3M$) was used instead of the usual KCl in the reference bridge because NAS_{11-18} glass is 100 times less sensitive to Rb^+ than to K^+ ions. Using the sodium cell of Figure 9 *in vitro*

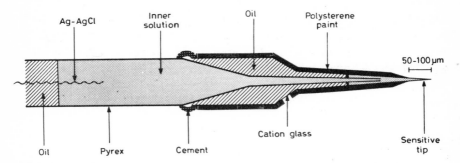

Figure 8. Concentric cation glass microelectrode with external insulation.

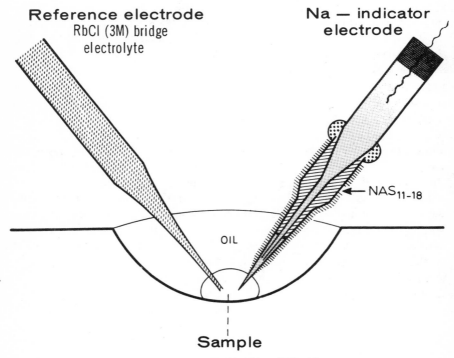

Figure 9. Na⁺ microelectrode — RbCl (3*M*) cell (for Na⁺ measurement).

and *in vivo* as represented in Figure 3, the Na⁺ activity of serum, glomerular fluid, and proximal tubular fluid were essentially the same in Necturus [4].

3. *Potassium Glass Electrodes*

The potassium-selective glasses like KAS_{20-5} and NAS_{27-4} are only 10 times more sensitive to K⁺ than to Na⁺ ions. The K⁺-glasses have the following selectivity order: $H^+ > K^+ > Na^+ --- >> Ca^{++}$. These are, therefore, truly "mixed" electrodes. In plasma the concentration ratio of Na^+/K^+ is 35-40. Having at best a K:Na selectivity of 10:1, a separate measurement of Na^+ concentration is needed to obtain the K^+ concentration. Therefore, using a Na-glass reference against the K-glass electrode (see Fig. 1), Khuri, *et al.* [4,5] did not increase the steps involved in the potentiometric determination of K^+. Besides the rationale for the use of the K-Na all-glass cell presented in Section I-A, no salt bridge could be identified to which the K-glass was sufficiently insensitive.

Using the all-glass cell (Fig. 1) and the sodium cell (Fig. 9) in succession, Khuri, *et al.* [4,5] measured K^+ in proximal tubular fluid and plasma in Necturus and the rat. A mean concentration ratio of potassium in tubular fluid/glomerular fluid of 1.8 ± 0.1 was obtained in Necturus. This contrasts with the mean potassium concentration ratio of tubular fluid/plasma of 0.70 ± 0.03 obtained in the rat.

K^+-sensitive glass electrodes were used by Gotoh, *et al.* [47] and Portnoy, *et al.* [57] to monitor K^+ activity of the brain of experimental animals *in vivo*. Gotoh, *et al.* [47] used a collodion-coated C-0150 glass after the design of Ling [46] to measure K^+ activity.

In intracellular applications of K^+-sensitive microelectrodes, Lev [7] and Hinke and McLaughlin [36] found that K^+ is essentially free in the myoplasm. Hinke [35] reached a similar conclusion in studies of the squid axon.

Figure 10 shows a cation sensitive electrode with the internal capillary configuration. Microcapillaries of the sodium electrode glass NAS_{11-18} fuse readily with Corning C-1720, whereas the potassium glass KAS_{20-5} fuses with C-0080. In Table 1, the soft point and the coefficient of thermal expansion of the pH, sodium and potassium electrode glasses are tabulated along with those of the inactive glasses with which they readily fuse.

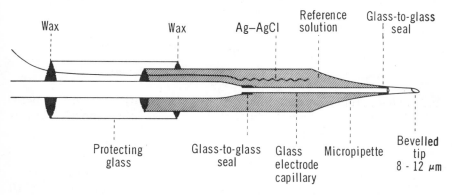

Figure 10.   Glass ultra-microelectrode, internal capillary type, glass-to-glass seal.

Table 1. Some thermal properties of the electrode and "inert" glass pairs that account for their readiness to fuse together.[a]

Glass		Soft point °C	Thermal expansion 10^{-7} in/in/°C
pH electrode:	Corning 0150	655	110
	Corning 0120	630	89
Na$^+$ electrode:	NAS$_{11-18}$	> 970	53
	Corning 1720	915	42
K$^+$ electrode:	KAS$_{20-5}$	796	102
	Corning 0080	695	92

[a] Tabulated values are quoted from Dr. N. C. Hebert, Corning Glass Works, Corning, New York.

B. NON-GLASS ELECTRODES

1. Metallic Electrodes

There are several subgroups of metallic electrodes:

a. A metal in contact with a solution having an ion of that metal. These are referred to as electrodes of the "first kind" like Ag|Ag$^+$ (| designates solid-solution interface).

b. A metal coated with a sparingly soluble salt of that metal. This has been referred to as an electrode of the "second kind." An example of this group is Ag/Ag$^+$Cl$^-$ (or Ag/AgCl) which is a Cl$^-$ reversible electrode.

c. Metal amalgams like the amalgam electrodes for sodium and other cations.

In general, metal electrodes are poorly suited for potentiometric analyses of biological systems. The metal ions may poison a living system, and some biological constituents like proteins may poison metallic electrodes. Also, metallic electrodes are quite sensitive to the oxidation-reduction reactions that are prevalent in living systems.

The silver-silver chloride (Ag/AgCl) electrode is reversible to chloride. It is most widely used as a metallic internal reference element for the measuring and reference electrodes. Hansen, *et al.* [61] used Ag/AgCl electrodes to measure the chloride concentration in sweat by placing the electrochemical cell on the skin surface. Infants suffering from cystic fibrosis had a higher Cl^- concentration in sweat than normal infants. $Ag/AgCl$ electrodes have been used to measure Cl^- in various biologic solutions. Several workers have used $Ag/AgCl$ electrodes to measure intracellular Cl^- activity although it is known that protoplasm has constituents that are capable of reducing the silver ion. Also protein constituents may adsorb on the $Ag/AgCl$. Intracellular Cl^- was measured with $Ag/AgCl$ microelectrodes in the giant axon by Mauro [62] and Strickholm, et al. [63]. Hinke and McLaughlin [36], in an intracellular microelectrode study of the barnacle muscle, concluded that a significant fraction of the fiber's Cl^- and Na^+ are bound to constituents of the myoplasm, as opposed to the K^+ ion which is free.

The antimony electrode (antimony/antimony oxide) is a metallic electrode sensitive to H^+ ion. Antimony electrodes were used to measure the in situ pH of dental tissues by Thompson and Brudevald [64,65]. Kurella and coworkers [66,67] used antimony microelectrodes to measure the intracellular pH of large plant cells. Recently, Vieira and Malnic [31] used antimony microelectrodes to measure the intraluminal pH of proximal tubules of the rat kidney. However, in all these applications one should keep in mind that antimony could be oxidized by oxygen, that antimony oxide may be reduced by the protoplasmic reducing agents and that the electrode may be poisoned by proteins.

2. Oxidation-Reduction Electrodes

The quinhydrone electrode represents this class. Its reaction involves the reversible oxidation-reduction of the hydroquinone – quinone system. It is of limited biological usefulness as an electrode for measuring pH in view of its sensitivity to amino-acids, proteins and oxidation-reduction reactions. For about forty years the quinhydrone electrode has been used in the measurement of pH of several biologic fluids [68,69].

In 1935, Pierce and Montgomery [70] described the technique of constructing micro-quinhydrone electrodes and used their electrodes to study the site of acidification within the renal tubule of amphibia [71]. Several renal physiologists [72,73] subsequently utilized micro-quinhydrone electrodes to measure pH in vivo in single renal nephrons.

3. Ion-Exchange Membrane Electrodes

This represents a new class of ion-selective electrodes. A number of the electrodes of this class are "mixed" electrodes with relatively low selectivity. The two major subgroups of this class are the solid-state and the liquid membrane electrodes.

a. Solid-State Membranes. These are further subdivided into the crystalline membrane electrodes and the precipitate-impregnated (heterogeneous) membrane electrodes.

The crystalline membrane electrodes have a sensitive membrane sectioned from a single inorganic crystal of low solubility characteristics. Electrodes sensitive to the halides F^-, Cl^-, Br^-, and I^- have been developed by Orion Research, Inc. Of this group, the fluoride electrode of Frant and Ross [74] has received a great deal of interest in view of the biologic and medical importance of fluoride. The sensitive portion of the electrode is a small flat crystalline membrane. The fluoride electrode exhibits a Nernstian response over a wide range of fluoride activity. It is highly selective with a F^-:Cl^- selectivity of more than 10^6:1. Hydroxide ion, the only interference, does not present a problem in the near-neutral biologic systems. Fluoride ion activities have been determined with the Orion fluoride electrode in serum, mineralized tissue, saliva and in pharmaceutical pastes, mouthwashes, and vitamins.

Durst and Taylor [75] modified the fluoride electrode for microchemical analysis. By using the crystalline fluoride-sensitive membrane as a cup to contain the sample, the electrode was rendered capable of measuring F^- activity on samples as small as 10 μl in volume.

Taves [76] made a comparative study, determining serum fluoride ion concentration with the fluoride-electrode and with other methods. Concentration of the serum and isolation of the F^- by diffusion was essential since normal levels of serum F^- are in the range where the electrode response begins to be uncertain. He found the fluorescent method rather superior to the colorimetric method. Because of the hysteresis that the electrode exhibits when subjected to extremes in F^- concentration over a short span, Taves advises bracketing the unknown closely with standards. In another study of serum fluoride utilizing the fluoride-electrode and the morin-thorium reagent, Taves [77] obtained results which are consistent with the hypothesis that there are two forms of fluoride in human serum, an exchangeable and a non-exchangeable moeity.

Singer and Armstrong [78] determined fluoride in bone using the fluoride electrode. The bone was ashed and the latter dissolved in an aqueous solution of constant pH and ionic strength. The mean fluoride content obtained by the electrode was in close agreement with the value obtained by a chemical method. McCann [79] using the Orion electrode determined fluoride activity in enamel, dentine, bone and apatite and found the values to be in good agreement with the colorimetric method.

Gron, et al. [80] determined fluoride in human saliva with the fluoride electrode. Since the electrode is almost equally sensitive to F^- and OH^-, it is advantageous to acidify the saliva. Using a recovery technique, Gron, et al. found no evidence for F^- complexes in saliva. Saliva was noted to.

be a poor source of fluoride. They observed higher F^- salivary values after repeated ingestion of NaF. This was attributed to an overflow of F^- following the saturation of skeletal sites.

Aasenden, et al. [81] studied the effect of oral topical treatments with F^- solutions on salivary fluoride. Following such treatment, salivary F^- was elevated for over a day. Following the routine use of fluoride-containing toothpaste, the salivary F^- remained elevated for about 3 hours. The decay characteristics of the increment in salivary F^- can be described by a simple exponential. The protracted elevation of salivary F^- after a topical application was attributed to leaching of F^- from the treated teeth.

Shane and Miele [82] measured F^- in toothpastes with the fluoride electrode. Toothpaste was converted into an aqueous mixture for the F^- determination. Fluoride ion was detected in toothpastes in the range of 0.22% as NaF and 0.40% as SnF_2.

The precipitate-impregnated membrane electrodes consist of poorly soluble inorganic salts precipitated in the matrix of an inert membrane. The resulting membrane is a heterogeneous one, having a precipitate phase and an inert phase. These electrodes are insensitive to oxidation-reduction reactions and not as vulnerable to protein poisioning as the metallic electrodes. The precipitate-impregnated membrane electrodes currently available are selective for I^-, Br^-, and Cl^-. Arino and Kramer [83] used an iodide electrode consisting of a silicone rubber membrane impregnated with AgI to measure the activity of iodide in iodinated proteins.

b. Liquid-Liquid Membrane Electrodes. The ion-exchanger in this group is in the liquid state. Being organic the liquid ion exchanger is hardly miscible with water. The design that is currently being followed with these electrodes is to hold the organic liquid ion exchanger within the framework of a porous membrane. Using liquid anionic exchangers, electrodes selective to Cl^- and NO_3^- have been developed. However, it is the Orion calcium electrode which occupies the position of prominence among this group. The liquid ion exchange electrode with a favorable Ca^{++} selectivity became available through the pioneering work of Ross [84]. The calcium electrode is highly selective for Ca^{++} over Mg^{++}. Its sensitivity for the group Ia monovalent cations is even lower than for Mg^{++}. The only significant source of interference is H^+ ion to which the electrode is 10^4 times more selective. For this reason alkalinization of the solutions may be in order in some studies. The electrode response time is less than 30 seconds.

Perris and Whitfield [85] used the Orion calcium electrode to study the influence of Ca^{++} activity on mitosis. They observed that mitotic activity is affected by the level of ionized calcium in the cellular environment.

Woodward and Davidson [86] utilized a specific calcium electrode to study the Ca^{++}-binding ability of the protein polysaccharides of cartilage. The stoichiometry of the binding process suggests that each calcium ion is bound by two separate sulfate groups of the polysaccharide chains. The protein polysaccharides of cartilage were found to chelate Ca^{++} ions very effectively.

IV. References

[1] Friedman, S. M., Jamieson, J. D., Nakashima, M., and Friedman, C. L., Science 130, 1252 (1959).
[2] Friedman, S. M., and Friedman, C. L., Anat. Rec. 138, 129 (1960).
[3] Garrels, R. M., in Glass Electrodes for Hydrogen and Other Cations, G. Eisenman, Ed., Marcel Dekker, New York, 1967, pp. 344-361.
[4] Khuri, R. N., Goldstein, D. A., Maude, D. L., Edmonds, C., and Solomon, A. K., Amer. J. Physiol. 204, 743 (1963).
[5] Khuri, R. N., Flanigan, W. J., and Oken, D. E., J. Appl. Physiol. 21, 1568 (1966).
[6] Lev, A. A., Biophysica 9, 686 (1964).
[7] Lev, A. A., Nature 201, 1132 (1964).
[8] Bates, R. G., Determination of pH; Theory and Practice, Chap. 3, John Wiley and Sons, New York, 1964.
[9] Ling, G. N., and Gerard, R. W., J. Cell. Comp. Physiol. 34, 382(1949).
[10] Siggaard-Andersen, O., Scand. J. Clin. Lab. Invest., Suppl. 15, 70 (1963).
[11] Khuri, R. N., Rev. Sci. Instrum. 39, 730 (1968).
[12] Grundfest, H., Kao, C. Y., and Altamirano, M., J. Gen. Physiol. 38, 245 (1954).
[13] Semple, S. J. G., J. Appl. Physiol. 16, 576 (1961).
[14] Khuri, R. N., Agulian, S. K. and Harik, R. I., Phys. Med. Biol. 13, 23 (1968).
[15] Khuri, R. N., and Merril, C. R., Phys. Med. Biol. 9, 541 (1964).
[16] Mueller, P., and Rudin, D. O., Biochem. Biophys. Res. Commun. 26, 398(1967).
[17] Ussing, H. H., J. Gen. Physiol. 43, 135 (1960).
[18] Giebisch, G., J. Gen. Physiol. 44, 659 (1961).
[19] Hodgkin, A. L., and Horowicz, P., J. Physiol. 153, 370 (1960).
[20] Hodgkin, A. L., and Keynes, R. D., J. Physiol. 128, 61 (1955).
[21] Hinke, J. A. M., in Glass Electrodes for Hydrogen and Other Cations, G. Eisenman, Ed., Marcel Dekker, Inc., New York, 1967, pp. 464-477.
[22] Khuri, R. N., in Glass Electrodes for Hydrogen and Other Cations, G. Eisenman, Ed., Marcel Dekker, Inc., New York, 1967, ppp. 478-518.
[23] Lavallee, M., Schanne, O., and Hebert, N., Eds., Intracellular Glass Microelectrodes, John Wiley and Sons, Inc., New York (in press-1969).
[24] Friedman, S. M., in Glass Electrodes for Hydrogen and Other Cations, G. Eisenman, Ed., Marcel Dekker, Inc., New York, 1967, p. 443.
[25] Friedman, S. M., Meth. Biochem. Anal. 10, 71 (1962).
[26] Friedman, S. M., Jamieson, J. D., Hinke, J. A. M., and Friedman, C. L., Proc. Soc. Exptl. Biol. Med. 99, 727 (1958).
[27] Friedman, S. M., Jamieson, J. D., Hinke, J. A. M., and Friedman, C.L., Amer. J. Physiol. 196, 1049 (1959).
[28] Rechnitz, G. A., in Glass Electrodes for Hydrogen and Other Cations, G. Eisenman, Ed., Marcel Dekker, Inc., New York, 1967, pp. 335-339.
[29] Khuri, R. N., and Agulian, S. K., Proc. Intl. Union Physiol. Sciences 7, 236 (1968).
[30] Rector, F. C., Carter, N. W., and Seldin, D. W., J. Clin. Invest. 44, 278 (1965).

[31] Vieira, F. L., and Malnic, G., Amer. J. Physiol. 214, 710 (1968).
[32] Caldwell, P. C., J. Physiol. 126, 169 (1954).
[33] Caldwell, P. C., J. Physiol. 142, 22 (1958).
[34] Hinke, J. A. M., Nature 184, 1257 (1959).
[35] Hinke, J. A. M., J. Physiol. 156, 314 (1961).
[36] Hinke, J. A. M., and McLaughlin, S. G. A., Can. J. Physiol. Pharm. 45, 655 (1967).
[37] Lev, A. A., Nature 201, 1132 (1964).
[38] Kostyuk, P. G., and Sorokina, Z. A., Membrane Transport and Metabolism, A. Kleinzeller and A. Kotyk, Eds., Academic Press, New York, 1961, pp. 193-203.
[39] Lavallee, M., Circ. Res. 15, 185 (1964).
[40] Carter, N. W., Clin. Res. 9, 177(1961).
[41] Carter, N. W., Rector, F. C., Campion, D. S., and Seldin, D. W., J. Clin. Invest. 46, 920 (1967).
[42] Eisenman, G., Rudin, D. O., and Casby, J. U., Science 126, 831 (1957).
[43] Eisenman, G., Biophys. J. 2, 259 (1962).
[44] Eisenman, G., Advances in Analytical Chemistry and Instrumentation, Vol. 4, C. N. Reilley, Ed., Wiley-Interscience, New York, 1965.
[45] Lev, A. A., in Intracellular Glass Microelectrodes, M. Lavallee, O. Schanne, and N. Hebert, Eds., John Wiley and Sons, Inc., New York (in press-1969).
[46] Ling, G. N., J. Gen. Physiol. 43, 149 (1960).
[47] Gotoh, F., Tazaki, Y., Hamaguchi, K., and Meyer, J. S., J. Neurochem. 9, 81 (1962).
[48] Garrels, R. M., Sato, M., Thompson, M. E., Truesdell, A. H., Science 135, 1045 (1962).
[49] Dubuisson, M., J. Physiol. 90, 47P (1937).
[50] Dubuisson, M., J. Physiol 94, 461 (1939).
[51] Disteche, A., and Dubuisson, M., Rev. Sci. Instrum. 25, 869 (1954).
[52] Sonnenschein, R. R., Walker, R. M., and Stein, S. N., Rev. Sci. Instrum. 24, 702 (1953).
[53] Meyer, J. S., and Gotoh, F., Arch. Neurol. 3, 739 (1960).
[54] Meyer, J. S., Gotoh, F., and Tazaki, Y., J. Appl. Physiol. 16, 869 (1961).
[55] Khuri, R. N., Agulian, S. K., Oelert, H., and Harik, R. I., Pflugers Archiv. 294, 291 (1967).
[56] Khuri, R. N., Agulian, S. K., and Harik, R. I., Pflugers Archiv. 301, 182 (1968).
[57] Portnoy, H. D., Thomas, L. M., and Gurdgian, E. S., Arch. Neurol. 8, 597 (1963).
[58] Moore, E. W., and Wilson, D. W., J. Clin. Invest. 42, 293 (1963).
[59] Moore, E. W., and Dietschy, J. M., Amer. J. Physiol. 206, 1111 (1964).
[60] Sekelj, P., and Goldbloom, R. B., in Glass Electrodes for Hydrogen and Other Cations, G. Eisenman, Ed., Marcel Dekker, New York, 1968, pp. 540-553.
[61] Hansen, L., Buechele, M., Koroshec, J., and Warwick, W. J., Amer. J. Clin. Path. 49, 834 (1968).
[62] Mauro, A., Fed. Proc. 13, 96 (1954).
[63] Strickholm, A., and Wallin, B. G., Nature 208, 790 (1965).
[64] Thompson, F. C., and Brudevold, F., J. Dent. Res. 33, 849 (1954).
[65] Brudevald, F., and Thompson, F. C., J. Dent. Res. 33, 854(1954).
[66] Kurella, G. A., and Popov, G. A., Biofizika (Russian) 5, 373 (1960).
[67] Vorobiev, L. N., Kurella, G. A., and Popov, G. A., Biofizika (Russian) 6, 581 (1961).
[68] Lang, E. P., J. Biol. Chem. 88, 551 (1930).
[69] Pierce, J. A., J. Biol. Chem. 111, 501 (1935).
[70] Pierce, J. A., and Montgomery, H., J. Biol. Chem. 110, 763 (1935).
[71] Montgomery, H., and Pierce, J. A., Amer. J. Physiol. 118, 144 (1937).

[72] Gottschalk, C. W., Lassiter, W. E., and Mvlle, M., Amer. J. Physiol. **198**,581 (1960).
[73] Clapp, J. R., Watson, J. F., and Berliner, R. W., Amer. J. Physiol. **205**, 693 (1963).
[74] Frant, M. S., and Ross, J. W., Science **154**, 1553 (1966).
[75] Durst, R. A., and Taylor, J. K., Anal. Chem. **39**, 1483 (1967).
[76] Taves, D. R., Talanta **15**, 1015 (1968).
[77] Taves, D. R., Nature **217**, 1050 (1968).
[78] Singer, L., and Armstrong, W. D., Anal. Chem. **40**, 613 (1968).
[79] McCann, H. G., Arch. Oral Biol. **13**, 475 (1968).
[80] Gron, P., McCann, H. G., and Brudevold, F., Arch. Oral Biol. **13**, 203 (1968).
[81] Aasenden, R., Brudevold, F., and Richardson, B., Arch. Oral Biol. **13**, 203 (1968).
[82] Shane, N., and Miele, D., J. Pharm. Sci. **57**, 1260 (1968).
[83] Arino, H., and Kramer, H. H., Nucl. Applic. **4**, 356 (1958).
[84] Ross, J. W., Science **156**, 1378 (1967).
[85] Perris, A. D., and Whitfield, J. F., Nature **216**, 1350 (1967).
[86] Woodward, C., and Davidson, E. A., Biochem. **60**, 201 (1968).

CHAPTER 9

ANALYTICAL STUDIES ON ION-SELECTIVE MEMBRANE ELECTRODES

Garry A. Rechnitz

*Department of Chemistry
State University of New York
Buffalo, New York 14214*

I. Introduction

The development and continuing improvement of ion-selective membrane electrodes during the last few years has been of particular benefit to analytical chemistry [1]. From the analytical viewpoint such electrodes are nearly ideal measurement tools because of their ability to selectively monitor the activity of certain ions in solution both continuously and nondestructively. It is not surprising, therefore, that a large number of analytical applications of the electrodes have already been developed.

To focus attention only upon the direct analytical applications of ion-selective electrodes would be a disservice both to the scope of the electrodes and the catholic interests of modern analytical chemists, however. The range of what can be called "analytical studies" using ion-selective electrodes as measurement devices and of the electrodes themselves has been very wide indeed. This review is an attempt to communicate something of this range by a description of relevant studies involving the use of electrodes in equilibrium and kinetic solution chemistry as well as of the interesting and challenging problems raised regarding the method of operation of ion-selective membrane electrodes; the latter also illustrates the interplay between application needs and fundamental investigation which is so necessary to the further development of new electrode systems.

II. Principles

While I have been specifically asked to emphasize the newer kinds of membrane electrodes in preference to glass electrodes, it must nevertheless be recognized that much of our present understanding arises from basic studies performed on glass electrodes and that much of our reasoning concerning ion-selective electrodes is by analogy to glass electrodes.

The continuum of cation-selective glass electrodes is now known to belong to the "fixed-site" category [2] of ion-exchange membrane electrodes. This simply means that the active sites on the surface or in the

313

hydrated layer of the glass are not free to move about during the time scale of the measurement. It is further recognized that the electrode potential arises from a combination of cation exchange and cation mobility factors. The quantitative physical meaning of the observed selectivity ratio of such electrodes is, in fact, the product of the ion-exchange equilibrium constant between the sites and the solution and the mobility ratio of the exchanging ions in the hydrated layer of the glass. Thus, the selectivity properties of a desired electrode can be produced by appropriate adjustment of these parameters through alteration of the glass composition or by appropriate surface treatment. This simple model ought to be applicable to fixed-site types of electrode membranes, in general, and is indeed useful in the study of solid matrix or crystalline membrane electrodes.

These considerations are also useful in the treatment of liquid membrane electrodes with the added complication that the "sites" are also free to move in the active phase of these electrodes. This is an important advantage from the point of view of practical electrodes because it makes possible the design of electrodes having appreciable selectivity for multivalent ions over univalent ions.

Because the potential of ion-selective electrodes is actually composed of two or more discrete contributions arising from the various processes at the interfaces and in the bulk of the active membrane material, it follows that these several components can be separately discerned under certain experimental conditions. This is particularly true when such electrodes are used under non-steady state conditions, say in flowing samples or in changing reaction systems. The resulting behavior can have significant consequences to the interpretation of experimental measurements carried out under dynamic conditions.

Specifically, when the potential of an ion-selective electrode is monitored as a function of time in a system of rapidly changing composition, the potential determining processes at and in the electrode membrane may also be rate determining and result in various "transient" phenomena.

This effect has recently been demonstrated for cation-sensitive glass electrodes [3]. When such electrodes are subjected to a sudden change in activity of divalent cations such as Ca^{++} or Sr^{++} in the presence of a constant background concentration of univalent cations, the electrode potential undergoes a momentary (<100 msec) excursion far beyond that predicted by the equilibrium selectivity of the electrode for the ions involved (Fig. 1). At slightly longer times, the potential returns to the expected value. This behavior, while initially puzzling, can now be explained on the basis of the above mentioned two components which make up the potentiometric selectivity of the electrode, i.e., the ion-exchange equilibrium

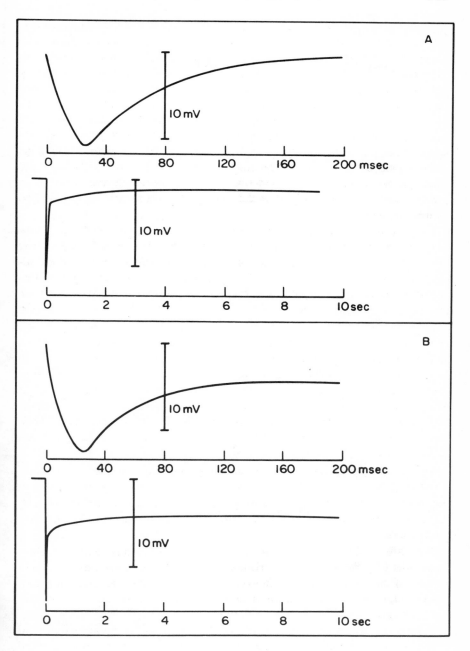

Figure 1.   Transient response to divalent cations of cation-sensitive glass electrodes. K$^+$
background $= 10^{-4}M$, pH $= 9$. A) $0.0538M$ Ca$^{++} \rightarrow 0.0100M$ Ca^{++}. B) $0.0538M$ Sr^{++}
$\rightarrow 0.0100M$ Sr^{++}.

constant and the mobility ratio. In the experimental system illustrated in Figure 1, we have a situation where the ion-exchange equilibrium between Ca^{++} or Sr^{++} and K^+ substantially favors the up-take of the divalent ion by the electrode. This effect is momentarily dominant when the activity of the divalent ion is changed near the electrode surface and gives rise to the initial excursion of the potential. The mobility of divalent ions in the hydrated layer is vastly lower than that of univalent cations in the hydrated layer of the glass; thus, the mobility ratio factor more than cancels the favorable ion-exchange equilibrium constant and causes the potential to return to the final steady-state value when both factors are in full effect.

Ordinarily, such phenomena would not be noticeable in experiments carried out with ion-selective electrodes on the normal laboratory time scale. In the study of fast reactions, to be described below, these effects can pose a practical limitation to accurate experimentation, however. More seriously, similar effects are also observed on liquid membrane electrodes where the time scale of electrode response is very much expanded (Fig. 2). As a result, the effective use of such electrodes for rate studies is difficult even for moderately rapid reactions under certain circumstances.

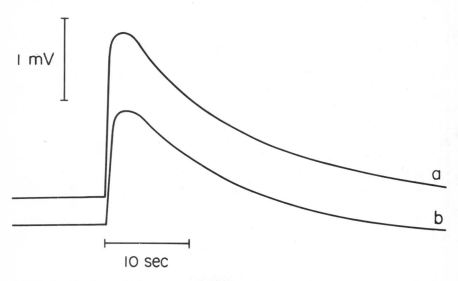

Figure 2. Transient Mg^{2+} response of Ca^{2+}-selective liquid membrane electrode. pH = 9.63; $I = 0.01M$ 25°C. (a)$[Mg^{++}] = 0 \to 2.5 \times 10^{-4}M$; $[Ca^{++}] = 3.9 \times 10^{-4}M$. (b) $[Mg^{++}] = 2.5 \times 10^{-4}M \to 4.9 \times 10^{-4}M$; $[Ca^{++}] = 3.7 \times 10^{-4}M$.

Because the equilibrium selectivity of liquid membrane electrodes having "mobile" sites involves at least three separate components [2], the observed transient effects cannot yet be unambiguously interpreted.

Another common and, as yet, unexplained phenomenon is the "slowing" of electrode response in the presence of interfering ions. The sodium selective glass electrode, for example, shows (Fig. 3) a more sluggish response to changes in Na^+ activity in the presence of K^+ ions than in their absence. Similarly, the calcium selective liquid membrane electrode responds more slowly to changes in Ca^{++} activity when magnesium ions are present than when they are not (Fig. 4). A systematic investigation of these effects is currently underway but, in the meantime, it must be recognized that this slowing of response rates could be a source of error in the investigation of practical systems under dynamic conditions.

Equilibrium selectivity considerations, alone, present one of the limiting factors in the use of ion-selective electrodes for analytical studies. In this connection, it is convenient to speak in terms of accessibility "windows" for each electrode in a given system. For the LaF_3 crystal, fluoride selective electrode, for example, there is an accessibility window with the solution pH as the variable because the usefulness of this electrode is limited by OH^- interference at high pH values and by the formation of hydrogen fluoride species at low pH's. Similarly, the liquid membrane cupric ion-selective electrode has a pH window defined by its response to the hydrogen ion in acidic media and by the formation of cupric hydroxide in more alkaline media.

Such accessibility windows may be enormously large, as in the case of the pH type glass electrode, or distressingly narrow, as is the case for some of the recently developed liquid membrane electrodes. Naturally, the solution pH is not the only determining variable in the definition of those windows. Any interfering ion, "poisoning" material, or physical variable has an effect which can be expressed in terms of such windows for any given electrode. It has been my experience that most of the problems encountered by users, especially new users, of ion-selective electrodes can be traced to a lack of appreciation of this concept, the violation of some simple rule regarding electrode treatment and handling, or confusion about the elementary activity relationships used for the interpretation of potentiometric data. It should not be necessary to do this but it must be stated again: ion-selective electrodes measure activity — not concentration!

III. Complexes

An especially attractive consequence of the fact that ion-selective electrodes measure the activity of unassociated ions is that such electrodes can be used directly and elegantly in the study of complexes and other associated chemical species. In principle, all that is necessary is to measure the activity of the ion of interest under noncomplexing solution conditions

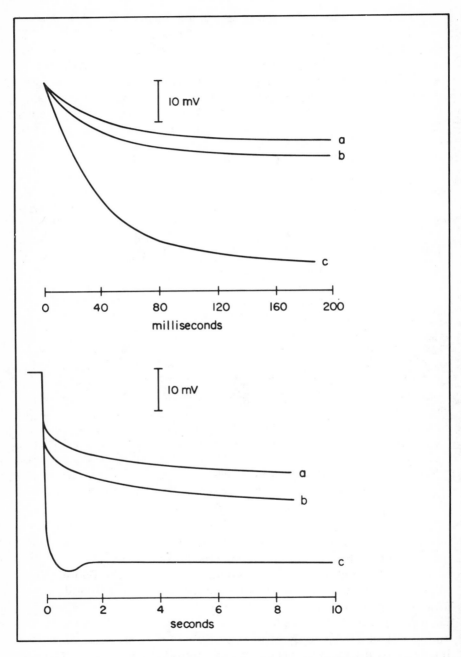

Figure 3.   Effect of K^+ background upon dynamic response of Na^+-selective glass electrode to change in Na^+ concentration from $0.0538M$ Na^+ to $0.0100M$ Na^+. K^+ background (a) $0.1000M$; (b) $0.0500M$; (c) 0.0.

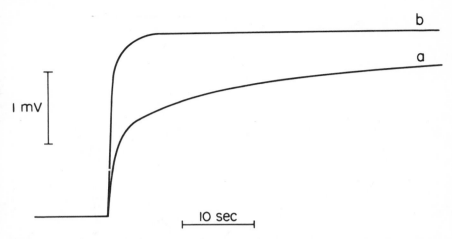

Figure 4. Slowing effect of Mg^{2+} on response rate of Ca^{2+}-selective liquid membrane electrode. $pH = 9.63$; $I = 0.01M$; 25 °C. $[Ca^{++}] = 1.0 \times 10^{-4}M \rightarrow 1.33 \times 10^{-4}M$. (a) $3 \times 10^{-4}M$ Mg^{++}. (b) no Mg^{++}.

and then again in the presence of the complexing agent. From these measurements and knowledge of the initial concentrations of the reagents involved, both the stoichiometry and the formation constant of the resulting complex can be obtained by standard methods. Situations involving series of complexes, additional equilibria, kinetic complications, *etc.*, can also be handled through proper design of experiments and use of appropriate computational techniques.

Practically every category of ion-selective electrodes has, by now, been employed for complex formation studies. The species involved have ranged from simple inorganic ion pairs to large complexes of biological interest. The fluoride sensitive membrane electrode is, because of its large accessibility window, a particularly convenient device for the purpose of studying fluoride complexes. It also has the desirable property of time stability as is demonstrated in Figure 5 where two calibration curves obtained with the same electrode but with a two-month time interval are displayed. Both calibration curves have the theoretical slope.

As already mentioned, the accessibility window of the fluoride electrode is limited in acidic solutions by the tendency of the fluoride ion to form hydrogen fluoride species. It should, therefore, be possible to study the formation of such species using the electrode to monitor the decreasing activity of free fluoride ion as the acidity of the medium is increased. Incidentally, if the results agree well with independent studies we should also have a confirmation of the hypothesis that the electrode indeed is only responsive to uncomplexed fluoride.

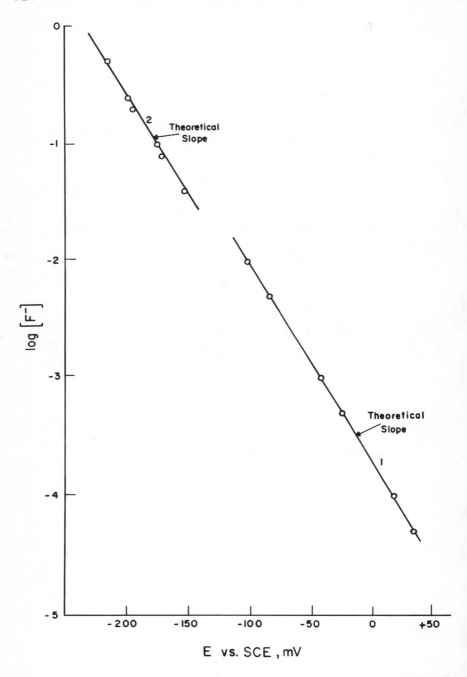

Figure 5.   Calibration curves of LaF$_3$ type F$^-$-selective electrode. Taken with 2 month time interval.

The equilibria

$$H^+ + F^- \rightleftarrows HF \tag{1}$$

and

$$HF + F^- \rightleftarrows HF_2^- \tag{2}$$

should be dominant in acidic, aqueous solutions of fluoride. With this model in mind, it is then appropriate to carry out simultaneous determinations of H^+ and F^-, using the pH type glass electrode and the LaF_3 crystal electrode, respectively, on a series of solutions of systematically varying composition, but of constant ionic strength and temperature. The results [4] of such a series of measurements are shown in Table 1 which gives $\bar{n}$, the average number of fluoride ions bound per hydrogen ion, over a wide range of conditions. These data can then be converted into a Bjerrum plot (Fig. 6) which indeed shows two "breaks" indicative of the formation of

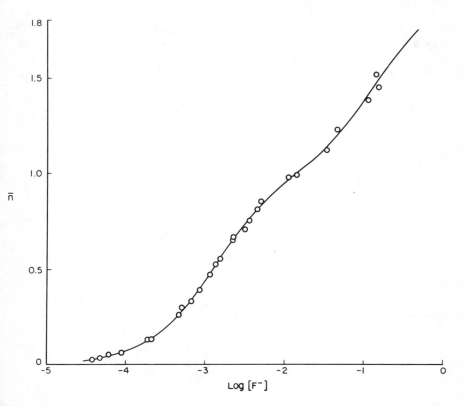

Figure 6. Bjerrum plot for H^+-F^- interaction in aqueous solution. Data taken with F^--selective electrode.

Table 1.   Free fluoride concentration and average number of fluoride ions bound per hydrogen ion at different total fluoride and acid concentrations.

$[F^-]_T$	$[H^+]_T$	$-\log [F^-]$	$\bar{n}$
0.0040	0.1500	4.430	0.026
0.0040	0.1162	4.347	0.034
0.0080	0.1500	4.222	0.053
0.0040	0.0581	4.066	0.067
0.0080	0.1162	4.061	0.068
0.0040	0.0291	3.735	0.131
0.0200	0.1500	3.683	0.132
0.0400	0.1500	3.331	0.264
0.0010	0.0020	3.328	0.265
0.0040	0.01162	3.298	0.301
0.0010	0.0010	3.176	0.333
0.0600	0.1500	3.071	0.394
0.0080	0.001162	2.934	0.471
0.0800	0.1500	2.863	0.524
0.0080	0.01162	2.810	0.555
0.0400	0.05809	2.660	0.651
0.1000	0.1500	2.648	0.652
0.0100	0.01162	2.652	0.669
0.0040	0.001162	2.498	0.708
0.0080	0.005809	2.442	0.755
0.0400	0.04357	2.348	0.815
0.0100	0.005809	2.298	0.855
0.0400	0.02905	1.943	0.985
0.0200	0.005809	1.848	0.998
0.1000	0.0581	1.463	1.129
0.2981	0.2033	1.331	1.237
0.3974	0.2033	0.939	1.389
0.4968	0.2324	0.799	1.454
0.5347	0.2558	0.837	1.522

HF and HF_2^-, respectively. The experimental results may also be quantitatively evaluated in terms of the equilibrium constants for Equations (1) and (2); the results of this evaluation are given in Table 2 yielding mean values of $10^{2.90}$ and $10^{0.77}$ for K_1 and K_2, respectively. Since these values are in excellent agreement with prior studies, our hypothesis regarding the response of the electrode can be considered as confirmed.

With this knowledge of the properties of the LaF_3 electrode and the information about fluoride equilibria in acidic media, the electrode can then

Table 2. Formation constants of HF and HF_2^- calculated for each experimental set of $[F^-]$ and $\bar{n}$.

$$K_1 = \frac{[HF]}{[H^+][F^-]} \; ; \; K_2 = \frac{[HF_2^-]}{[HF][F^-]}$$

$\bar{n}$	$[F^-]$	$\log K_1$	$\log K_2$
0.131	0.0001842	2.91	0.72
0.132	0.0002075	2.86	0.77
0.264	0.0004666	2.88	0.75
0.265	0.0004700	2.88	0.75
0.301	0.0005035	2.93	0.71
0.333	0.0006670	2.87	0.77
0.394	0.0008491	2.88	0.76
0.471	0.001165	2.87	0.76
0.524	0.001371	2.89	0.74
0.555	0.001548	2.89	0.74
0.651	0.002188	2.91	0.73
0.652	0.002249	2.90	0.74
0.669	0.002229	2.94	0.70
0.708	0.003176	2.85	0.79
0.755	0.003617	2.89	0.75
0.815	0.004488	2.93	0.70
0.855	0.005035	2.97	0.81
0.985	0.01140	2.93	0.87
0.998	0.01419	2.89	0.80
1.129	0.03443	2.88	0.76
1.237	0.04662	2.88	0.88
1.389	0.1151	2.88	0.76
1.454	0.1589	2.91	0.73
1.522	0.1455	2.89	0.89

Mean value $\quad$ 2.90 ± 0.03 $\quad$ 0.77 ± 0.05

be employed with confidence for more challenging complex formation studies. Of particular interest and practical importance is the interaction of fluoride with heavy metal ions, which is difficult to monitor directly with other techniques. Some representative data for the formation of iron(III) complexes of F^-, using the techniques described above, are given in Table 3. Here $\bar{n}$ is defined as the average number of F^- bound per Fe^{3+}, and it is clear that the predominant species under these conditions are FeF^{2+} and FeF_2^+. At higher fluoride concentrations it is also

Table 3. Average number of fluoride ions bound per ferric ion at different concentrations of free fluoride ion.

$[F^-] \times 10^5\ M$	$\bar{n}$	$[H^+]\ M$	$\bar{n}\left(1 + \dfrac{K_h}{[H^+]}\right)$
0.06731	0.07215	0.1316	0.07306
0.06702	0.07235	0.1316	0.07326
0.08919	0.08557	0.06887	0.08763
0.1129	0.09513	0.03722	0.09938
0.1005	0.1050	0.1316	0.1063
0.1443	0.1367	0.06646	0.1401
0.1393	0.1412	0.1316	0.1430
0.2094	0.1633	0.03359	0.1714
0.1862	0.1684	0.06887	0.1724
0.2379	0.1880	0.03722	0.1964
0.2057	0.2040	0.1316	0.2065
0.3146	0.2621	0.06645	0.2686
0.3035	0.2657	0.1316	0.2690
0.2987	0.2689	0.1316	0.2723
0.4453	0.3179	0.03359	0.3336
0.4128	0.3225	0.06887	0.3303
0.3887	0.3259	0.1316	0.3299
0.4479	0.3612	0.1316	0.3657
0.5458	0.3624	0.03722	0.3785
0.5517	0.3906	0.06887	0.4000
0.7366	0.4425	0.03722	0.4622
0.5662	0.4434	0.1316	0.4490
0.7187	0.4657	0.06646	0.4773
0.9421	0.5535	0.06646	0.5673
1.115	0.5604	0.03359	0.5878
1.528	0.6552	0.03359	0.6875

possible to form the species FeF_3, FeF_4^-, FeF_5^{2-}, FeF_6^{3-} and to evaluate their formation constants; such a quantitative study is currently in progress. Further relevant details [5] with regard to fluoride complexes are also given below in connection with the formation kinetics of the monofluoroaluminum(III) complex.

The crystalline Ag_2S membrane electrode, which is sensitive to the sulfide ion, is also well suited for complex formation studies because of its remarkable lack of interferences. Unfortunately, the chemistry of sulfide ion in aqueous solution is complicated by the tendency of that ion to interact with the solvent to form HS^- and H_2S species to which the electrode is not responsive. This tendency is illustrated in Figure 7 where the

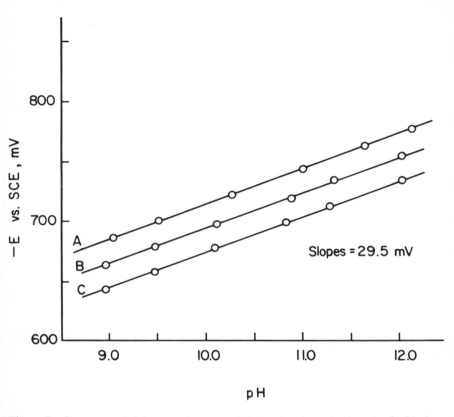

Figure 7. Response of Orion $S^=$ electrode to $S^=$ as function of pH, at $I = 0.1M$. A $=$ $5 \times 10^{-3}M$ Na$_2$S; B $= 1 \times 10^{-3}M$ Na$_2$S; C $= 2 \times 10^{-4}M$ Na$_2$S.

decreasing response of the electrode with decreasing pH values at other-wise constant conditions is clearly visible. Because of this effect, the elec-trode has its optimum sensitivity in alkaline media [6].

In such media, however, the electrode is admirably suited to the study of sulfide complexes. The formation of the thiostannate complex ion, for example, proceeds according to

$$SnS_2(s) + S^{2-} \rightleftarrows SnS_3^{2-} \tag{3}$$

and can be very precisely evaluated by simultaneous measurements with the pH type and sulfide ion-selective electrodes. Some relevant results are shown in Table 4. The average value for K_f, 2.062×10^5, agrees very well with a previously reported value of 1.1×10^5, obtained under slightly different solution conditions. Because the electrode gives a direct mea-sure of the sulfide activity, the present value has an uncertainty of only $\pm 5\%$ and is probably quite accurate, as well.

Table 4. Formation constants of thiostannate complex ion at 25 °C and $I = 0.1M$.

$[Na_2S] \times 10^3$ M	$-E$ V	$[S^{2-}] \times 10^8$ g–ion/1	pH	$[H^+]$ g–ion/1	$[S^{2-}]_t \times 10^3$ g–ion/1	$[SnS_3{}^{2-}] \times 10^3$ g–ion/1	$K_f \times 10^{-5}$
8.000	0.6673	0.6310	8.298	3.827×10^{-9}	6.643	1.358	2.152
12.00	0.6762	1.259	8.450	2.697×10^{-9}	9.341	2.659	2.112
7.969	0.6747	1.122	8.610	1.866×10^{-9}	5.758	2.211	1.970
12.00	0.6836	2.239	8.760	1.321×10^{-9}	8.136	3.865	1.726
3.993	0.6732	1.000	8.998	7.811×10^{-10}	2.149	1.844	1.844
9.963	0.6850	2.512	9.104	5.980×10^{-10}	4.133	5.831	2.321
6.000	0.6806	1.778	9.450	2.697×10^{-10}	1.319	4.681	2.633
8.000	0.6871	2.951	9.728	1.422×10^{-10}	1.154	6.847	2.320
3.020	0.6776	1.413	10.00	7.600×10^{-11}	0.2954	2.724	1.928
9.963	0.6924	4.467	10.30	3.810×10^{-11}	0.4682	7.532	1.609

Average 2.062
± 0.098

While liquid membrane electrodes require somewhat greater skill and care for reliable use in fundamental studies, they are also excellent and useful tools for complex formation studies. As a general statement, it can be said of liquid membrane electrodes that they have more restricted accessibility windows than either glass or crystal membrane electrodes. This is a direct consequence of the fact that liquid membrane electrodes are more prone to potentiometric interference from both cations and anions. On the other hand, the liquid membrane electrodes are responsive exactly to those ions, e.g., Ca^{++}, ClO_4^-, NO_3^-, BF_4^-, etc., which are extremely difficult to monitor by other techniques. Thus any extra effort required in the handling of the electrodes and the selection of optimum conditions is well repaid by the possibility of studying previously inaccessible systems.

The cupric ion-selective electrode, for example, responds selectively to Cu^{++} over the 10^{-2} to 10^{-5} molar range in the pH region of 3.5 to 6.5. Thus, the electrode can be used to study soluble copper complexes involving ligands of appropriate acid-base properties. The results of such a study are summarized in Table 5 where the complexing ligands have been chosen, in part, because of their biological significance. The results agree well with available literature data, and the method, using the direct measurement of Cu^{++} activities, is thought to be superior to alternate methods

Table 5. Formation constants of copper (II) complexes determined with the cupric ion–selective electrode (at 25 °C and $I = 0.1 M$).

Ligand	pH	K_f(measured)	K_f(literature)
Glycine	6.06	$K_1 = 10^{8.20}$	—
	$(I = 0.01 M)$	$K_2 = 10^{14.96}$	—
	6.00	$K_1 = 10^{8.36}$	$K_1 = 10^{8.38}$
	$(I = 0.1 M)$		$(I = 0.1 M, 25 °C)$
Glutamic Acid	6.00	$K_1 = 10^{8.48}$	$K_1 \sim 10^8$
		$K_2 = 10^{14.55}$	$K_2 \sim 10^{15}$
THAM[a]	6.00	$K_1 = 10^{4.97}$	$K_1 = 10^{4.44}$
			$(I = 1.0 M, 20 °C)$
Acetate	5.75	$K_1 = 10^{2.04}$	$K_1 \sim 10^2$

[a] $Tris$[hydroxymethyl]aminomethane

(such as pH titration) because of its simplicity and potential applicability to a wide range of ionic media.

Because of the difficulty of measuring free calcium activity by conventional analytical methods, the use of the Ca^{++} selective membrane electrodes of the liquid membrane type is particularly attractive in the study of calcium complexes. For such studies, we [8] made use of the equation

$$E = E^\circ + 0.0295 \, \log \left\{ \frac{\gamma_{Ca^{2+}} \, [Ca^{2+}]}{1 + \Sigma \beta_j [L]_j} + \Sigma K_i(\gamma_i) \, [M_i]^{2/z_i} \right\} \qquad (4)$$

where γ and [ ] signify activity coefficients and analytical concentrations while β_j and $[L]_j$ are the overall formation constants and ligand concentrations, respectively, of any ligand which complexes Ca^{2+}. K_i and z_i denote the selectivity ratios and charges of any interfering cations which may be present; fortunately the electrode is sufficiently selective for Ca^{2+} so that the second term in Equation (4) can be minimized.

The chelating agents ethylenediaminetetraacetic acid (EDTA) and nitrilotriacetic acid (NTA) were studied in detail and their interaction with Ca^{2+} is graphically presented in Figure 8, as a function of pH, in terms of a "titration" of a constant amount of Ca^{2+} by increasing quantities of ligand. The resulting curves can be mathematically analyzed to yield the quantitative overall formation constants shown in Tables 6 and 7 for EDTA and NTA, respectively. Formation constant values obtained at other pH's were as follows: for Ca(II)-NTA, 1.32×10^5 (pH = 7.8-8.1), 3.2×10^5 (pH = 8.4-8.5) and for Ca(II)-EDTA, 8.80×10^5 (pH = 5.26). These results are in good agreement with reported literature values.

These studies were extended to some biologically important Ca^{2+} complexes using the interesting new Beckman 39608 Ca^{2+} selective electrode which utilizes a solid matrix ion exchanger and, thus, has somewhat different selectivity characteristics than the Orion or Corning liquid membrane electrodes. The results for calcium malate, citrate, and DCTA (trans-1,2-diaminocyclohexane-N,N,N',N'-tetraacetic acid) complexes are given in Tables 8-10; once again the formation constants obtained are in good agreement with the literature values shown at the foot of each table.

It should not be thought that the general method described is restricted to cation selective liquid membrane electrodes. Indeed, the recent development of electrodes for Cl^-, NO_3^-, ClO_4^-, BF_4^-, etc., has opened a whole new field of investigation involving the association of these anions with other ions. This possibility is particularly attractive because of the lack of independent techniques for the selective and direct measurement of the activity of these ions.

A relevant illustration is provided by our recent studies involving the perchlorate electrode [9]. This electrode has a useful response to ClO_4^-

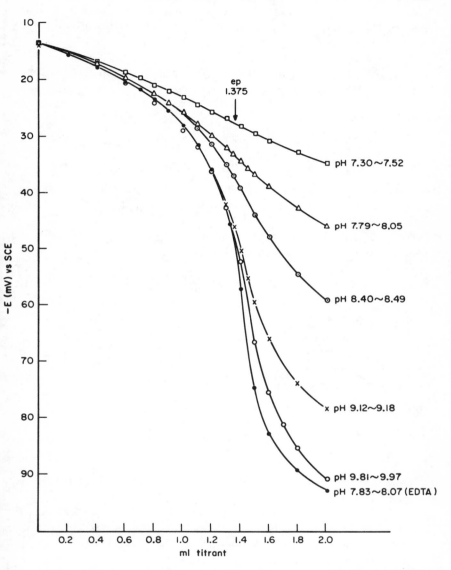

Figure 8. Titration curves monitored with Ca^{2+}-selective electrode. 77 ml of $3.573 \times 10^{-4}M$ Ca^{2+} with $0.02M$ TEA–NTA or TEA–EDTA ($I = 0.01M$, TEA-borate media, 25 °C).

in the 10^{-1} to $10^{-3.5}$ molar range in aqueous systems of pH 4 to 11, and has reasonable selectivity for ClO_4^- over common anions such as nitrate, bicarbonate, and the halides. The response of the electrode to ClO_4^- activity is illustrated by Figure 9 as a function of temperature, and the results of some solubility determinations, obtained by measuring

Table 6.   Titration data of 77.0 ml of $3.57_3 \times 10^{-4}$ M Ca^{2+} with 0.0200 M
TEA–EDTA, $I = 0.01$, pH $= 4.75$, TEA-acetate.

EDTA ml	$[Ca^{+2}]_t$ $\times 10^4$ M	$[EDTA]_t$ $\times 10^4$ M	$[Ca^{+2}]_e$ $\times 10^4$ M	$[CaY]_e$ $\times 10^4$ M	$[L]_{et}$ $\times 10^5$ M	K' $\times 10^{-4}$ M^{-1}
0.40	3.55_3	1.03_4	2.67_0	0.88_3	1.5_1	2.19^a
0.60	3.54_4	1.54_6	2.34_6	1.11_8	4.2_8	1.12^a
0.80	3.53_5	2.05_6	2.02_0	1.51_5	5.4_1	1.39^a
1.00	3.52_6	2.56_4	1.78_0	1.74_6	8.1_8	1.20
1.20	3.51_6	3.06_9	1.53_0	1.98_6	10.8_3	1.20
1.30	3.51_2	3.32_1	1.43_0	2.08_2	12.3_9	1.18
1.35	3.50_9	3.44_6	1.38_0	2.12_9	13.1_7	1.17
1.40	3.50_8	3.57_2	1.33_0	2.17_8	13.9_4	1.18
1.50	3.50_3	3.82_2	1.25_0	2.25_3	15.6_9	1.15
1.60	3.49_9	4.07_1	1.16_5	2.33_4	17.3_7	1.15
					mean	1.18×10^4

$[\ ]_t$: total concentration, $[\ ]_e$: equilibrium concentration,

$[L]_{et}$: total ligand species concentration at equilibrium,

[a]: not included in average; $K' = [CaY]_e / (Ca^{2+})_e (L)_{et}$

the activity of free ClO_4^- in equilibrium with the relevant precipitate,
are shown in Table 11.

It certainly seems that the general utility of ion-selective electrodes for
complex formation and other ion association studies has already been
demonstrated and that a widespread use of electrodes for such measurements can be expected in the future.

IV. Kinetics

Since ion-selective membrane electrodes are capable of monitoring
changes in ion activities continuously and with generally good dynamic
response, one of the more fruitful areas of application of electrodes ought
to be in chemical and biochemical kinetics. We have, thus, been trying to
demonstrate the usefulness of ion electrodes for reaction rate measurements and mechanistic investigations through the study of a number of

Table 7. Titration data of 77.0 ml of 3.57×10^{-4} M Ca^{2+} with 0.0200 M
TEA–NTA, $I = 0.01$, pH $= 7.3 - 7.6$, TEA–borate.

NTA ml	$[Ca^{+2}]_t$ $\times 10^4$ M	$[NTA]_t$ $\times 10^4$ M	$[Ca^{+2}]_e$ $\times 10^4$ M	$[CaY]_e$ $\times 10^4$ M	$[L]_{et}$ $\times 10^5$ M	K' $\times 10^{-4}$ M^{-1}
0.40	3.55_3	1.03_4	2.72_0	0.83_3	2.0_1	1.52^a
0.60	3.54_4	1.54_6	2.26_5	1.27_9	2.6_7	2.12^a
0.70	3.54_0	1.80_2	2.06_0	1.48_0	3.2_2	2.23^a
0.80	3.53_5	2.05_6	1.84_0	1.69_5	3.6_1	2.55^a
0.90	3.53_0	2.31_0	1.62_0	1.91_0	4.0_0	2.95^a
1.00	3.52_6	2.56_4	1.44_5	2.08_1	4.8_3	2.98
1.10	3.52_1	2.81_7	1.29_2	2.22_9	5.8_8	2.93
1.20	3.51_6	3.06_9	1.15_0	2.36_6	7.0_3	2.93
1.30	3.51_2	3.32_1	1.03_5	2.47_7	8.4_4	2.84
1.40	3.50_8	3.57_2	0.90_6	2.59_2	9.8_0	2.92
1.50	3.50_3	3.82_2	0.79_5	2.70_8	11.1_4	3.06
1.60	3.49_9	4.07_1	0.69_7	2.80_2	12.6_9	3.17^a
					mean	2.94×10^4

$[\ ]_t$: total concentration, $[\ ]_e$: equilibrium concentration,

$[L]_{et}$: total ligand species concentration at equilibrium,

^{a}: not included in average; $K' = [CaY]_e/(Ca^{2+})_e (L)_{et}$

model systems. It will be seen below that this effort has been largely successful.

Our work in this area began with the application of cation-sensitive glass electrodes to the study of heterogeneous reactions involving the precipitation of various alkali metal ions with tetraphenylboron [10]. This early work is important because it demonstrated that even rather fast reactions (rate constants in the 10^8 range) could be studied with electrodes whose response times (see above) might ordinarily be considered rate limiting. The method used to overcome this limitation is, of course, the steady-state approach; specifically, the reactants are rapidly mixed in a continuous flow system and streamed past the sensing electrode at a controlled rate. The electrode "sees" only a constant environment and,

Table 8. Formation constants of Ca–malate complexes at $I = 0.1\,M$
and 25 °C.

$[Ca^{2+}]_t$ $\times 10^3\,M$	$[H_2A]_t$ $\times 10^3\,M$	pH	$-E$ mV	$[Na^+]$ $\times 10^2\,M$	$[Ca^{2+}]_e$ $\times 10^3\,M$	$[CaA]_e$ $\times 10^3\,M$	$[A^{2-}]_e$ $\times 10^3\,M$	K $\times 10^{-2}$
2.010	1.010	6.04	47.3	9.3	1.688	0.322	0.659	2.89
3.140	4.040	6.46	45.7	8.7	1.949	1.191	2.801	2.18
4.019	3.030	6.33	42.0	8.5	2.644	1.375	1.618	3.22
5.024	6.010	6.51	41.4	7.9	2.789	2.235	3.72	2.16
6.029	5.050	6.49	39.4	7.7	3.297	2.732	2.28	3.64
7.002	7.979	6.64	39.8	7.1	3.197	3.805	4.13	2.88
8.007	6.969	6.60	37.3	6.9	3.908	4.009	2.84	3.70
9.043	9.999	6.73	36.9	6.3	4.060	4.983	4.97	2.47

Mean $= 2.89$

$\log K = 2.46$

Literature values: $\log K = 2.06$ at $I = 0.16$

$= 2.66, 2.24$ at $I = 0$

Table 9. Formation constants of Ca–citrate complexes at $I = 0.1\,M$
and 25 °C.

$[Ca^{2+}]_t$ $\times 10^3M$	$[H_3A]_t$ $\times 10^3M$	pH	$-E$ mV	$[Na^+]$ $\times 10^2M$	$[Ca^{2+}]_e$ $\times 10^3M$	$[CaA^-]_e$ $\times 10^3M$	$[A^{3-}]_e$ $\times 10^3M$	K $\times 10^{-3}$
6.000	5.000	6.62	47.5	6.7	1.721	4.279	0.616	4.04
6.000	7.000	6.88	56.5	6.1	0.825	5.175	1.665	3.77
8.000	7.000	6.67	46.8	5.5	1.843	6.157	0.730	4.58
8.000	10.000	6.98	58.9	4.6	0.699	7.302	2.511	4.17
10.000	8.000	6.61	42.7	4.6	2.576	7.424	0.489	5.89
10.000	9.000	6.71	46.6	4.3	1.895	8.105	0.785	5.45
10.000	10.000	6.78	50.2	4.0	1.420	8.580	1.270	4.76

Mean $= 4.66$

$\log K = 3.67$

Literature values: $\log K = 4.68, 4.90$ at $I = 0$

$= 3.17$ at $I = 0.15$

Table 10. Formation constants of Ca–DCTA complexes at $I = 0.1M$ and 25 °C.

$[Ca^{2+}]_t$ $\times 10^3 M$	$[H_4A]_t$ $\times 10^3 M$	pH	$-E$ mV	$[Na^+]$ $\times 10^2 M$	$[Ca^{2+}]_c$ $\times 10^3 M$	$[CaA^{2-}]_c$ $\times 10^3 M$	$[A^{4-}]_c$ $\times 10^{13}$	K $\times 10^{-12}$
8.006	7.006	4.46	46.9	7.0	1.805	6.201	6.475	5.31
8.006	9.004	4.27	48.5	6.7	1.585	6.442	8.318	4.87
7.003	5.996	4.38	44.6	7.3	2.159	4.844	6.274	3.58
7.003	7.994	4.36	53.1	7.1	1.073	5.930	10.030	5.51
5.997	5.007	4.38	46.4	7.7	1.857	4.140	4.973	4.65
5.997	7.006	4.40	52.4	7.5	1.134	4.863	1.321	3.25
4.994	3.997	4.34	45.5	8.1	1.988	3.006	4.357	3.47
4.994	5.996	4.39	56.4	7.9	0.795	4.119	10.132	5.22

Mean $= 4.48$

$\log K = 12.65$

Literature values: $\log K = 12.3, 12.5\ 13.15$ at $I = 0.1$

thus, its response time is not critical within reasonable limits. This same approach is now being successfully applied to kinetic investigations using the more sluggish liquid membrane electrodes.

The first really comprehensive investigation undertaken was the kinetic study [11] of the exchange reaction between Ag(I)-EDTA and Ni(II). This study, which yielded the mechanisms (where Y denotes EDTA)

$$Ni^{2+} + AgY^{3-} \xrightarrow{k_1} NiY^{2-} + Ag^+ \tag{5}$$

$$Ni^{2+} + AgHY^{2-} \xrightarrow{k_2} NiY^{2-} + Ag^+ + H^+ \tag{6}$$

$$Ni^{2+} + HY^{3-} \xrightarrow{k_3} NiY^{2-} + H^+ \tag{7}$$

$$Ni^{2+} + Y^{4-} \xrightarrow{k_4} NiY^{2-} \tag{8}$$

for the 9.2-10.2 pH region and

$$NiOH^+ + AgY^{3-} \xrightarrow{k_{1'}} NiY^{2-} + Ag^+ + OH^- \tag{9}$$

$$Ni^{2+} + AgY^{3-} \xrightarrow{k_1} NiY^{2-} + Ag^+ \tag{10}$$

for the pH 10.8 to 11.4 range, was conducted by continuously measuring the activity of silver(I) with a cation sensitive glass electrode and demonstrates the use of such electrodes in homogeneous kinetic systems.

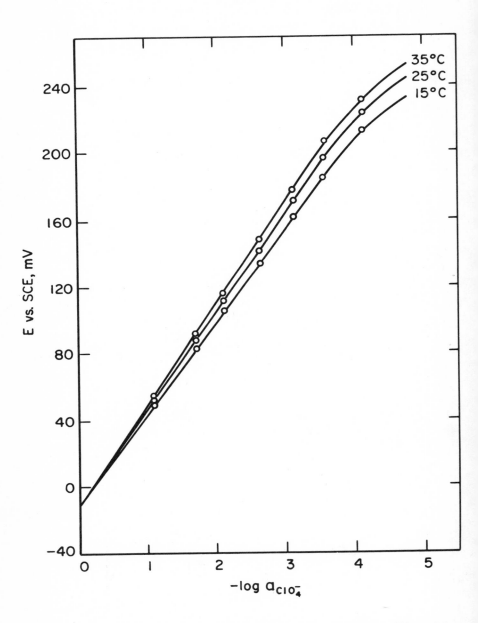

Figure 9.   Response of Orion liquid membrane ClO_4^- selective electrode to ClO_4^- activity
at various temperatures.

Table 11. Solubility product constants of perchlorate salts.

	t °C	E, mV	$A_{ClO_4^-}$ (M)	pH	Solubility	K_{sp}
$KClO_4$ white	15	49.7	7.16×10^{-2}		7.16×10^{-2}	5.127×10^{-3}
	25	47.0	9.806×10^{-2}	5.19	9.806×10^{-2}	9.616×10^{-3}
	35	43.8	1.263×10^{-1}		1.263×10^{-1}	1.595×10^{-2}
$[Co(NH_3)_6](ClO_4)_3$ yellowish orange	15	63.6	4.063×10^{-2}		1.354×10^{-2}	9.082×10^{-7}
	25	61.2	5.634×10^{-2}	4.95	1.878×10^{-2}	3.359×10^{-6}
	35	58.4	7.283×10^{-2}		2.428×10^{-2}	9.380×10^{-6}
$[Cu(C_5H_5N_4)](ClO_4)_2$ blue	15	68.4	3.341×10^{-2}		1.671×10^{-2}	1.865×10^{-5}
	25	70.4	3.935×10^{-2}	6.39	1.968×10^{-2}	3.047×10^{-5}
	35	69.6	4.772×10^{-2}		2.386×10^{-2}	5.433×10^{-5}
$[Fe(C_{12}H_8N_2)_3](ClO_4)_2$ red	15	125.4	3.274×10^{-3}		1.637×10^{-3}	1.755×10^{-8}
	25	132.0	3.555×10^{-3}	5.53	1.778×10^{-3}	2.247×10^{-8}
	35	133.3	4.310×10^{-3}		2.155×10^{-3}	4.003×10^{-8}

These two studies stimulated our interest in using the newer liquid membrane and solid crystal electrodes for quantitative rate measurements. Because of the importance of Ca^{2+}-EDTA reactions to analytical chemistry we [8] undertook an investigation of the reaction

$$Ca^{2+} + Mg\text{-EDTA} \quad \rightleftarrows \quad Ca\text{-EDTA} + Mg^{2+} \qquad (11)$$

in conjunction with the study of Ca-EDTA complexes already discussed above.

For this purpose, we used the Orion liquid type Ca^{2+}-selective electrode with careful attention to possible interferences and control of kinetic conditions so as not to exceed the effective response time limits of the overall measuring system. By carrying out the kinetic study with Ca^{2+} in excess, useful data could be obtained from the early portion of the reaction course. Figure 10 shows some of the rate data as a function of the

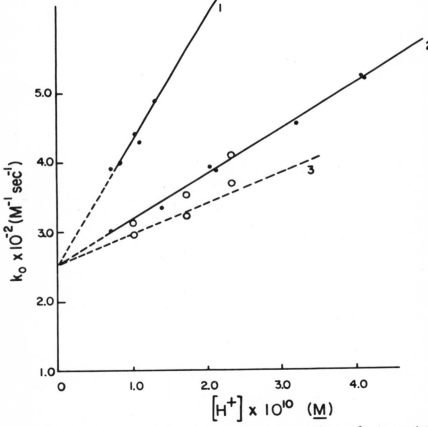

Figure 10. Ca^{2+}-Mg^{2+}EDTA exchange reaction. pH dependence of rate constant. Conditions as in Reference [8].

solution pH and gives an indication of the precision and accuracy of the method. From these and similar measurements it was possible to arrive at the overall mechanism

$$Ca^{2+} + Mg(II)Y \xrightleftharpoons{k_I} CaY + Mg^{2+} \qquad (12)$$

$$Ca^{2+} + HY^- \xrightleftharpoons{k_{II}} CaY + H^+ \qquad (13)$$

$$Ca^{2+} + Mg(II)HY^+ \xrightleftharpoons{k_{III}} CaY + Mg^{2+} + H^+ \qquad (14)$$

$$Ca^{2+} + Y^{2-} \xrightleftharpoons{k_{IV}} CaY \qquad (15)$$

where k_I, k_{II}, k_{III}, and k_{IV} have the values of $2.7 \times 10^2\,M^{-1}\,sec^{-1}$, 2.3×10^7 $M^{-1}\,sec^{-1}$, $1.3 \times 10^{11}\,M^{-2}\,sec^{-1}$, and $2 \times 10^9\,M^{-1}\,sec^{-1}$, respectively. This mechanism may be compared with the paths for the Ag(I)-EDTA + Ni(II) reaction, above, and shows that liquid membrane electrodes can also be used for the study of moderately rapid reactions.

Because of their rapid response and minimal interferences, solid crystal membrane electrodes can be easily used for kinetic studies. The fluoride-selective electrode is particularly useful in this connection because the continuous measurement of fluoride activity in solution is a difficult analytical problem. We, therefore, used [5] this electrode to measure the rates of formation of the monofluoro complexes of iron(III) and aluminum(III). The first system was chosen because some kinetic measurements had already been done using optical techniques and could, thus, give a good indication of the reliability of the new method; the second system had never been studied from the kinetic viewpoint, because of measurement difficulties associated with conventional techniques, and thus provides a challenging test of the electrode method.

Figure 11 is typical of the emf *vs.* time curves recorded during the reaction between ferric and fluoride ions. The potential of the fluoride-ion selective electrode becomes progressively more positive with respect to the calomel electrode indicating a decrease in the free fluoride ion concentration resulting from the formation of FeF^{2+}. From a series of experiments carried out at different initial H^+, Fe^{3+}, and F^- concentrations, the rate constants shown in Table 12 could be obtained and the general results yielded the mechanism

$$Fe^{3+} + F^- \rightleftarrows FeF^{2+} \qquad (16)$$

$$Fe^{3+} + HF \rightleftarrows FeF^{2+} + H^+ \qquad (17)$$

under the conditions used, any contribution from HF_2^- could be neglected.

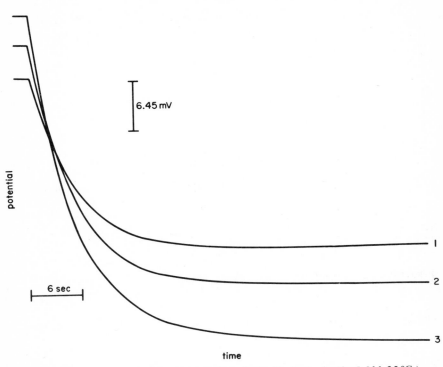

Figure 11.   FeF^{2+} formation reactions monitored with F$^-$ electrode. ($I = 1.0M$, 25 °C.) [Fe^{3+}]$_{total}$ = 0.001584M. [F$^+$]$_{total}$ = 0.0009259M. (1) [H$^+$] = 0.13116M. (2) [H$^+$] = 0.06887M. (3) [H$^+$] = 0.03722M

The formation of AlF^{2+} is very much more complicated than that of FeF^{2+} and, as Figure 12 shows, the rate of formation is quite slow. For this reason, the kinetic data were analyzed using the initial rate method (results in Table 13) and led to the overall rate law

$$\frac{d[AlF^{2+}]}{dt} = k_I[H^+][Al^{3+}][F^-] + k_{II}[Al^{3+}][F^-] + k_{III}[Al^{3+}][F^-]^2 \quad (18)$$

where k_I, k_{II}, and k_{III} are 346 M^{-2} sec^{-1}, 5 M^{-1} sec^{-1}, and 1.03 × 10^5 M^{-2} sec^{-1}, respectively. This rate law corresponds to the proposed mechanism

$$Al^{3+} + HF \rightleftarrows AlF^{2+} + H^+ \quad (19)$$

$$Al(H_2O)^{3+} + F^- \rightleftarrows AlOH^{2+} + HF \quad (20)$$

$$AlOH^{2+} + HF \rightleftarrows AlF^{2+} + H_2O \quad (21)$$

which is confirmed also by independent chemical evidence.

Table 12. Values of rate constant K' for the formation of FeF^{2+} at 25 °C and at an ionic strength of 1.0 M.

$[H^+] M$	$[Fe^{3+}]_t \times 10^3 M$	$[F^-]_t \times 10^3 M$	$K' \times 10^{-3} (M^{-1} sec^{-1})$	
0.1316	1.584	0.9259	10.80,	10.90
0.1316	0.8223	0.7692	11.21,	12.59
0.1316	1.584	0.7407	10.73,	10.40
0.1316	0.8223	0.3846	11.19,	11.43
0.1316	1.584	0.3704	10.24,	10.05
0.1316	0.8223	0.1923	11.07,	10.46
0.1316	1.584	0.1852	9.92,	9.52
0.06887	1.584	0.9259	7.24,	7.20
0.06646	0.8223	0.7692	8.28,	8.84
0.06887	1.584	0.7407	7.62,	7.98
0.06646	0.8223	0.3846	7.75,	8.30
0.06887	1.584	0.3704	6.71,	6.69
0.06646	0.8223	0.1923	7.44,	8.48
0.06887	1.584	0.1852	6.63,	6.64
0.03722	1.584	0.9259	4.87,	5.75
0.03359	0.8223	0.7692	6.47,	6.79
0.03722	1.584	0.7407	6.04,	5.22
0.03359	0.8223	0.3846	5.98,	6.27
0.03722	1.584	0.3704	4.70,	4.81
0.03359	0.8223	0.1923	5.24,	5.40
0.03722	1.584	0.1852	4.71,	4.60

While the use of ion-selective electrodes for such rate studies holds considerable promise in itself, one should not conclude that the range of application in kinetics is restricted to straightforward rate measurements. Recently for example, we [12] used the fluoride ion electrode, less directly, in a kinetic study of the iron(III)-iodide reaction in fluoride media where fluoride is not involved as one of the reactants.

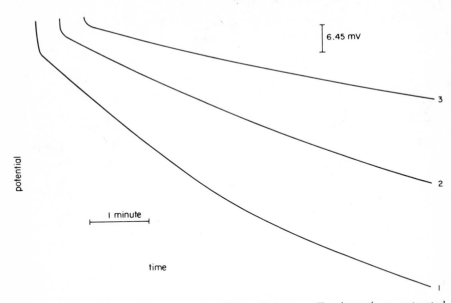

Figure 12.   AlF^{2+} formation as function of time. LaF$_3$ type F$^-$ electrode *vs.* saturated calomel reference. Runs 1-3, show increasing F$^-$/Al^{3+}ratio.

It had been known that fluoride ions inhibit the reaction between iron(III) and iodide, but there was no way to distinguish between the main alternative mechanisms, *e.g.*, one in which the inhibition results because FeF^{2+} reacts more slowly with I$^-$ than Fe^{3+} or one in which the inhibition occurs because FeF^{2+} is unreactive toward I$^-$, and the presence of F$^-$ lowers the equilibrium concentration of Fe^{3+} available. Work on the analogous reactions involving FeCl^{2+} or FeBr^{2+} had favored the first alternative. By monitoring the concentration of free fluoride ion during the reaction and using our knowledge of FeF^{2+} formation constants, we were able to demonstrate, however, that the second mechanism is operative, *i.e.*, that FeF^{2+} does not oxidize iodide ion. This, then, is an example of the use of ion-selective electrodes as a diagnostic tool in the characterization of reaction mechanisms—a use which should become more popular as kineticists learn about the capabilities of these electrodes.

V. Analysis

While this review is primarily devoted to physico-chemical studies, it would be a disservice to the potentialities of ion-selective electrodes not to include some comment on their usefulness in chemical analysis. Obviously, that usefulness is very great indeed and surely accounts for the bulk of the electrodes in use today.

Table 13. Initial rates of formation of AlF^{2+} at 25 °C and at an ionic strength of 1.0 M.

Acid conc.	$[Al^{3+}] \times 10^2 M$	$[F^-] \times 10^4 M$	Rate $\times 10^5$ (M sec^{-1})	Corrected rate (M sec^{-1})
0.1316 M	1.357	0.3211	2.277	1.913
"	0.7245	0.3445	1.343	1.129
"	1.358	0.1587	1.025	0.882
"	0.3790	0.3640	0.682	0.561
"	0.7298	0.1738	0.604	0.517
"	1.360	0.07917	0.426	0.363
"	0.3783	0.1809	0.340	0.293
"	0.7308	0.08687	0.253	0.215
"	0.3794	0.09068	0.144	0.124
0.06353	1.359	0.6627	2.913	1.847
"	1.362	0.3340	1.491	1.106
"	1.360	0.1624	0.623	0.476
0.05849	0.7214	0.7591	1.793	1.090
"	0.7275	0.3815	0.833	0.584
"	0.7301	0.1917	0.400	0.302
0.05568	0.3736	0.8371	1.009	0.582
"	0.3768	0.4186	0.467	0.319
"	0.3791	0.2109	0.219	0.161
0.0408	1.332	0.9414	3.702	1.855
"	1.360	0.5063	1.628	0.923
"	1.357	0.2414	0.611	0.365
0.03412	0.7222	1.285	2.868	1.172
"	0.7266	0.6411	1.028	0.487
"	0.7206	0.2900	0.393	0.226
0.0304	0.3615	1.457	1.586	0.529
"	0.3636	0.7001	0.574	0.263
"	0.3731	0.3554	0.259	0.144

The accompanying Tables (14 and 15) indicate something of the present range of application of ion-selective electrodes. That range extends from measurements of industrial and geological samples to determinations carried out in actual living beings. The promise of ion-electrodes in clinical and chemical laboratories, perhaps in conjunction with automated equipment and computer processing, seems especially great. It is my personal opinion that ion-electrodes represent an exciting new tool for chemical measurement and that their use will significantly extend the frontiers of scientific investigation.

Table 14. Analysis by direct potentiometry using ion–selective electrodes.

A. Inorganic systems	Ion determined	Conditions and remarks	Ref
Synthetic samples	BF_4^- (boron)	Orion 92–07 electrode, direct potentiometry after conversion and ion exchange; NO_3^- and I^- interfere	[13]
Synthetic samples	F^-	Modified Orion F^- electrode; microanalysis by linear null-point technique; 10^{-3} to 2×10^{-6} M F^- in 10 μl samples	[14]
Synthetic samples	F^-	Orion electrode; 10^{-4} to 10^{-5} M F^- using standard addition technique; interferences masked with phosphoric acid	[15]
Synthetic samples	F^-	Orion electrode; F^- to $10^{-6.7}$ M using 60% ethanol medium	[16]
Bone	F^-	Orion 94–09 electrode; determination after ashing of bone	[17]
Minerals	F^-	Orion electrode; determination in fluorite, cryolite, topaz, etc.	[18]
Water	Na^+	GEA 28 Na^+ glass electrode; direct Na^+ determination in 0.004–25 ppm range; pH control with ammonia vapor	[19]
Tungsten	F^-	Orion electrode; dissolution of sample by fusion; determination in 2–100 ppm range	[20]

Table 14. Analysis by direct potentiometry using ion–selective electrodes. (continued)

A. Inorganic systems	Ion determined	Conditions and remarks	Ref
Chromium plating solutions	F^-	Orion F^- electrode; direct determination of plating bath samples	[21]
Synthetic samples	NO_3^-	Evaluation of Orion NO_3^- electrode; pH range 4–7	[22]
Synthetic samples	Ca^{2+}	Evaluation of Orion Ca^{2+} electrode; gives cation selectivity ratios, other interferences	[23]
Synthetic samples	K^+	Macrotetrolide impregnated membrane electrode; response not Nernstian but good K^+ to Na^+ selectivity	[24]
Synthetic samples	ClO_4^-	Evaluation of Orion ClO_4^- electrodes; pH range selectivities, dynamic response	[9]
Synthetic samples	$S^=$	Evaluation of Orion $S^=$ electrode; direct potentiometry and titrations	[6]
Synthetic samples	F^-	Orion F^- electrode in acidic media; effect of HF and HF_2^- formation	[4]
Synthetic samples	Ca^{2+}	Evaluation of Corning and Orion liquid membrane Ca^{2+} electrodes; analytical, equilibrium and kinetic studies	[8]
Synthetic samples	Cu^{2+}	Evaluation of Orion Cu^{2+} electrode; pH effect, study of complexes	[7]
Soils	K^+	Beckman 78137 V electrode; conc $\geq 10^{-5}$ M, troubled by interferences (Na^+, NH_4^+)	[25]

Table 14.   Analysis by direct potentiometry using ion—selective electrodes. (continued)

A. Inorganic systems	Ion determined	Conditions and remarks	Ref
Soils and slurries	Na^+	Beckman 78137 V electrode, 1.6 to 500 meq/l; 0.2% relative agreement with flame photometry	[26]
Clay suspensions and marine muds	Na^+	– –	[27]
Boiler water	Na^+	Beckman 78178 V electrode; ppb level, continuous monitoring	[28, 29]
Acidic sol systems	Na^+	Beckman 78137 V electrode; 12–300 ppm Na^+ 5.7% relative deviation compared to flame photometry	[30]
Basin waters	Na^+	Beckman 78178 electrode; 10 to 1.3×10^5 ppm Na^+	[31]
Sea water	Ca^{2+}	Orion Ca^{2+} electrode; Mg^{2+} interferes; 0.3 mV reproducibility	[32]
Sea water	Mg^{2+}	Orion Mg^{2+} electrode	[33]
Synthetic samples	F^-	Orion 94–90 F^- electrode, only OH^- interferes seriously	[34]
Synthetic samples	NH_4^+ (urea, urease)	Beckman 39137 electrode; 3% relative accuracy in millimolar range	[35]
Synthetic samples	$R_n NH_{4-n}^+$	Beckman 39137 electrode; response is size dependent	[36]
Synthetic samples	I^-	AgI membrane electrode, Nernstian response to 10^{-7} M I^-	[37]
Synthetic samples	Cl^-, Br^-	AgCl and AgBr membrane electrodes	[38]
Synthetic samples	Ag^+	Beckman 39278 electrode; little interference from alkali metal ions	[39]

Table 14.   Analysis by direct potentiometry using ion—selective
electrodes. (continued)

A. Inorganic systems	Ion determined	Conditions and remarks	Ref
Synthetic samples	Ag$^+$	Electronic Instruments, Ltd. GNA 23 electrode; good response to 10^{-6} M Ag$^+$, puzzling interference by iron (II).	[40]

B. Biological and living systems	Ion determined	Conditions and remarks	Ref
Blood	Na$^+$, K$^+$ H$^+$, Cl$^-$	Automated determination using glass and silver electrodes in flow system; automatic computation	[41]
Urine	Na$^+$	Beckman 39278 electrode; good agreement with flame photometry	[42]
Serum, plasma, urine, cerebrospinal fluid	Na$^+$	No interference from proteins or uric acid	[43]
Bile	Na$^+$, K$^+$	Find Na$^+$ association	[44]
Tissue extract	Na$^+$, K$^+$	Study of Na$^+$, K$^+$ binding in brain extract	[45, 46]
Nerve and muscle tissue	Na$^+$, K$^+$	Uses microelectrodes to follow ion flux across cell membranes	[47]
Kidneys	Na$^+$, K$^+$	Measurement of ion activities in single kidney tubules	[48]
Cerebral cortex	Na$^+$, K$^+$	Analysis of cerebrospinal fluid as function of physiological variables variables	[49]
Body fluids	Na$^+$, K$^+$	Determination of Na$^+$ and K$^+$ using differential measurement with with analog computer	[50]

Table 15. Potentiometric titrations using ion–selective indicator electrodes.

Ion determined	Titrant	Conditions and remarks	Ref
ClO_4^-	tetraphenyl-arsonium chloride	Orion 92–81 electrode; pH 4–7 range	[51]
F^-	tetraphenyl-antimony sulfate	Orion F^- electrode; involves extraction with chloroform	[52]
F^-	Th^{4+}, La^{3+} Ca^{2+}	Orion F^- electrode; tests usefulness of various titrants and conditions	[53]
Ag^+	$MgCl_2$	Uses NAS_{27-8} electrode; good accuracy but smaller ΔE at end point than same titration with Ag metal electrode	[39, 54]
Ag^+	CN^-	Only AgCN end point (not $Ag(CN)_2^-$ end point) is seen owing to moderate Ag^+ sensitivity of NAS_{27-8} electrode	[54]
K^+	$Ca(B\Phi_4)_2$	Uses NAS_{33-5} electrode; 0.25% relative accuracy at 30 mg level	[55]
K^+, Cs^+, Rb^+, NH_4^+, Ag^+	$Ca(B\Phi_4)_2$	Beckman 39137 electrode; 10–110 mg range, accuracy limited by volumetric technique; sharp "S"– shaped titration curves	[56]
K^+	$Zn(SiF_6)$	Uses NAS_{27-8} electrode; determination of 2–160 mg K^+ in water-methanol solvent with 0.1% relative accuracy; Ca^{2+}, Mg^{2+}, Al^{3+} interfere owing to reaction with F^-	[57]
I^-	$AgClO_4$	AgI membrane electrode; 0.2% relative accuracy at 10^{-4} M I^- level with $\sim$400 mV break at end point	[37]
Ca^{2+}	EDTA	Orion 92–20 Ca^{2+} electrode; pH adjusted to 11 with NH_4OH, rather poor end-point break	[58]

Table 15. Potentiometric titrations using ion-selective indicator electrode. (continued)

Ion determined	Titrant	Conditions and remarks	Ref
F⁻	La(NO₃)₃	Orion 94–09 F⁻ electrode; about 120 mV end-point break for 0.1 M solutions, good agreement with calculated end point	[34]

VI. References

[1] Rechnitz, G. A. Chem. Eng. News 43 (25), 146 (1967).
[2] Eisenman, G., Anal. Chem. 40, 310 (1968).
[3] Rechnitz, G. A., and Kugler, G. C., Anal. Chem. 39, 1682 (1967).
[4] Srinivasan, K., and Rechnitz, G. A., Anal. Chem. 40, 509 (1968).
[5] Srinivasan, K., and Rechnitz, G. A., Anal. Chem. 40, 1818 (1968).
[6] Hseu, T. M., and Rechnitz, G. A., Anal. Chem. 40, 1054 (1968).
[7] Rechnitz, G. A., and Lin, Z. F., Anal. Let. 1, 23 (1967).
[8] Rechnitz, G. A., and Lin, Z. F., Anal. Chem. 40, 696 (1968).
[9] Hseu, T. M., and Rechnitz, G. A., Anal. Let. 1, 629 (1968).
[10] McClure, J. E., and Rechnitz, G. A., Anal. Chem. 38, 136 (1966).
[11] Rechnitz, G. A., and Lin, Z. F., Anal. Chem. 39, 1406 (1967).
[12] Srinivasan, K., and Rechnitz, G. A., Anal. Chem. 40, 1955 (1968).
[13] Carlson, R. M., and Paul, J. L., Anal. Chem. 40, 1292 (1968).
[14] Durst, R.A., Anal. Chem. 40, 931 (1968).
[15] Baumann, E. W., Anal. Chim. Acta 42, 127 (1968).
[16] Lingane, J. J., Anal. Chem. 40, 935 (1968).
[17] Singer, L., and Armstrong, W. D., Anal. Chem. 40, 613 (1968).
[18] VanLoon, J. C., Anal Lett. 1, 393 (1968).
[19] Hawthorn, D., and Ray, N. J., Analyst 93, 158 (1968).
[20] Raby, B. A., and Sunderland, W. E., Anal. Chem. 39, 1304 (1967).
[21] Frant, M. S., Plating, June 1967.
[22] Potterton, S. S., and Shults, W. D., Anal. Lett. 1, 11 (1967).
[23] Ross, J. W., Science 156, 1378 (1967).
[24] Stefanac, Z., and Simon, W., Microchem. J. 12, 125 (1967).
[25] Mortland, M. M., Quart. Bull. Mich. Agric. Exp. Station 43, 491 (1961).
[26] Bower, C. A., Soil Sci. Am. Proc. 23, 19 (1959); 25, 18 (1961).
[27] Siever, R., and Garrels, R. M., Kanwisher, J., Berner, R. A., Science 134, 1071 (1961).
[28] Jones, R. H., Ind. Water Eng. 1, March-April 1964.
[29] Mattock, G., Anal. Chem. Proc. Intern. Symp. 59, 247 (1963).
[30] Taulli, T. A., Anal. Chem. 32, 186 (1960).
[31] Truesdell, A. H., Jones, B. F., and VanDenburgh, A. S., Geochim. Cosmochim. Acta 29, 725 (1965).
[32] Thompson, M. E., and Ross, J. W., Science 154, 1643 (1966).
[33] Thompson, M. E., Science 153, 866 (1966).
[34] Frant, M. S., and Ross, J. W., Science 154, 1553 (1966).
[35] Katz, S. A., and Rechnitz, G. A., Z. anal. Chem. 196, 248 (1963).

[36] Rechnitz, G. A., and Kugler, G., Z. anal. Chem. **210**, 174 (1965).

[37] Rechnitz, G. A., Kresz, M. R., and Zamochnick, S. B., Anal. Chem. **38**, 973 (1966).

[38] Rechnitz, G. A., and Kresz, M. R., Anal. Chem. **38**, 1786 (1966).

[39] Budd, A. L., J. Electroanal. Chem. **5**, 35 (1963).

[40] Bishop, E., and Dhaneshwar, R. G., Analyst **88**, 424, 442 (1963).

[41] Dahms, H., Clin. Chem. **13**, 437 (1967).

[42] Annino, J. S., Clin. Chem. **13**, 227 (1967).

[43] Moore, E. W., and Wilson, D. W., J. Clin. Invest. **42**, 293 (1963).

[44] Diamond, J., J. Physiol. (London) **161**, 442 (1962).

[45] Ungar, G., Cytologia **1**, 622 (1959).

[46] Ungar, G., and Romano, D. V., Fed. Proc. **18**, 162 (1959).

[47] Hinke, J. A., Nature **184**, 1257 (1959); J. Physiol. **156**, 314 (1961).

[48] Khuri, R. N., et al., Amer. J. Physiol. **204**, 743 (1963).

[49] Portnoy, H. D., Thomas, L. M., and Gurdjian, E. S., Arch. Neurol. **8**, 597 (1963).

[50] Friedman, S. M., and Bowers, F. K., Anal. Biochem. **5**, 471 (1963).

[51] Baczuk, R. J., and DuBois, R. J., Anal. Chem. **40**, 685 (1968).

[52] Orenberg, J. B., and Morris, M. D., Anal. Chem. **39**, 1776 (1967).

[53] Lingane, J. J., Anal. Chem. **39**, 881 (1967).

[54] Geyer, R., Chojnacki, K., and Stief, C., Z. anal. Chem. **200**, 326 (1964).

[55] Geyer, R., and Grank, H., Z. anal. Chem. **179**, 99 (1961).

[56] Rechnitz, G. A., Zamochnick, S. B., and Katz, S. A., Anal. Chem. **35**, 1322 (1963).

[57] Geyer, R., Chojnacki, K., Erxleben, W., and Syring, W., Z. anal. Chem. **204**, 325 (1964).

[58] Instruction Manual, Model 92-20 Electrode, Orion Research, Inc., Cambridge, Mass., 1966.

CHAPTER 10

INDUSTRIAL ANALYSIS AND CONTROL WITH ION-SELECTIVE ELECTRODES

Truman S. Light

The Foxboro Company
Foxboro, Massachusetts

I. Introduction

Industrial analysis is a term applied to analytical composition information derived from a continuous signal which may be used for monitoring or control purposes. Industrial analysis ("continuous analysis," "on-line analysis" or "process analysis") for the most part derives its principles from laboratory analytical practices and procedures. However, laboratory analytical instrumentation is seldom suitable for direct use in the plant. The industrial analysis instrument continuously receives samples from the process or environment and continuously sends out a signal with information about the composition of the sample. A person must bring a sample to the "automatic" laboratory instrument, read the answer, interpret the results and take appropriate action. The process analytical instrument is not privileged to sit with the chemist in an air-conditioned laboratory, but must receive its sample "as is" from a process which often runs at extreme temperatures and pressures.

It is not surprising that ion-selective electrode applications should appear promising to the industrial analytical field. Ion-selective electrodes may be placed into a process solution and will transmit an electrical signal that characterizes the composition of the solution. This information is obtained rapidly and may be utilized to operate a controller, or as a process computer input. Large-scale industrial production has created waste problems. The composition of plant effluents, both liquid and gaseous, have become of considerable concern. In many cases, ion-selective electrodes could permit continuous analysis of these effluent streams.

The present paper discusses the principles and operation of ion-selective electrodes related to their use in industrial analytical instrumentation. Many applications for ion-selective electrodes have been recognized and developed since the first industrial uses were discussed two years ago [1].

II. Ion-Selective Electrodes

An ion-selective electrode is defined simply as an indicator or measuring electrode with a relatively high degree of specificity for a single ion or a class of ions. The glass electrode for pH measurement (hydrogen ion activity) was the earliest ion-selective electrode to attain widespread use. It became commercially available with accompanying instrumentation in the 1930's. The theory and application of the glass pH electrode for both laboratory and industrial use have been well documented [2,3]. Around 1959, two more ion-selective electrodes of the glass electrode family became commercially available. One of these was for sodium, the other for potassium, silver and other univalent cations. The glass electrode family has also been thoroughly treated in the literature [4,5]. Beginning in 1966, two new classes of ion-selective electrodes, solid-state and liquid ion exchange, were introduced. New electrodes are still being introduced and, consequently, the literature is in a state of growth. Detailed discussion of the construction, characteristics, limitations, and applications of these electrodes are presented elsewhere in this publication, *e.g.*, Chapters 2 and 3. In Table 1, a current list of the commercially available laboratory model ion-selective electrodes is given with some of their chemical limitations. This list, which can be divided into three classifications — glass, solid-state and liquid ion exchange — now numbers over 20 electrodes.

Table 1. Commercially available ion—selective electrodes, 1969.

Electrode designated for	Class[a]	pH range	Principal interferences
Bromide	S	0 – 14	CN^-, I^-, $S^=$
Cadmium	S	1 – 14	Ag^+, Hg^{++}, Cu^{++}, Fe^{++}, Pb^{++}
Calcium	L	5.5 – 11	Zn^{++}, Fe^{++}, Pb^{++}, Cu^{++}, Ni^{++}
Chloride	S	0 – 14	Br^-, I^-, $S^=$, CN^-, SCN^-, NH_3
Chloride	L	2 – 10	ClO_4^-, I^-, NO_3^-, Br^-, OH^-, OAc^-, HCO_3^-, $SO_4^=$, F^-
Cyanide	S	0 – 14	$S^=$, I^-
Cupric	S	0 – 14	Ag^+, Hg^{++}, Fe^{+++}

Table 1. Commercially available ion–selective electrodes, 1969 (continued).

Electrode designated for	Class[a]	pH range	Principal interferences
Fluoride	S	0 – 8.5	OH^-
Fluoroborate	L	2 – 12	I^-, NO_3^-, Br^-, OAc^-, HCO_3^-
Iodide	S	0 – 14	$S^=$, CN^-
Lead	S	2 – 14	Ag^+, Hg^{++}, Cu^{++}, Cd^{++}, Fe^{++}
Lead	L	3.5 – 7.5	Cu^{++}, Fe^{++}, Zn^{++}, Ca^{++}, Ni^{++}, Mg^{++},
Nitrate	L	2 – 12	ClO_4^-, I^-, ClO_3^-, Br^-, $S^=$, NO_2^-, CN^-, HCO_3^-, Cl^-, OAc^-, $CO_3^=$, $S_2O_3^=$, $SO_3^=$
Perchlorate	L	4 – 10	OH^-, I^-, NO_3^-
Hydrogen (pH)	G	0 – 14	
ORP (OX–RED POT.)	S	0 – 14	All redox systems
Potassium	G	7 – 13	H^+, Ag^+, NH_4^+, Na^+, Li^+
Silver	S	0 – 14	Hg^{++}
Silver	G	4 – 8	H^+
Sodium	G	3 – 12	Ag^+, H^+, Li^+, K^+
Sulfide	S	0 – 14	
Thiocyanate	S	0 – 14	I^-, Br^-, Cl^-, $S_2O_3^=$, NH_3
Water Hardness	L	5.5 – 11	Zn^{++}, Fe^{++}, Cu^{++}, Ni^{++}, Ba^{++}, Sr^{++}

[a] G = Glass; L = Liquid Ion Exchange; S = Solid State.

Application of any of these electrodes to a given problem should be made only after consideration of the manufacturer's and other literature, and the physical and chemical limitations of the electrodes. The principles of construction of these three classes of electrodes may be seen in Figures 1 and 2. In Figure 1, the construction of the glass electrode with its glass

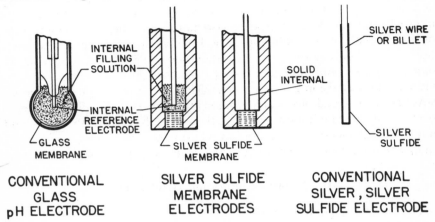

Figure 1.   Construction of glass electrode and silver sulfide membrane electrode.

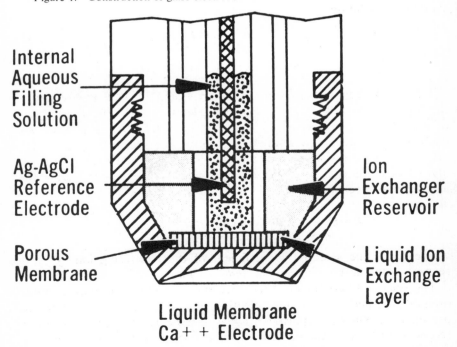

Figure 2.   Construction of liquid ion exchange electrode (Orion Research Inc.).

ion-selective membrane, internal filling solution and internal reference electrode is compared with the solid-state sulfide ion electrode. Also shown in Figure 1 is a slightly different form of the sulfide ion electrode with a solid internal contact to the membrane [6]. This form is of special interest to industrial process monitoring because it minimizes the pressure and temperature limitations imposed upon electrodes with aqueous internal solutions. The electrode is also more stable due to the elimination of the internal solution/solid interface. Finally, Figure 1 shows a conventional silver-silver sulfide wire electrode which is susceptible to oxidation-reduction potential errors [7]. Figure 2 shows a cross-section view of the liquid ion exchange electrode. These electrodes have more severe chemical and physical limitations than the glass or solid-state electrodes; yet these limitations are more than offset by the fact that the liquid ion exchange electrodes are able to measure certain cations and anions that have not previously been accessible by direct potentiometry [8].

III. Nernst Equation and Modifications

The Nernst equation provides the basic means of interpreting the potentiometric output of an ion-selective electrode in terms of the ion activity in the solution[1]:

$$E = E° + (0.19841T/n) \log a_i \tag{1}$$

A. SELECTIVITY COEFFICIENT

The simple form of the Nernst equation, Equation (1), explains most of the performance of the pH sensitive glass electrode. With the introduction of additional ion-selective glass electrodes, solid-state and liquid ion exchange electrodes, it was found that many electrodes responded to ions other than those for which they were designated. A modified form of the Nernst equation is now commonly used to describe the performance of ion-selective electrodes [4,5].

$$E = E° + (0.19841T/n) \log (a_i + K_{ij}a_j^m + . . .) \tag{2}$$

where K_{ij} is the selectivity coefficient of the interfering ion "j" with respect to the designated ion "i" and "m" may be an integer or fraction.

The selectivity coefficient "K_{ij}" becomes a useful quantitative tool to predict whether a given ion-selective electrode may be used in the presence of known impurities. Table 1 indicates the principal interferences for most of the presently available ion-selective electrodes. For

[1]Nomenclature is appended to this chapter.

quantitative evaluation of the selectivity coefficient, it is usually necessary to consult the manufacturer's literature. For example, a common form of the sodium sensitive glass electrode is made from a glass designated as $NAS_{11\text{-}18}$. For this glass, K_{NaH} is approximately 30 [9]. The electrode is then understood to be 30 times more sensitive to the hydrogen ion than to the sodium ion, even though it is designated as sodium sensitive. If the sodium electrode of this example is to be used to measure a one millimolar solution of sodium ion with an accuracy of 3%, then the hydrogen ion concentration must be less than $10^{-6}M$ (pH greater than 6). For direct measurement of sodium ion activity, it follows that the sodium ion electrode is more useful in alkaline solutions than in acid solutions. However, Equation (2) also indicates the possibility of using multiple ion-selective electrodes. For example, if sodium ion must be measured in acid solutions, an additional glass electrode may be introduced to measure the pH of the solution and from Equation (2) and the known selectivity coefficient, K_{NaH}, the corrected activity of the sodium ion in the acid solution may be calculated.

B. TEMPERATURE COEFFICIENTS

The fundamental form of the Nernst equation given in Equation (1) is valid only at constant temperature.

The temperature variation of ion-selective electrodes may be described by differentiating Equation (1) with respect to temperature [10]:

$$(dE/dT)_{th} = (dE°/dT)_{th} + (0.19841/n) \log a_i +$$

$$(0.19841T/n) (d \log a_i/dT) \tag{3}$$

The overall effect of changing the temperature of an ion-selective electrode immersed in a solution, $(dE/dT)_{th}$, may be better understood if it is divided into three separate contributions:

1. $(dE°/dT)_{th}$ is the standard temperature coefficient of the ion-selective electrode. This is a quantity that is characteristic of the particular ion-selective electrode, or of the ion-selective electrode and its reference electrode in a cell. Very little has been reported to date on temperature coefficients for ion-selective electrodes. In such cases as the sulfide ion electrode, the temperature coefficients of ion-selective electrodes and classical electrode systems coincide [7]. In other cases, such as the glass pH sensitive electrode, the standard temperature coefficient is a function not only of the electrode's membrane material but also of the internal electrode and the internal filling solution. Here the standard temperature coefficient may depend upon the manufacturer's design and individual batch variations. The temperature coefficients may be

minimized by adjustment of internal electrode composition and matching to the reference electrode.

2. $(0.19841/n)$ log a_i is the temperature coefficient slope term of the Nernst equation. This is the temperature correction usually performed by the manual or automatic temperature compensator of the modern pH or ion-selective meter. This temperature coefficient term corrects for the temperature slope change of the log a_i vs. E relationship of the Nernst equation. A frequently occurring error in using pH or ion-selective meters is caused when it is assumed that this is the only cause for variation of observed emf's with temperature.

3. $(0.19841T/n)(\mathrm{d}$ log $a_i/\mathrm{d}T)$ is the solution temperature coefficient term. The activity of an ion may be affected by its activity coefficient and for weak or complex forming electrolytes by its equilibrium relationships. Since activity coefficients and equilibrium constants may each have temperature coefficients of their own, the "solution temperature coefficient" term may become quite complex. For the pH standard solutions used in the calibration of pH meters, Bates and coworkers of the National Bureau of Standards have painstakingly prepared temperature coefficient tables [11]. The establishment of reference materials, solutions, and the temperature coefficients for ion-selective electrodes largely remains to be done.

Another small, but measurable temperature coefficient effect is contributed by the third term for the "solution temperature coefficient." The Nernst equation is valid for the use of any suitable units for the activity term a_i. Concentration or activity expressed in "molal" units are dependent on mass and are, therefore, temperature independent. However, it is more common to express concentration in molar units which are volume (and, therefore, temperature) dependent. Thus, the latter temperature coefficient term also includes the dilution correction caused by the expansion of most solutions upon heating. Quantitatively, this would be measured by the temperature dependence of the solution density.

C. Accuracy

The accuracy of measurements derived from any analytical system is a composite of all contributing variables. There are several possible sources of error in ion-selective electrode measurement. These include: the measuring electrode, the reference electrode, including the liquid junction potential, the measuring system (converter and recorder), temperature, solution errors, and the Nernst equation relationship.

The relationship between overall emf errors, ΔE, and concentration, C, may be derived from the Nernst equation, Equation (1), by taking the derivative with respect to concentration:

$$\Delta E = (0.2568/n)\,(100\,\Delta C/C) \qquad \text{(mV at 25°C)} \qquad \text{(4a)}$$

$$\Delta E = (0.2568/n)\,(RE) \qquad\qquad \text{(4b)}$$

A plot of Equation (4b) is given in Figure 3. The relative error in concentration, RE, is dependent only on the error in the emf and is independent of the concentration range, and of the size of the sample being measured. For an electrode responding to univalent ions, an overall error of

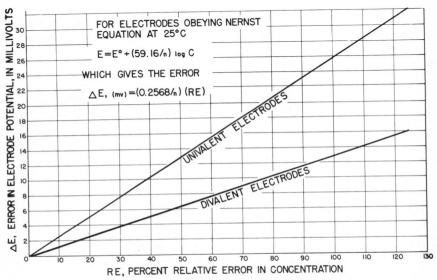

Figure 3.   Theoretical error in potential as a function of relative error in concentration.

1 mV corresponds to a 3.9 percent relative error in concentration; for an electrode responding to divalent ions, the relative error is 7.8 percent per mV.

Measuring instruments using ion-selective electrodes have become commercially available with an accuracy of ± 0.1 mV. They are capable of measuring through the high impedance characteristic of the electrodes. Glass electrodes for pH have almost perfect response, following the Nernst equation over a wide pH range with measuring instruments capable of ± 0.1 mV accuracy [12]. The accuracy attained to date has been limited by the measuring instruments and reference electrodes rather than the ion-selective electrodes. Stability and accuracy of about 0.01 mV may be predicted from properly planned and interpreted ion-selective electrode measurements. Meaningful interpretation of analytical information to 0.1 percent relative error is then possible.

IV. Activity and Concentration

Analytical composition information may be desired either in terms of the ionic activity, a_i of Equation (1), or in terms of the analytical concentration, C_i, as determined by many classically used analytical chemistry procedures. Either activity or concentration information may be obtained from properly planned ion-selective measurement readings. The relationship between activity and concentration is given simply by:

$$a_i = \gamma_i C_i \tag{5}$$

The single ion activity coefficient, γ_i, may be derived both theoretically and empirically; in "real" chemical solutions, it usually differs significantly from unity. It is principally a function of the ionic strength of the solution, I:

$$I = (1/2) \sum_i C_i z_i^2 \tag{6}$$

Correlation of the single ion activity coefficient with the ionic strength of a solution has been provided by the Debye-Hückel equation applicable to dilute solutions:

$$-\log \gamma_i = \frac{A z_i^2 \sqrt{I}}{1 + B\sqrt{I}} \tag{7}$$

Tabulated data for estimated single ion and mean ionic activity coefficients in solutions of various ionic strengths are available [13,14].

In practice, more information is available for mean ion activity coefficients than for single ion activity coefficients. Single ion activity coefficients are not accessible to direct measurement and require adoption of a convention, such as the Debye-Hückel Equation (7). Single ion activity coefficients, nevertheless, are needed for interpretation of ion-selective electrode data derived from Equation (1).

Since the standardization, interpretation and application of ion-selective electrodes depend on standard reference materials of known activity, it is encouraging to note that Bates and coworkers of the National Bureau of Standards have initiated studies dealing with the standardization of ion-selective electrodes [15] and ionic activity scales [16].

A. FREE AND TOTAL ION CONCENTRATION

Ion-selective electrodes measure ionic activity, as shown in Equations (1) and (2). The ionic activity is frequently less than the ionic concentration, the relationship being expressed by the activity coefficient of Equation (5). There is still another factor which may make the observed ion activity less than the total ion concentration. This is the tendency for ions in solution to associate with other ions to form undissociated molecules. Examples of this are the formation of weak acids, weak bases, insoluble precipitates and complex molecules or ions. For example, the weak acid, HA, is slightly dissociated:

$$HA = H^+ + A^- \tag{8}$$

and obeys the following equilibrium expression:

$$K_a = \frac{a_{H^+} a_{A^-}}{a_{HA}} \tag{9}$$

Using the activity coefficient concept introduced in Equation (5), the equilibrium expression may be written in terms of the concentrations and activity coefficients:

$$K_a = \frac{\gamma_{H^+} C_{H^+} \gamma_{A^-} C_{A^-}}{\gamma_{HA} C_{HA}} \tag{10}$$

and solved for the activity of the hydrogen ion,

$$a_{H^+} = \gamma_{H^+} C_{H^+} = \left(\frac{C_{HA} \gamma_{HA}}{C_{A^-} \gamma_{A^-}}\right) K_a \tag{11}$$

The Nernst equation for the glass pH electrode may then be written in terms of concentrations and activity coefficients:

$$E = E° + (0.19841 T/n) \log\left(\frac{C_{HA} \gamma_{HA}}{C_{A^-} \gamma_{A^-}}\right) K_a \tag{12}$$

In practice, Equation (12) is difficult to use for interpretation of ion-selective electrode emf's. Not only does it lack simplicity, but frequently, data for activity coefficients and equilibrium constants are not available for "real" solutions of varying ionic strength and unknown quantities of impurities.

B. HIGH IONIC STRENGTH MEDIUM

By introducing the concept of the high ionic strength medium, Equation (12) may be simplified and made to be direct in terms of concentration. The high ionic strength medium contains an inert electrolyte, not normally present in the test solution, in large enough concentration to swamp out the ionic strength contribution of the test solution itself. Equation (12) may then be simplified for interpretation in terms of concentration:

$$E = E^{\circ\prime} + (0.19841\,T/n)\,\log C_{H^+}. \tag{13}$$

The constant, $E^{\circ\prime}$, of Equation (13) may be determined by calibrating the ion-selective electrode cell with a standard solution of known concentration which has been suitably mixed with the high ionic strength medium. By treating the unknown solution in the same fashion as the standard, one calibration curve serves to determine the concentration of a given ion in a solution regardless of the original environment of that ion. In some cases, the high ionic strength medium may be refined to include a pH buffer and complexing agents to eliminate the effect of interferences. An excellent example is furnished by the medium called "TISAB" (Total Ionic Strength Adjustment Buffer) [17], and used for directly measuring the concentration of fluoride ion in public water supplies and many other media. The composition of TISAB is given in Table 2.

Table 2. Composition of "TISAB", a high ionic strength buffered complexing medium for measuring fluoride ion concentration [Anal. Chem. **40**, 1169 (1968)].

Sodium Chloride	1.0M
Acetic Acid	0.25M
Sodium Acetate	0.75M
Sodium Citrate	0.001M
pH	5.0
Ionic Strength	1.75M

In use, equal volumes of the sample and TISAB are mixed thus fixing the ionic strength high enough to make the activity coefficients of unknowns and standards virtually identical. The optimum pH range for the fluoride electrode is at pH 5 and this is provided by the sodium acetate-acetic acid buffer. Some citrate ion is added to preferentially complex metal ions such as iron and aluminum and insure that the fluoride ion is displaced into the solution as "free" fluoride.

V. Industrial Modes for Using Ion-Selective Electrodes

Industrial analytical instruments differ from laboratory instruments in that operation must be continuous without operator attention and that more extreme sampling and environment conditions may be encountered. Operations such as zeroing and standardization must be automatic and maintenance should be minimal. The final signal emitted from the industrial analytical instrument must be a known function of the process composition and compatible with recording, controlling, and computing equipment.

Several methods of incorporating ion-selective electrodes in continuous process analytical instruments may be devised. Figure 4 shows an ion-selective electrode, *M*, and a reference electrode, *R*, monitoring a

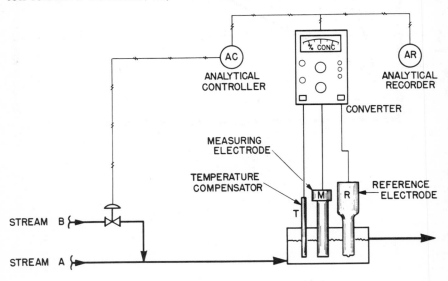

Figure 4.   Ion-selective electrode process control system.

stream by direct potentiometry in a flow-through cell. The process or sample stream is continuously flowing past the electrodes. The outputs of the electrodes and the temperature compensator, *T*, are fed into a converter which then permits continuous analytical recording, *AR*, and controlling, *AC*, of the process stream. This system is applicable to streams in which the ion-selective electrodes encounter no interferences. The monitoring of pH in a variety of process and waste monitoring systems is well established.

The feasibility of monitoring ion exchange water purification units with water hardness electrodes has been demonstrated [18]. A continuous monitor for fluoride ion analysis in potable water supplies has also been described [19]. Figure 5 illustrates the analysis of two water supplies, with and without added fluoride, as performed by the continuous analysis system and shows that 40 mV of "signal" exists between the two concentration levels. Furthermore, this continuous analysis system makes use of

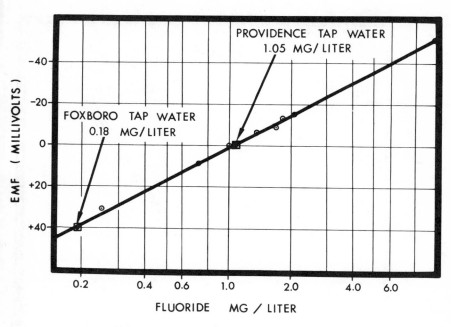

Figure 5.   Fluoride in potable water supplies.

the symmetrical cell principle [2] to achieve measurements independent of the temperature at the iso-potential point of 1 mg F$^-$/l. This reduction of the temperature coefficient to virtually zero is illustrated in Figure 6 and is achieved by filling both the measuring and reference electrodes with the same internal solution. A schematic drawing of the continuous fluoride monitor is shown in Figure 7.

The monitoring of the sulfide ion in the paper and pulp industry is another application of the direct monitoring system which is being studied. The digesting liquor of the Kraft pulping process is an alkaline mixture of sodium sulfide. At many points in the process stream, there exists a need for sulfide analysis information. At one stage in the process, the spent black liquor is subjected to oxidation by air or oxygen to reduce sulfur losses and minimize release of malodorous gases such as hydrogen sulfide, mercaptans and methyl sulfides. Figure 8, based on laboratory studies [20], shows the monitoring of black liquor with both a sulfide and an ORP (oxidation-reduction potential) platinum electrode while the solution is being purged with oxygen to reduce the sulfide content.

At the start of the oxidation, it can be learned from a suitable calibration curve used in conjunction with Figure 8 that the sodium sulfide content is equivalent to 4 g Na_2S/l (corresponding to -810 mV).

This is reduced by 99.9 percent (*i.e.*, three 30 mV decades) within a half hour. Within the next half hour, the sulfide decreases substantially

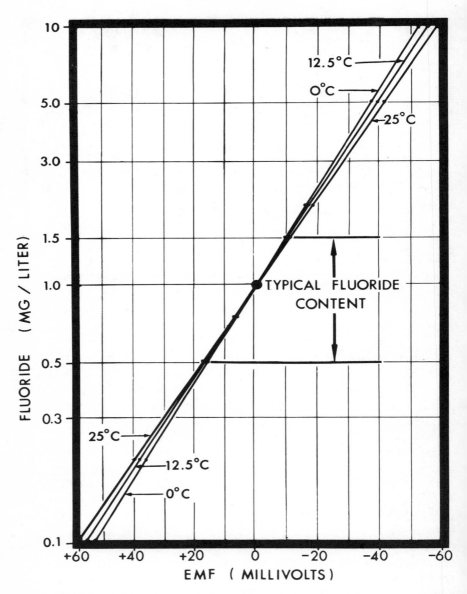

Figure 6. Response of matched fluoride and reference electrodes as a function of temperature.

further by 12 more decades (360 mV), but at a different rate than the reaction of the first half hour. The third half hour brings even more startling results in that the sulfide ion activity now increases as oxygen continues to bubble through the solution. Finally, in the fourth half hour, the

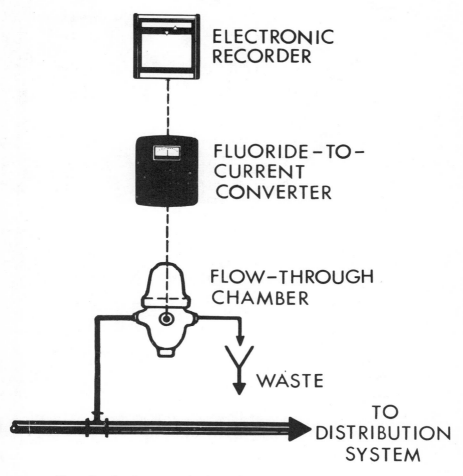

ELECTRONIC
RECORDER

FLUORIDE-TO-
CURRENT
CONVERTER

FLOW-THROUGH
CHAMBER

WASTE

TO
DISTRIBUTION
SYSTEM

Figure 7. Continuous monitoring of fluoride in potable water supplies.

new supply of sulfide is also oxidized and the sulfide content is reduced to the "mud" level of the solution and the electrode, about -300 mV corresponding to 10^{-18} molar sulfide ion. Although studies are incomplete, it appears that the sulfide is present in two main forms. Inorganic sulfides, such as sodium sulfide, which are 50 percent or more dissociated to "free" sulfide ion in the strongly alkaline (pH>12) black liquor, and organic sulfides, such as the mercaptans and methyl sulfides, which are dissociated in only trace amounts, are both found in the black liquor. The inorganic sulfides are readily oxidized within the first half hour. The organic sulfides are oxidized more slowly, with the rate of dissociation being the limiting step of the reaction. The reappearance of sulfide has been noted when one of the products of oxidation is elemental sulfur [21,22]. The

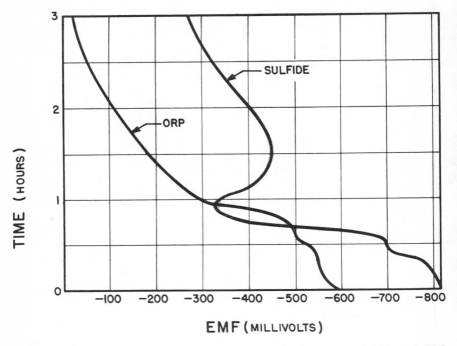

Figure 8. Oxygen purging of black liquor solution monitored with sulfide and ORP (oxidation reduction potential) electrodes.

ORP electrode follows the oxidation procedure in a manner similar to the sulfide electrode, but without the specificity to characterize the slope and rate changes observed by the sulfide electrode.

Figure 9 illustrates multiple ion-selective electrodes, M_A, M_B, and M_C, in a flow-through cell. Such an installation may be used for measuring several constituents simultaneously, or for permitting a correction to be made to an ion-selective electrode by a signal processor. For example, the cyanide ion electrode measures only free cyanide ion which exists for practical purposes only in alkaline solutions. If the cyanide ion electrode were to be used for monitoring pollution in a stream which might have neutral or acid pH, the electrode reading could not be interpreted without a knowledge of the pH. Introducing both the pH and cyanide ion electrodes and a signal processor for making the necessary pH correction derived from Equations (8) through (12) would permit continuous monitoring of the total cyanide content of the stream. A computer solution for cation analysis using sodium and potassium electrodes has been reported [23].

Figure 10 illustrates another possible method of compensating for the ion-selective electrodes which are not completely selective to the ion

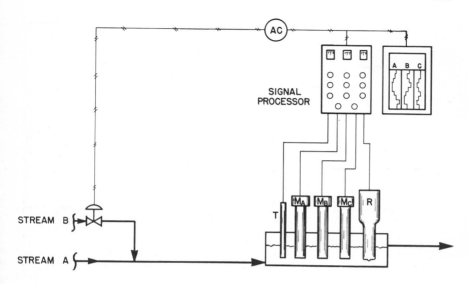

Figure 9. Multiple ion-selective electrodes process control system.

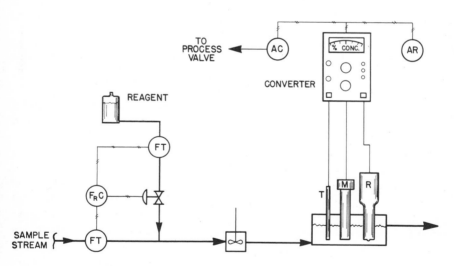

Figure 10. Ion-selective electrode system with reagent addition.

whose measurement is desired. This system would permit reagent addition to the sample stream before it is measured by the ion-selective electrode. For example, pH is a constantly recurring limitation of ion-selective electrodes. Injection of a suitable buffer in a sufficiently small quantity so as to not significantly dilute the stream would extend the useful measuring range of many electrodes. Figure 10 illustrates a flow ratio controller, $F_R C$, used to control the ratio of reagent to sample, each of which has been measured by passing through flow transmitters, FT. An application of the reagent addition system is afforded by looking again at fluoride analysis in public water supplies. Figure 11 shows that direct potentiometry for fluoride determinations at the 1 mg/l level is suitable in the

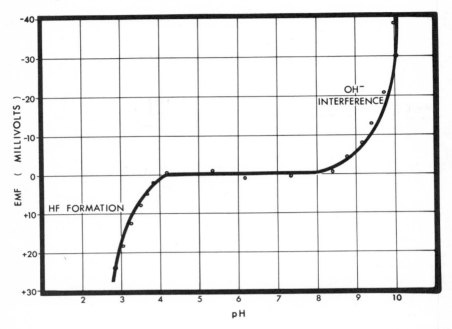

Figure 11.   Response of the fluoride electrode as a function of pH at the 1 mg F⁻/l level.

pH range of 4 to 8.5 [24]. This range includes over 90% of the public water supplies of the United States. Above pH 8.5, the electrode also responds to hydroxide ion. By using the reagent addition system in Figure 10 and a buffered reagent such as TISAB, the fluoride content of any water regardless of its pH could be monitored. Thus plants employing hydrofluoric acid would have a system for guarding against loss of this hazardous and corrosive reagent.

The reagent addition system in Figure 10 could also be used with gaseous reagents. The sodium ion electrode has already been noted as not useful for direct monitoring of low levels of sodium in acid solutions. A system for continuously monitoring the sodium level of high purity water used in boilers has been reported using injection of gaseous ammonia to assure that the solution is alkaline when sodium ion is measured [25].

Figure 12 illustrates the use of ion-selective electrodes as end-point detectors in continuous titration analysis. Such a system would involve measurement of both the sample and reagent, as well as provide a sequencing

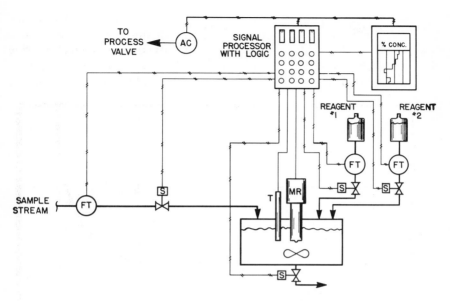

Figure 12. Continuous process titrator, ion-selective electrode end-point detector.

logic to control sample and reagent addition, readout and drain cycles. The inherent accuracy of a few tenths of a percent offered by the titration principle could be achieved with a system such as this. Also, the vast literature and methodology of titrations that are already used in quality control laboratories would become accessible to instrumentation.

Even though ion-selective electrodes are inherently devices for measuring ions in solution, Figure 13 shows how they could be adapted to monitoring gas streams. By scrubbing the gaseous constituents with a suitable reagent and measuring the quantity of gas and of reagent solution with flow transmitters, FT, and the concentration of the resulting solution with an ion-selective electrode, the quantity of the gas in the sample stream could be monitored with the signal processor. A system like that in Figure 12 might be applied to the monitoring of gaseous pollutants with the aid of ion-selective electrodes such as sulfide, cyanide and fluoride. The fluoride ion electrode has been applied to monitoring of fluoride in air and stack gas effluents such as are emitted from the environment of various industrial processes [26].

Ion-selective electrodes may even be applied to the analysis of ions for which ion-selective electrodes are not yet known. This is possible if the desired ion can be found to enter into a reaction with an ion for which an electrode exists. Such an application is shown in Figure 14 which involves the principle of differential analysis using reagent addition. If a

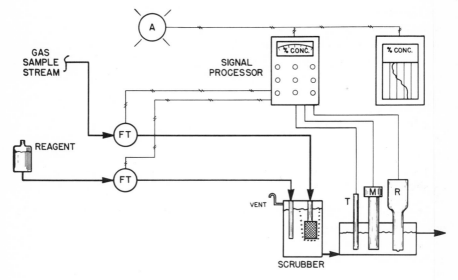

Figure 13.   Continuous gas analyzer using ion-selective electrode.

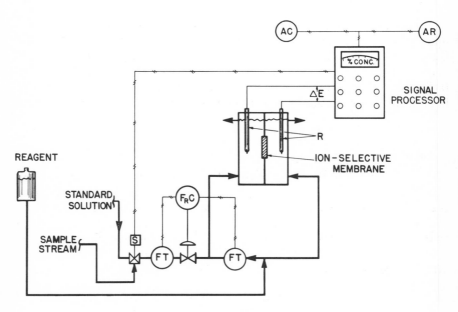

Figure 14.   Differential cell with ion-selective membrane.

flow-through cell is constructed as shown in Figure 14 with two compartments separated by an ion-selective membrane, then a reagent stream
may be made to flow directly over the surface of the membrane in the

right hand compartment. The same reagent stream, measured by a flow transmitter, FT, and mixed with the sample stream by a flow ratio controller, F_RC, then flows past the second surface of the membrane. The difference in activity between the two surfaces of the membrane is measured as the difference in potential, ΔE, between the two reference electrodes, R. Although similar in principle to the reagent addition system of Figure 10, greater measurement precision ought to be attainable because many minor errors, such as temperature drifting and changes in reagent solution, would be self-canceling. In practice, this instrument would be zeroed by permitting the reagent to flow past both membrane surfaces and calibrated to full scale by use of a standard solution injected as shown in Figure 14.

An application of this differential analysis cell may be illustrated in connection with the problem of aluminum analysis [18]. An electrode selective for aluminum ion does not yet exist, but aluminum is known to form a strong complex with fluoride:

$$Al^{3+} + \bar{n}F^- = AlF_{\bar{n}} \tag{14}$$

Table 3 shows some data obtained when small amounts of a standard aluminum solution are added to a specially prepared high ionic strength fluoride reagent solution buffered to pH 5. The composition of this reagent is similar to that of the TISAB solution of Table 2, except that $0.0526M$ sodium fluoride is added and the citrate is omitted. The change in emf, ΔE, upon the addition of aluminum solution to the fluoride reagent

Table 3. Addition of ΔV ml of 0.0945 M $AlCl_3$ to 100 ml of specially buffered fluoride solution (see text).

ΔV	E	ΔE	Y	X	K	K'
(ml)	(mV)	(mV)		(ml^{-1})	(mmoles Al)	(mg Al)
0	−26.6					
1	−23.6	3.0	1.124	0.1014	0.932	25.15
2	−20.2	6.4	1.283	0.1025	0.922	24.88
3	−16.4	10.2	1.487	0.1024	0.923	24.90
				(Average)	0.926	25.0

may be correlated to the concentration of the aluminum by the following equations:

$$C_{Al} = KX \tag{15}$$

where

$$X = \frac{[Y - 1 - (\Delta V / V_0)]}{Y \Delta V} \tag{16}$$

$$Y = 10^{(\Delta E / 0.19841 T)} \tag{17}$$

$$K = \frac{V_0 C_F}{\bar{n}} \tag{18}$$

From the data in Table 3, it is possible to show that $\bar{n}$, the fluoride to aluminum ratio, is 5.7 and this is sensibly constant over at least a 10 mV span for ΔE. This differential analysis system has been applied in the laboratory to the determination of aluminum in some simulated Bayer liquor solutions, which are process fluids in the aluminum industries. The principal ingredients of this liquor are sodium aluminate, sodium hydroxide and sodium carbonate.

Table 4 shows the results of several of these analyses and illustrates that relative errors of less than 4 percent for the analysis of aluminum may be obtained if the emf data are accurate to the order of 0.1 mV.

Table 4. Analysis of simulated Bayer liquor solutions containing $NaAlO_2$, $NaOH$ and Na_2CO_3.

Solution	ΔV (ml)	ΔE (mV)	Aluminum found (g/l)	Aluminum theoretical (g/l)	Relative error (%)
1	1.00	3.1	2.62	2.65	−1.1
2	1.00	4.9	4.13	4.23	−2.4
3	1.00	4.5	3.82	3.83	−0.3
4	1.00	7.9	6.44	6.21	+3.70

The preceding discussion has shown that applications of ion-selective electrodes to problems of industrial analysis are just emerging. A few of the applications have already resulted in commercially available analytical instrumentation; many of them have had feasibility demonstrated, and it may be anticipated they will be adopted as their significance becomes appreciated and indeed as ion-selective electrodes themselves become accepted as another modern tool required by analytical chemists to give quantitative information accurately and efficiently.

Table 5 singles out approximately half of the commercially available electrodes listed in Table 1 as having special promise for industrial and

Table 5. Suggested industrial and pollution monitoring applications of ion—selective electrodes.

Electrode designated for:	Possible application
Cadmium	Plating Solutions, Industrial Wastes
Calcium and/or Water Hardness	Boiler and Process Feedwater, Water Softening and Ion Exchange Equipment, Water Treatment Plants
Chloride	Water Brackishness, Desalination; Food, Pharmaceutical, and other Industries
Cyanide	Liquid and Gaseous Waste Pollution Monitoring, Cyanide Oxidation Systems, Plating and Rinse Tanks, Metal Finishing and Extraction Processes
Cupric	Plating and Rinse Tanks, Etching Baths for Printed Circuit Board Manufacture, Ore Extraction Processes, Industrial and Mining Waste Water
Fluoride	Potable Water Monitoring, Stream and Stack Gas Effluents in Aluminum and Phosphate Ore Industries, Monitoring for Hydrofluoric Acid Leaks in Industrial Processes
Fluoroborate	Plating Baths, Measurement of Boron Following Conversion to Fluoroborate
Nitrate	Water Supplies, Sewage
Silver	Photographic Industry — Emulsions and Fixing Solutions
Sodium	Food Industry, Natural, Brackish and Industrial Process Waters, Break Through of Ion Exchange Units
Sulfide	Water, Stack Gas and Air Pollution Monitoring, Paper Pulp and Petroleum Industry, Drilling Muds

pollution monitoring applications. Table 5 also lists some possible industrial and pollution monitoring applications of these electrodes. It is anticipated that this list will continue to grow within the next few years.

Nomenclature

A	constant of the Debye-Hückel equation
a_i	activity of ion "i"
B	constant of the Debye-Hückel equation
C_i	concentration of ion "i"
ΔC	error in concentration
E	emf of an electrode (in mV)
E°	standard emf of an electrode (in mV)
ΔE	change of emf of an electrode upon addition of aluminum solution; also used to denote error in electrode measurement (in mV)
K, K'	constant defined in Equation (18) and Table 3
K_a	acid dissociation constant
K_{ij}	selectivity coefficient of ion "j" with respect to ion "i"
m	an integer or fraction
n	an integer corresponding to the electron change in an electrode reaction
$\bar{n}$	the ratio of fluoride to aluminum in the complex $AlF_{\bar{n}}$
RE	percent relative error in concentration
I	ionic strength of solution, defined in Equation (6)
T	absolute temperature in °K
V_0	volume of fluoride reagent solution (in ml)
ΔV	volume of aluminum solution added (in ml)
X	function defined in Equation (16)
Y	function defined in Equation (17)
z_i	charge on ion "i"
γ_i	activity coefficient of ion "i"
$(dE/dT)_{th}$	thermal temperature coefficient of an electrode
$(dE^\circ/dT)_{th}$	standard thermal temperature coefficient of an electrode

Symbols Used in Figures

A	alarm
AC	analytical controller
AR	analytical recorder
FT	flow transmitter
F_RC	flow ratio controller
M	measuring electrode
MR	combination measuring—reference electrode

R	reference electrode
S	solenoid valve
T	temperature compensator

VI. References

[1] Light, T. S., "Selective Ion Electrodes" in Analysis Instrumentation, Vol. 5, L. Fowler, R. G. Harmon and D. K. Roe, Eds., Plenum Press, New York, 1968, pp. 73-87.

[2] Bates, R. G., Determination of pH, Theory and Practice, John Wiley and Sons, New York, 1964.

[3] Mattock, G., pH Measurement and Titration, The Macmillan Company, New York, 1961.

[4] Eisenman, G., Ed., Glass Electrodes for Hydrogen and Other Cations, Marcel Dekker, Inc., New York, 1967.

[5] Eisenman, G., Bates, R. G., Mattock, G., and Friedman, S. M.,The Glass Electrode, Interscience Publishers, Div. of John Wiley and Sons, New York, 1966.

[6] Frant, M. S., and Ross, J. W., Jr., Canadian Patent 763082, July 11, 1967.

[7] Light, T. S., and Swartz, J. L., Anal. Lett. 1, 825 (1968).

[8] Ross, J. W., Science 156, 1378 (1967).

[9] Moore, E. W., and Wilson, D. W., J. Clin. Invest. 42, 293 (1963).

[10] deBethune, A. J., Light, T. S., and Swendeman, N., J. Electrochem. Soc. 106, 616 (1959); also in Encyclopedia of Electrochemistry, C. A. Hampel, Ed., Reinhold, New York, 1964, pp. 412-434.

[11] Bates, R. G., J. Res. Nat. Bur. Stand. 66A, 179 (1962).

[12] Light, T. S., and Fletcher, K., III, Anal. Chem. 39, 70 (1967).

[13] Harned, H. S., and Owen, B. B., The Physical Chemistry of Electrolyte Solutions, Reinhold, New York, 1958.

[14] Meites, L., Ed., Handbook of Analytical Chemistry, McGraw-Hill, New York, 1963, pp. 1-6 to 1-13.

[15] Bates, R. G., Ed., Electrochemical Analysis Section: Summary of Activities July 1967 to June 1968, Technical Note 453, U. S. Department of Commerce, National Bureau of Standards, July 1968, pp. 37-45.

[16] Alfenaar, M., and Bates, R. G., "Scales of Ionic Activity and Standards of Ion-Specific Electrodes", paper presented at 156th American Chemical Society National Meeting, Atlantic City, Sept. 8-13, 1968.

[17] Frant, M. S., and Ross, J. W., Jr., Anal. Chem. 40, 1169 (1968).

[18] Light, T. S., and Mannion, R. F., unpublished results.

[19] Babcock, R. H., and Johnson, K. A., J. Amer. Water Works Assoc. 60, 953 (1968).

[20] Light, T. S., and Swartz, J. L., unpublished results.

[21] Chen, K. Y., and Morris, J. C., "Oxidation of Sulfide by Aqueous O_2", paper presented at the First Northeast Regional Meeting, American Chemical Society, Boston, Mass., Oct. 13-15, 1968.

[22] Murray, F. E., TAPPI 42, 9 (1959).

[23] Friedman, S. M., and Bowers, F. K., Anal. Biochem. 5, 471 (1963).

[24] Light, T. S., "Analytical Evaluation of the Fluoride Ion Electrode", paper presented at the Pittsburgh Conference on Analytical Chemistry and Applied Spectroscopy, Mar. 5-10, 1967.

[25] Diggens, A. A., "Determination of Low Levels of Sodium in Water with a Sodium Responsive Electrode", paper presented at Symposium on Automatic Analytical Systems in Water Analysis, Soc. for Anal. Chem., London, Nov. 17, 1967.

[26] Elfers, L. A., and Decker, C. E., Anal. Chem. **40**, 1658 (1968).

CHAPTER 11

ANALYTICAL TECHNIQUES AND APPLICATIONS OF ION-SELECTIVE ELECTRODES

Richard A. Durst

Institute for Materials Research
National Bureau of Standards
Washington, D.C. 20234

I. Introduction

The present analytical applications of ion-selective electrodes are many and varied, and certainly as new types of electrodes are developed, the list of uses will grow at an increasing rate. In general, the analytical techniques will fall into one of two classes; direct potentiometric measurements based on the Nernstian logarithmic relationship between emf and ionic activity, and potentiometric titrations which, when applicable, are usually more accurate and precise.

Although the analytical usefulness of these electrodes has already been presented for a number of systems, such as in the studies of complexes and reaction kinetics, for process and quality control, and in biomedical studies, this section will compliment these discussions by presenting applications to the more usual types of laboratory analyses. At present, these applications include studies on more than a dozen ionic species in fields ranging from the usual chemical research and development to diverse studies in agriculture, geology, oceanography, and water and air pollution.

II. Direct Potentiometry

A. THE NERNST EQUATION

An analytical determination based upon the application of the Nernst equation is experimentally very simple. It merely involves the measurement of the emf of a cell consisting of an electrode selective to the ion of interest and a suitable reference electrode, the potential of which is accurately known and stable. The Nernst equation is then solved for the activity of the analate species using the observed cell emf. Unfortunately, however, the interpretation of the measured emf is usually quite difficult, since the cell potential which is measured also includes a liquid junction potential term, E_j, that is,

$$E_{cell} = E_{ind} - E_{ref} + E_j \tag{1}$$

where E_{ind} and E_{ref} are the potentials of the ion-selective indicator and reference electrodes, respectively. For an ion-selective electrode responding, for example, to some univalent anion, X^-, we have

$$E_{cell} = E_{ind}^{\circ\prime} - \frac{RT}{F} \ln a_{X-} - E_{ref} + E_j \tag{2}$$

and

$$a_{X-} = \text{antilog} \frac{1}{0.1984T} (-E_{cell} + E_{ind}^{\circ\prime} - E_{ref} + E_j) \tag{3}$$

where T is the temperature in kelvins, and the various potential terms are in millivolts. It should also be noted that the $E_{ind}^{\circ\prime}$ is not the "standard potential" of the indicator electrode in the usual sense. Instead, it more closely resembles the "zero potential" of the glass pH electrode which includes the contributions from the inner reference electrode, the inner phase boundary potential of the membrane, and the asymmetry potential. The value of $E_{ind}^{\circ\prime}$ must therefore be evaluated for each electrode before Equation (3) can be applied.

Another disadvantage of the direct evaluation of the Nernst equation derives from the fact that the results are in terms of ionic activity. Since concentration is the usual quantity of interest in analyses, it is necessary to have activity coefficient data available to convert activity to concentration. For mixed electrolyte systems, these data are seldom, if ever, available.

From Equation (3), it is easily calculated that an error of one millivolt in any of the potential terms corresponds to an error of approximately 4% in a_{X-}. For a divalent ion, the response slope, $mV/pX^=$, is one-half that of a univalent ion, and the error increases to about 8%/mV.

Thus the uncertainty in $E_{ind}^{\circ\prime}$, E_j, and the activity coefficients plus the difficulty in measuring the E_{cell} to better than ± 0.1 mV, all combine to limit the precision of the direct technique based on the evaluation of the Nernst equation to about $\pm 0.5\%$.

B. CONCENTRATION CELL TECHNIQUES

One method of avoiding some of the above difficulties is to employ a concentration cell technique. The null-point technique, first performed by deBrouckere in 1928 [1], was refined by Malmstadt and coworkers [2-5] in the late fifties and early sixties. In principle, null-point potentiometry is a simple concentration cell technique that compares the solution to be analyzed (analate solution) with a solution of known composition. The usual procedure consists of adjusting the composition of one of the half-cell solutions to match the other as evidenced by zero cell potential when measured between identical indicator electrodes specific for the species being determined.

For the general case of a concentration cell of this type, the emf is given by

$$E_{cell} = \frac{RT}{nF} \ln \frac{C_1 \gamma_1}{C_2 \gamma_2} + E_j \tag{4}$$

where C and γ are the concentration and activity coefficient, respectively, of the species being determined, and the subscripts 1 and 2 indicate the analate and variable known solutions. If a sufficiently large excess of an inert electrolyte is used in both half cells, E_j will become negligible since it depends on the difference in the electrolyte concentration between the two half cells. Also, the activity coefficients of the ionic species in the two half cells will be approximately equal due to the constant high ionic strength maintained by the inert electrolyte.

Equation (4) then simplifies to

$$E_{cell} = \frac{59.16}{n} \log \frac{C_1}{C_2}. \tag{5}$$

That is, when both half cells are at the same temperature (usually 298K), the cell emf is dependent only on the concentration ratio of electrode-selective species. From Equation (5), when $E_{cell} = 0$, the analate concentration, C_1, is equal to the known concentration, C_2. If the concentration in the variable known half cell is varied volumetrically, i.e., by dilution with the inert electrolyte solution or by addition of a concentrated solution of the electrode-selective species [6], as opposed to coulometric generation of the species in situ [7], then the usual dilution correction factor must be applied to calculate the known concentration, C_2.

The null-point technique can be applied in two ways: 1) as a "dead-stop" method, or 2) as a linear interpolation "titration" technique. In the dead-stop method, diluent or a standard solution of the species of interest is added until the null point is reached, and the analate concentration is evaluated from the known concentration in the variable half cell. In the linear null-point potentiometric technique, aliquots of the diluent or standard solution are added incrementally, and emf measurements are made prior to and after the null point. These emf data are then plotted semi-logarithmically (E_{cell} vs. $\log C_2$) resulting in a "linear titration curve" with a slope of $59/n$ millivolts per decade change in concentration and an intercept at $E_{cell} = 0$ where $C_2 = C_1$. Computer techniques have been applied to the data evaluation for this method whereby the intercept (end-point concentration) of the linear least squares fit of the data is printed out along with the slope of the titration curve (which serves as a check on the electrode behavior).

The null-point technique easily lends itself to the analysis of very small volumes of solution. At the National Bureau of Standards, this technique has been used for the determination of fluoride [6] and silver [7] in volumes ranging from 5 to 100 μl. Using the concentration cell arrangement in Figure 1, 0.380 nanograms of fluoride were determined in a sample volume of 10 μl with an error of only 0.002 ng. Over the range 0.38 to 190 ng, fluoride was determined with an average error of about 1%. In the case of silver, it was possible to determine 0.054 μg in a volume of 100 μl with an error of 0.001 μg [8], while over the range 0.054 to 54 μg, the

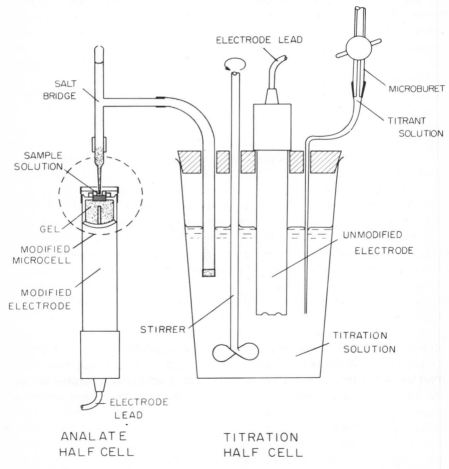

Figure 1.   Concentration cell used for the determination of fluoride by linear null-point potentiometry.

average error was less than 1%. In addition to its intrinsic simplicity, this technique has the additional advantages that the actual "titration" can be performed in any convenient volume of solution, e.g., 100 ml as used in the NBS investigations, while the sub-ml volume of test solution is unchanged, i.e., it serves only as a reference and is not modified or chemically reacted during the determination, and can therefore be recovered for use in subsequent studies.

C. Calibration Curves

A commonly used method for directly relating the electrode potential to the species activity or concentration is to construct an empirical calibration curve. The data are usually plotted on semi-logarithmic graph paper (E_{cell} vs. log a_i) which results in a linear calibration with a slope dependent on the ionic charge and electrode behavior. Basically, this can be done in two ways. One method employs pure solutions of some completely dissociated salt of the species of interest covering the range of concentration being studied. In this case, the presence of indifferent electrolytes, which are not true interferences in the usual sense of the word, will cause errors due to their effect on the activity coefficient of the ion under investigation through variations in the ionic strength of the system. For simple systems where activity coefficient data are available, corrections for ionic strength effects can be easily made in order to relate the observed cell potential and the activity or concentration of the species.

For more complex systems, it is necessary to use calibration solutions which either approximate the background of the test solutions or contain an excess of an inert electrolyte (plus non-electrolytes, buffers, etc.) which will swamp out interferences and variations in the test solution background. These two methods are equivalent to constructing a calibration curve of "formal potentials" which include the effects due to activity, liquid junction potentials and any background species which influence the cell emf.

The choice of which of these two alternate calibration methods is used depends primarily on the system itself. In cases where the background concentration of the test solution is high, such as in sea water and most biological systems, it would be very difficult to effectively swamp out the background, and a series of calibration solutions with backgrounds approximating that of the test solution would be required. However, very often the technique of standard additions will be of value in systems of this kind especially when the background is itself difficult to analyze or is variable. This technique is discussed in Section E below.

For less complex systems or for systems where it is desired to hold the activity coefficient relatively constant to relate emf and concentration more easily, an excess of an inert electrolyte or buffer solution will usually suffice. An important practical example of this method is demonstrated by the use of a total ionic strength adjustment buffer (TISAB) for the determination of fluoride in public water supplies [9]. This technique is based on a 1:1 dilution of both standards and samples with the TISAB solution (containing glacial acetic acid, sodium chloride, and sodium citrate with its pH adjusted to 5.0-5.5 using sodium hydroxide) which simultaneously performs three functions; 1) the ionic strength is fixed by the high level of ions contained in the TISAB, 2) the solution is buffered in a range where hydroxide does not interfere, and 3) any Fe^{3+} or Al^{3+} present is complexed by the citrate thereby releasing bound fluoride. This technique eliminates virtually all of the effects due to the background variations of water supplies, and makes possible the use of a single calibration curve for a wide range of water samples. In addition to public water supplies, this method should find application to the determination of low levels of fluoride in a wide variety of aqueous systems, such as fluoride in urine or from scrubbers in air pollution monitors.

D. Electrode Calibration

A technique closely related to the calibration curve methods depends on calibrating the electrode with one or more standard solutions and assuming a linear emf *vs.* ln(activity) relationship. This is essentially the same technique used in making pH measurements, and the activity of the unknown is defined in terms of the emf difference between the unknown and standard solutions (see Chapter 6).

The use of two standard solutions which bracket the unknown solution concentration increases the reliability of the method by establishing both the "zero potential", $E^{\circ\prime}$, for the electrode system and the response slope. This procedure will allow for most non-theoretical response characteristics of the electrode. The application of these calibration procedures to direct potentiometric determinations is facilitated by the use of a pH-type meter which is provided with a logarithmic readout of the cell potential corresponding to the ion activity or concentration. The conventional pH meter will suffice for the direct readout of monovalent cation-selective electrodes, *i.e.,* the alkali metals and silver, but for monovalent anions and divalent cations and anions a special type of meter is required. For the monovalent anions, a simple polarity-reversal switch on the pH meter would be sufficient (or reversal of the pH scale). For divalent ions, a newer type of meter (Orion Series 400) is needed in which provision is made for a Nernst factor of $RT/2F$ in relating the cell emf to ionic activity or concentration. Here again, a provision for polarity reversal is required to permit readings on both divalent cations and anions. In addition, a temperature compensating adjustment and/or a slope-modifier is needed to correct for the effect of temperature on the slope and to compensate for any deviation of the electrode response from the theoretical Nernst slope. Using appropriate calibrating solutions, a meter of this type can be made direct reading in various concentration terms, such as parts per million, molarity, normality, *etc.*, and can also be used in making water hardness measurements by again using the slope modifier to make the proper proportionality adjustments for direct readout.

The use of this type of meter simplifies ion-selective electrode determinations in much the same way as the measurement of pH has been facilitated by the use of pH meters. The time required for constructing calibration curves is saved in addition to the convenience of direct readout in remote or on-stream continuous measurements. However, whereas the glass pH electrode is more consistently Nernstian in its response, some of the ion-selective electrodes tend to be slightly less Nernstian, with response slopes as much as 2 or 3 millivolts less than theoretical. This necessitates, for the time being at least, the use of the bracketing method of calibration where the appropriate slope correction can be applied for direct readout. Except for a very slight decrease in sensitivity and precision, this effect is a relatively minor difficulty. It has also been shown in several studies that once the response of one of these electrodes is determined, it remains relatively stable so that only a periodic check of the "zero potential" using a single reference solution is necessary.

E. ADDITION TECHNIQUES

The standard addition technique, also called a "spike" or "known-increment" technique, is a very convenient method for the determination of the total concentration of a species in very complex systems. This technique avoids many of the difficulties usually encountered in solutions with backgrounds containing high concentrations of other ions or complexing agents.

In order to apply this technique, the only preliminary requirement is a knowledge of the electrode response to the species of interest. This response is evaluated with standard solutions and should be determined to as high a degree of precision as possible since the reliability of the results will be no better than this value. Once evaluated, this response slope or Nernst factor is usually quite stable and needs only periodic rechecking. The usual standard addition procedure involves the addition of one or more aliquots of the species of interest to the unknown sample solution, being careful that the increment does not significantly change the ionic strength of the system. Under these conditions, the activity coefficient (and liquid junction) can be assumed to remain constant, and the observed emf change can be related through the Nernst equation to the original unknown concentration (rather than activity).

The observed initial potential of the unknown sample solution as given by the Nernst equation is:

$$E_1 = E^{\circ\prime} + \frac{RT}{nF} \ln C_X \gamma_X + E_j \tag{6}$$

where C_X and γ_X are the concentration and activity coefficient of the test ion, respectively, and the other terms retain their previous definitions. On the addition of a known amount of the test ion, a new potential is measured:

$$E_2 = E^{\circ\prime} + \frac{RT}{nF} \ln (C_X + \Delta C) \gamma_X' + E_j \tag{7}$$

where ΔC is the increase in concentration of the test ion produced by the standard addition. Since the addition is made in such a way that the ionic strength and nature of the system are virtually unchanged, then $E^{\circ\prime}$, E_j, and the activity coefficient should remain unchanged by the addition of the spike. On taking the difference between the initial and final potentials, the "constant" terms $E^{\circ\prime}$, E_j, and $\gamma(i.e., \gamma_X = \gamma_X')$ cancel out, and we have

$$\Delta E = E_2 - E_1 = \frac{RT}{nF} \ln \left(\frac{C_X + \Delta C}{C_X} \right) \tag{8}$$

Rearranging, and substituting S for the Nernst slope, $2.3\,RT/nF$, which is experimentally confirmed by a series of known standard solutions covering the concentration range of interest, Equation (8) becomes:

$$\frac{\Delta E}{S} = \log \left(\frac{C_X + \Delta C}{C_X} \right) \tag{9}$$

and, taking antilogarithms and solving for the concentration of the original test solution:

$$C_X = \Delta C (10^{\Delta E/S} - 1)^{-1} \tag{10}$$

or, related back to the actual concentration of the standard addition solution:

$$C_X = C_s \left(\frac{V_s}{V_X} \right) (10^{\Delta E/S} - 1)^{-1} \tag{11}$$

where C_s is the standard solution concentration, V_s is the volume of the standard addition aliquot, and V_X is the test solution volume. Equation (11) was derived assuming the volume of the standard solution, V_s, is negligible in comparison to the original test solution volume, V_X. If this assumption does not hold, the most general form of the standard addition equation becomes:

$$C_X = C_s \left(\frac{V_s}{V_X + V_s'} \right) \left[10^{\Delta E/S} - \left(\frac{V_X + V_s}{V_X} \right) \right]^{-1} \tag{12}$$

which takes into consideration the changes in concentration of both the standard solution and the original test solution.

From Equation (12), it is seen that the precision to which C_X can be determined directly depends on the reliability to which C_s, V_s, V_X, S, and ΔE are known. The standard solution concentration, C_s, and the test solution and standard addition volumes can normally be prepared and/or measured quite accurately and should not limit the precision of the method. Similarly, the Nernst slope, S, can usually be determined with a relatively high degree of precision. In most cases, it will be the emf measurements, E_1 and E_2, which will cause the most difficulty. Also, the relative uncertainty of these measurements will become more significant the smaller the value of ΔE. This uncertainty can be reduced by making ΔE as large as possible, but the addition must not be so large as to affect the ionic strength of the solution, as discussed above. Thus, the optimum results are obtained by balancing the increased reliability in the measurement of ΔE by adding a large increment against possible variations in the activity coefficient and liquid junction potential caused by changes in the ionic strength.

In the presence of excess complexing agents, the standard addition technique is the only procedure available for determining the total concentration of the complexed species using ion-selective electrodes. This method works because the added species is complexed to the same degree as the test species, thus each emf measurement detects a constant fraction of the total concentration. Again, this constant factor cancels out when the difference emf, ΔE, is evaluated.

The standard addition procedure is further simplified by using a special scale, unique, at the present time, to the Orion Model 407 meter. This scale indicates the ratio of the amount of ion in the original solution to the amount of ion added in the known increment. It is therefore unnecessary to evaluate equations, such as Equations (10) and (11), with the possible introduction of computational errors.

The standard addition technique has been used in the determination of trace fluoride [10]. Determinations were made in the concentration range from 10^{-4} to $10^{-5}M$ fluoride in a variety of solutions without prior separation. Sample solutions of 50 ml were analyzed using 10-100 μl increments of a $0.1M$ sodium fluoride solution. Individual additions produced emf changes of about 10 mV and were continued until a total change of at least 40 mV was achieved. Less than 1 ml of the standard solution is required for this emf change. The calculation of fluoride concentration was performed in two ways: 1) by a linear least squares fit to Equation (9) of 5 to 10 data points with both the slope and unknown concentration computed, and 2) by calculating the unknown concentration from a single known increment sufficiently large to produce an emf change of at least 40 mV and using a previously determined value for the slope. Over the 10^{-4} to $10^{-5}M$ concentration range, the relative error of the technique was about 10% and the relative standard deviation less than 5%.

In a brief study of the fluoride concentration in sea water [11], direct emf measurements indicated a fluoride level of about 0.6 ppm, while the standard addition technique gave a value of 1.2-1.3 ppm. These results indicate that approximately half of the fluoride in sea water is complexed by the magnesium present. Of course, it should be pointed out that in many types of determinations, such as ionic species in biologic media, it is the activity of the free uncomplexed ions that is of interest, and in such cases, the standard addition technique could not be used unless the fraction complexed were known.

The inverse technique of standard additions, called "analate additions potentiometry" [12], is based on the addition of increments of the unknown (analate) solution to a known volume of a standard solution of the same species. The change in emf is then related to the unknown concentration by means of the Nernst equation as in the standard addition technique. Equation (13) is derived by the simultaneous solution of the Nernst equation for the change in emf produced by delivery of an aliquot of the analate solution into the standard, and rearranged for evaluation of the unknown concentration, C_X:

$$C_X = C_s \left[\left(\frac{V_s + V_X}{V_X} \right) 10^{\Delta E/S} - \left(\frac{V_s}{V_X} \right) \right] \tag{13}$$

where all of the symbols retain their previous definitions. If the substitution $N = (V_s + V_X)/V_X$ is made, Equation (13) more simply becomes:

$$C_X = C_s [N \cdot 10^{\Delta E/S} - (N - 1)] \tag{14}$$

Again, the only assumptions involved in the derivation of Equations (13) and (14) are the constancy of the activity coefficient and the liquid junction potential. However, in this case, the ionic strength is controlled by the background inert electrolyte of the standard solution.

The singular advantage of this technique over standard additions lies in the fact that the minimum volume requirement for electrode immersion is satisfied by the standard solution so that the increment of unknown solution need only be as large as necessary to produce a useable emf response. This analate volume requirement decreases as the volume and concentration of the standard solution is reduced. The standard solution concentration, however, is limited to the range where the response slope is greatest and reproducible. The method suffers from the disadvantage that the solution background does not correspond to the unknown solution background but to that of the standard, and changes in the degree of complexation (if present) could introduce error. In general, the same limitations and uncertainties of measurement, *e.g.*, emf, volumes, *S*, *etc.*, apply to this technique, and aside from its use as a microtechnique, the two methods are otherwise comparable. This technique has been successfully applied to the determination of fluoride in solutions containing electrochemically generated fluoride ion [13]. The precision of the technique at the millimolar concentration level is about 0.5% (95% confidence limits).

In summary, the method of standard additions is recommended as the first-choice technique with analate additions used only in cases where the volume of unknown is severely limited or where it is desired to avoid dilution of a concentrated test solution.

The above sections briefly summarize the direct potentiometric techniques available for use with ion-selective electrodes. In general, they offer a means of rapid analysis and can be applied to an almost unlimited variety of systems. The technique of choice, obviously, will depend on the nature of the system of interest.

III. Potentiometric Titrations

In contrast to the direct potentiometric methods based on the Nernst equation, potentiometric titrations generally offer an increase in accuracy and precision at the cost of increased time and difficulty. The increase in accuracy comes about for two main reasons: 1) measured potentials are used to detect rapid changes in concentration (activity) that occur at the equivalence point of the titration and this rate of emf change is usually considerably greater than the response slope which limits precision in direct potentiometry, and 2) since it is the change in emf (*vs.* the volume of a standard reagent) rather than the absolute value of the emf which is of interest, the influences of liquid junction potentials and activity coefficients have little or no effect. The accuracy of these titrations is primarily determined by the accuracy of standardization and volume measurement of the titrant and by the sharpness of the potential "break" at the end point (as determined by the equilibrium constant of the titration reaction).

Titration techniques are widely applicable and can be based on a variety of reactions: neutralization (acid-base), precipitation, redox, and complexation. In addition, the titration reaction must be stoichiometric, relatively fast, and must go to completion.

The critical problem in a titration, of course, is to identify the point at which the reacting species are present in equivalent amounts. This equivalence point either exactly or virtually coincides with the inflection point of a plot of the cell emf vs. the volume of reagent added. In the case of non-1:1 reactions, this can be easily realized by standardizing the titrant against a known amount of the analate using the same titration procedure and arbitrarily designating the inflection point of the unsymmetrical titration curve as the equivalence point.

The equivalence point of a typical sigmoid titration curve can be located in two ways: 1) the equivalence-point emf can be calculated or measured beforehand using standards and then the volume of reagent required to reach that potential is found, or 2) the inflection point can be located graphically.

Titration to the equivalence-point potential is exactly analogous to ordinary indicator titrations, and, since recording the data is unnecessary, it is convenient and rapid. The precision of this simple method depends on the reproducibility of the equivalence-point potential, but because of the normally steep slope of the emf-volume curve near the equivalence point, a knowledge of this potential to ± 10 mV usually results in sufficiently high precision.

The most obvious graphical method for locating the equivalence point is by inspection of the emf vs. volume titration curve to find the point of maximum slope (Fig. 2a). With this method, relatively large aliquots of the titrant are added until the equivalence point is approached, where the increments are reduced until the equivalence point is passed. After each increment sufficient time is allowed for the system to reach equilibrium. Often, this is most easily done using a recorder to display the emf vs. time. Constructing the curve and locating the point of maximum slope may introduce error due to personal judgment.

The equivalence point can usually be located more conveniently and accurately by adding small, equal-volume increments of the titrant in the vicinity of the equivalence point and evaluating the equivalence point from the first or second derivative curves of the titration data (Figs. 2b and 2c). In the case of the first derivative, the point where the slope of the data, $\Delta E/\Delta V$, is a maximum corresponds to the equivalence point. Another method, using second derivative data, calculates the equivalence point from the point where $\Delta^2E/\Delta V^2$ becomes zero, i.e., corresponding to the maximum of the first derivative. This latter method does not require graphical evaluation but is readily calculated using procedures outlined in most basic analytical textbooks. Since the equivalence point is computed without the need of plotting and interpreting a graph, this method is less prone to the personal error cited above.

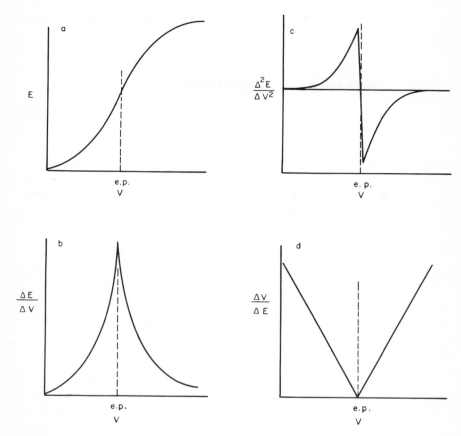

Figure 2. Titration curves. a) Potential *vs.* titrant volume (*E vs. V*); b) 1st derivative curve (Δ*E*/Δ*V vs. V*); c) 2nd derivative curve (Δ²*E*/Δ*V*² *vs. V*); d) Extrapolated Δ*V*/Δ*E vs. V* curve.

One final method of evaluating titration data, which has received little attention, is based on plotting $\Delta V/\Delta E$ *vs.* titrant volume [14]. Although somewhat less convenient to calculate than its reciprocal, $\Delta E/\Delta V$, since the values of ΔE will not be uniform integers, certain advantages are obtained by this method. For a typical plot of this type (Fig. 2d), it is seen that in the vicinity of the equivalence point, the curves consist of two straight lines which intersect each other and the volume axis (according to Gran [14]) at the equivalence point. Under some conditions, a deviation from the straight lines occurs just at the equivalence point. However, if the straight portions are extrapolated, they will intersect at the volume axis. Also, the slopes of the lines are indicative of the charges of the reacting ions, *i.e.,* for ions of the same charge, the lines are symmetrical about the equivalence point, while for ions of different charges, the slopes will differ. This technique is equally applicable to neutralization, precipitation, complexation, and redox titrations.

The high accuracy and precision of potentiometric titrations are widely accepted. Since the equivalence point volume is independent of E_j, $E°$, and E_{ref}, the titration methods are also generally useable in non-aqueous systems, where, except for matched concentration cell measurements, direct potentiometric data are difficult to evaluate. Except for speed and the application to very dilute solutions, the only distinct advantage of direct potentiometry over potentiometric titrations is for the continuous monitoring of changing systems where high accuracy is not essential.

One additional advantage of potentiometric titrations over direct potentiometry that deserves mention is the possibility of using the selective ion as the titrant in the determination of other species for which ion-selective electrodes are not available. This simple device greatly extends the usefulness of ion-selective electrodes to many other ions of interest.

A case in point which provides an excellent example of this is the determination of lithium by titration with fluoride [15]. This method was developed for the analysis of concentrated LiCl and LiNO₃ solutions used in the Tramex process for the separation of lanthanides from actinides. The analytical technique utilizes the quantitative precipitation of LiF in alcohol as the basis for the potentiometric titration with the fluoride electrode. No bias existed between the fluoride titration results and those obtained by an ion exchange procedure in which the acid displaced from an acid-form cation exchange resin is titrated. The two methods generally agreed to within 1%. The precision of the method for solutions approximately $11M$ in LiCl was 0.4% (relative standard deviation) and 0.3% for $0.085M$ LiCl. Figure 3 shows the effect of NaCl on the shape of the LiCl titration curve. Sodium causes less than 3% error when present in amounts up to 50 mole percent of the lithium. It is expected that other alkali metals would interfere less than sodium. Interferences by free acid and certain other metal ions can be eliminated by adding NH_4OH and $(NH_4)_2S$, respectively.

The above discussions of direct potentiometry and potentiometric titrations have of necessity been highly general in nature and were by no means intended as rigorous treatments. For this reason, exceptions to various points will occur, and discretion on the part of the analyst is necessary in the selection of the most suitable technique for a particular problem.

IV. Applications

The past several years have seen a rapid increase in the use of ion-selective electrodes in widely divergent disciplines. In fact, since the first paper concerned with the present generation of commercial,

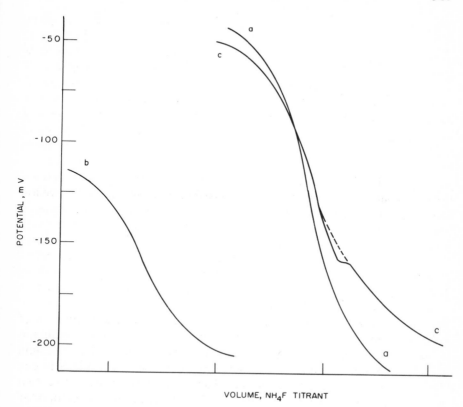

Figure 3.   Titration curves of lithium and sodium chlorides in ethyl alcohol with ammonium fluoride. a) LiCl only; b) NaCl only; c) LiCl + NaCl (Na⁺/Li⁺ ∼ 0.5). From E. W. Baumann [15].

non-glass types of ion-selective electrodes appeared in 1965, the yearly rate of publication has increased exponentially. In addition to the applications of these electrodes already discussed in the preceding sections, selected applications illustrating various techniques and sample systems will be described in this section. A bibliography of additional references is given in an addendum to this chapter.

A number of general papers have appeared which have briefly surveyed all or a part of the development and applications of these newer types of ion-selective electrodes. Since even the most recent of these reviews is already outdated by the latest developments, instead of discussing them individually they are merely listed chronologically in the addendum.

A. FLUORIDE

Of all the ion-selective electrodes developed in recent years, the fluoride electrode has probably been the most outstanding for two reasons: 1) the importance of fluoride in commerce and technology, and 2) the difficulty in determining fluoride by previous techniques. Some feeling for the importance of a rapid and reliable method for monitoring fluoride can be gained by considering a list of materials in which fluoride occurs: 1) public water supplies (fluoridation), 2) pharmaceuticals (e.g., vitamins), 3) consumer products (toothpaste), 4) water and air (pollution by discharge of industrial wastes), 5) soils (ecological effects of fluoride), 6) electroplating, cleaning, etching, and pickling baths (continuous monitoring for fluoride level regulation), 7) manufactured materials (e.g., fertilizers, pesticides, glass, etc.), and 8) biological materials (present in tooth enamel, bone, urine, and plant materials).

Obviously, only a few of these varied applications can be presented here, especially since the methods that have been developed are almost as numerous as the materials themselves. A general paper on the direct potentiometric determination of fluoride [16] describes the working characteristics of the electrode and the influence of foreign substances, including non-electrolytes, on the observed emf. The use of the standard addition technique and a novel form of the equation used to calculate results are also discussed.

Lingane has published two important papers [17,18] on the titration of fluoride with lanthanum, thorium, and calcium. In the first study, comparing the three titrant species, lanthanum was found to be the best titrant in neutral, unbuffered solution based on the titration curve slope at the equivalence point as shown in Figure 4. Although the thorium titrant produced the greatest overall change in emf, it was more drawn out than the lanthanum titration in the vicinity of the equivalence point, while calcium showed no inflection at all in unbuffered aqueous solution. In addition, the equivalence point potential is independent of fluoride sample size when titrated with lanthanum, but varies significantly in the thorium titration. This is an important consideration if a manual or automatic titration to the equivalence-point potential is used as the analysis technique.

Since the fluoride-lanthanum titration is a 3:1 reaction, the titration curve is not symmetrical, and the point of maximum slope does not correspond to the true equivalence point (assuming so will result in a negative error). Using fluoride standards, the equivalence-point potential can be determined, or the titrant can be standardized in such a way that the point of maximum slope does coincide with the true equivalence point. Further studies[18] of the lanthanum titration in 60 to 70 volume percent ethanol solution showed a considerable improvement in the titration curve, i.e., the slope at the equivalence point is increased (see Fig. 5) because of the decrease in the solubility of lanthanum fluoride.

Proceeding to some applications to specific analysis problems, the use of the fluoride-selective electrode in the determination of fluoride in

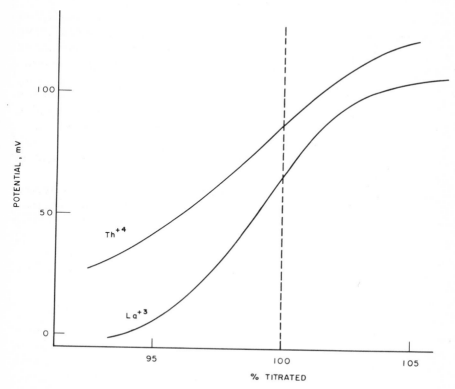

Figure 4. Comparison of the equivalence point slope for the titration of fluoride with lanthanum and thorium (aqueous, unbuffered solutions). From J. J. Lingane [17].

toothpastes has been reported by Shane and Miele[19]. Previously, the determination of fluoride in toothpaste required a steam distillation separation step ordinarily followed by titration with thorium nitrate using a colored dye indicator. In the fluoride electrode procedure, no separations are required. The fluoride concentration at the 0.1% level (equivalent to 0.22% sodium fluoride or 0.4% stannous fluoride) was measured using a direct potentiometric method. The ionic fluoride content in an aqueous dispersion of toothpaste was determined by relating the observed emf to a semi-logarithmic calibration curve constructed by adding known amounts of fluoride to a blank toothpaste formulation. The calibration curve is linear in the range of interest, *i.e.*, between 0.18 and 0.25% NaF. The potentiometric technique is simpler and more rapid (5-9 min *vs.* 40-45 min) than the distillation-thorium titration method and gives results which indicate no significant difference between the two methods.

Another direct potentiometric technique has been used for the determination of fluoride in bone [20]. The procedure consisted of ashing the

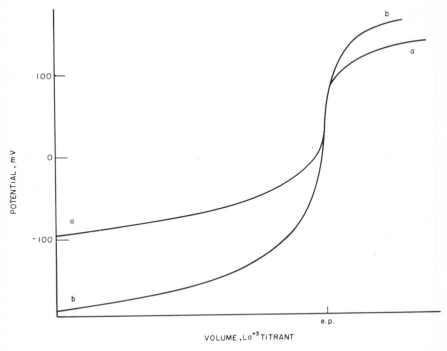

Figure 5.   Titration of fluoride with lanthanum in neutral, unbuffered solution — influence
of ethanol. a) Aqueous; b) 70% ethanol. From J. J. Lingane [18].

bone samples at 500 °C, dissolving the ash in HCl, nearly neutralizing
the excess HCl with NaOH, adjusting the final pH to 4.7 with sodium
acetate, and diluting to volume (5 ml). This procedure produced essentially the same ionic strength and pH in both the bone and standard solutions. A linear calibration curve was used to convert the emf readings of
the bone ash solutions to fluoride concentration. The results on replicate
analyses of a single sample solution were highly reproducible and agreed
well with the results obtained by a reference method. The authors believe
that similar procedures would be applicable to the determination of
fluoride in the ash of other normal and pathological calcifications, *e.g.*,
kidney stones.

   In the area of fluoride air pollution by industry, the presence of certain
fluoride compounds (such as HF, SiF₄, and H₂SiF₆) in excess can cause
harmful effects on vegetation. The absorption of fluoride into the leaf is
cumulative and will result in necrosis of the leaf. Vegetation which has
been seriously contaminated in this way by air pollution can subsequently
cause fluorosis when ingested by animals.

   A procedure for the determination of water-soluble fluoride in air and
stack gas at ambient levels of 1 μg/m³ or less has been described [21] in

which the gaseous and particulate fluoride are quantitatively collected by filtration and chemisorption on cellulose acetate filters impregnated with sodium formate. Aluminum and iron, present in most atmospheric samples, are prevented from interfering by complexation with an added sodium citrate buffer, which also maintains a pH of 7.5 and controls the total ionic strength of the solution. Comparison of this technique with the Spadns-zirconium lake method for the analysis of stack gas samples has shown these methods to be statistically equivalent. The authors conclude that the fluoride electrode technique is more rapid, convenient, and appears to be less susceptible to interferences than existing methods for determining fluoride to levels as low as 0.25 ppb.

In oceanography, the variations of fluoride concentration in sea water may have a possible correlation to submarine volcanic activity or outcrops of fluorine-rich minerals. Previous studies using colorimetric methods have located anomalously high fluoride/chloride ratios in several deep water locations of the North and South Atlantic. These studies suffered from the basic disadvantages of sampling by hydrographic casts, i.e., 1) the delay between sampling and analysis, and 2) the discontinuous nature of the sampling. Using a unique device developed by Spencer and Brewer [22,23] for measuring continuous F^-/Cl^- profiles, these two problems have been overcome. In this method, a fluoride electrode is incorporated into an *in situ* meter with a chloride reference electrode. The electrode pair is mounted on a piston floating in silicone oil which provides pressure equalization and electrical insulation simultaneously. The necessary electronic components are battery operated and located in a pressure housing adjacent to the electrodes to minimize noise pickup. The entire unit is self-contained and is lowered on hydrographic wire. Novel features incorporated into the design of this device include the replacement of the internal filling solution of the electrode with gelled sea water to counteract changes in the activity of the measured medium with temperature and also to enable the measurement of emf about a null point. The chloride ion-selective reference electrode is also filled with sea water; thus the whole system measures the parameter of interest: the fluoride to chlorinity ratio. Although this device operates as well as expected, it appears that fluoride variations in sea water are rare (if they occur at all), since measurements made during two cruises did not detect any variations. However, this study has shown that devices of this type are definitely feasible and provide a convenient method for deep sea monitoring. The use of ion-selective electrodes in conjunction with deep submersibles is extremely attractive since these techniques are for all practical purposes the only way chemical measurements can be made directly from these craft.

The future of ion-selective electrodes in oceanographic research is promising but not without first overcoming some extremely difficult problems. Some of the more formidable ones include the fact that the ratios of the major ions to chlorinity are remarkably constant, and none of the presently available electrodes have a high enough precision to be useful. Also, many of the elements which do exhibit a wide range of concentrations, such as the transition metals, are present only at the parts per billion level, and the development of electrodes to detect such species looks doubtful at the present time. The most fruitful area for research would seem to be electrode studies of nutrients, such as nitrate, phosphate, and silicate, which exhibit wide variations in sea water although they, too, are present at very low concentrations. It might be easiest to sum up the future of ion-selective electrodes in oceanographic studies by describing the characteristics of the ideal electrode [23]. Such an electrode would be capable of good response in the parts per billion range, tolerant of massive excesses of Na^+, Mg^{++}, Ca^{++}, K^+, Cl^-, and Br^-, and would have a fairly low impedance for working in this salty environment.

The microdetermination of fluorine in organic compounds is beset by many difficulties in both the decomposition and determination procedures. Recently, a procedure has been proposed by Light and Mannion [24] which employs a potentiométric titration of fluoride with thorium and a fluoride electrode for end point detection. In contrast with Lingane's conclusion [18], these authors found that thorium gave a better end point "break" than did lanthanum (see Fig. 6) which apparently is due to the differences in the system backgrounds (neutral, unbuffered and 70% ethanol vs. $0.01M$ nitric acid and 80% ethanol). The unique features of their decomposition procedure include the use of a clear, polycarbonate flask instead of glass for the oxygen combustion and dodecyl alcohol as a combustion accelerator.

The results of determinations on typical microchemical fluorine compounds, containing 13 to 76% fluorine, in the sample range of 1 to 10 mg were within $\pm 0.3\%$ (absolute) of the theoretical fluorine content, and the standard deviation for 25 determinations was 0.2%. But as has been pointed out many times and in many ways before, the analysis of fluorine is a highly subjective art, and the proof of this technique awaits its acceptance by other microchemists.

Additional fluoride references are addended to this chapter.

B. CALCIUM

The calcium ion-selective electrode is probably the second most important non-glass type of electrode developed to date, if total number of publications and diversity of application are any sort of criteria. Included in this wide variety of applications are: studies of scale formation; monitoring calcium levels in food processing; determining the calcium content of minerals, pharmaceuticals, fertilizers, and explosives; and, in

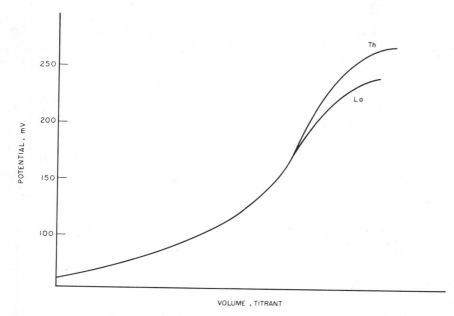

Figure 6.   Titration of fluoride with thorium and lanthanum in 0.01 M HNO$_3$ and 80% ethanol solutions. From T. S. Light and R. F. Mannion [24].

biomedicine, the study of calcium in teeth, bone, and serum (see Chapt. 7).

For the determination of ionic calcium in serum and other biologic fluids, a special electrode device has been developed for anaerobic, flow-through measurements on only 200 μl of sample (Orion, Model 99-20 Serum Calcium Activity Flow-Thru System). A precision syringe pump delivers the solution anaerobically through the calcium and reference electrode system. The calcium electrode was developed especially for serum measurements and has a higher selectivity for calcium over sodium and potassium.

In addition to the calcium liquid ion-exchange electrode, a solid ion-exchange type has recently been developed [25] and evaluated [26] by direct potentiometry and in potentiometric titrations. This type of electrode exhibits an improved calcium/hydrogen ion selectivity and is suited to both analytical and biochemical measurements.

An early paper by King and Mukherji [27] describes the complexometric titration of calcium with di-sodium EDTA at a pH adjusted to about 10 with NH$_4$OH. Beyond the end point, the potential remains fairly constant or rises slightly due to the response of the electrode to sodium added with the EDTA (see Fig. 7). Other divalent cations, which complex with EDTA, and the fluoride, carbonate, and oxalate anions interfere with the titration.

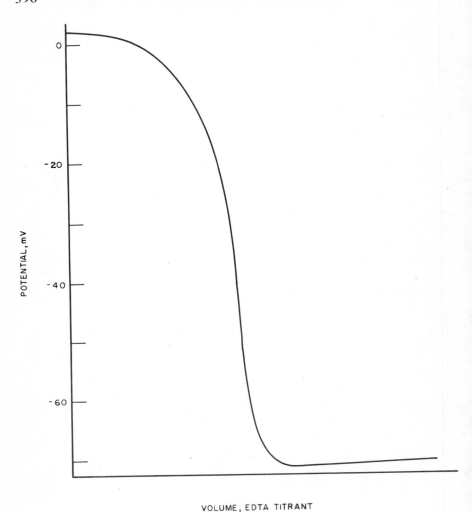

Figure 7.   Titration of calcium with EDTA.

A standard addition procedure for the determination of calcium in beer offers the same precision as the standard EDTA titration at the normal calcium levels in beer, but is considerably more convenient to perform [28]. The method assumes that a 50 to 100-fold excess of complexing agents, *e.g.*, proteins, is present in the beer samples. After determination of the electrode response slope with standard solutions, only two emf measurements are required; one prior to and one after the addition of the known calcium increment to the beer sample. A simple equation is then used to calculate the total calcium level in the original solution.

Muldoon and Liska have compared an ion-exchange method with the direct potentiometric determination of calcium in skim milk [29,30]. The two techniques were used in a study on the effect of heat treatment on the level of ionized calcium in skim milk. Statistical analysis of the data showed that there was no significant difference between the results obtained by the two methods on raw, pasteurized, and sterilized milk. Results indicated that the pasteurization process significantly lowers the ionized calcium level while rapid sterilization has little effect. In addition to accuracy, the electrode technique offered the advantages of convenience and repeatability.

The calcium electrode has also been applied to sea water determinations using direct potentiometric measurements [31]. The electrode is calibrated using solutions with backgrounds so like sea water that activity coefficients can be assumed constant, and the empirical electrode equation is written in terms of concentration rather than activity. The results obtained indicate that the ionized calcium concentration in sea water is $0.0086 \pm 0.0002M$, which corresponds to about 84% of the total calcium concentration at the 19.373 parts per thousand chlorinity level.

Dyrssen [32], in attempting to obtain a precision of at least 0.1% for calcium in sea water by the potentiometric titration of calcium with EGTA [ethyleneglycol bis(2-aminoethylether)tetraacetic acid], found that the sodium in sea water interfered with the titration by limiting the emf break in the vicinity of the equivalence point. That is, as the calcium level is reduced by the titration reaction, the electrode becomes poised by and responsive to the high level of sodium in the system and no longer senses changes in the calcium activity.

Several other applications of the calcium electrode are listed in the addendum.

C. Nitrate

The nitrate electrode should be of considerable importance in the pharmaceutical, explosive, and photographic industries, but especially in the areas of agricultural analysis and pollution control. It is used for the determination of nitrate in biological materials, fertilizers, and soils. In addition, this electrode can be used for nitrite determinations in cases where it is convenient to oxidize the nitrite to nitrate. Direct nitrite measurements are not recommended.

In soil and ground water, the amount of nitrate present is an indication of fertility and possible pollution due to excessive fertilization. The pollution problem arises when the nitrate (and phosphate) from agricultural fertilization enters streams and lakes (reservoirs) causing excessive aquatic plant growth and eutrophication.

The direct determination of water soluble nitrate in soil using the nitrate electrode is superior to the standard colorimetric brucine method [33]. It is suitable for both laboratory and field analyses since determinations can be made directly on soil slurries when it is not convenient to filter the prepared soil samples. Determinations were reportedly made with an error of about 5% in the 2 to 30 ppm NO_3^- (as nitrogen) range. Standard deviations of 12.5% were found for laboratory determinations and about 25% for measurements made directly on soil slurries. Again, the electrode method exhibits greater convenience over earlier techniques without sacrificing the reliability of the results.

The nitrate content of plants is critical for proper growth and maximum yield and excessive amounts may be dangerous to infants. In the technique developed by Paul and Carlson [34], the aqueous extract of dried plant tissues in the 1 to 50 ppm range is determined by direct potentiometry. The nitrate-selective electrode response is linear over this range. A cation exchange resin in the aluminum form is added during extraction to eliminate interference by bicarbonate and to reduce organic anion interferences. A resin in the silver form added during the extraction will remove any chloride interference. For practical purposes, the electrode technique agreed closely enough with the usual phenoldisulfonic acid method for it to be used in the latter's place. The average relative standard deviation for the 16 plant materials studied was 3.1% for the electrode method.

Two other nitrate references are given in the addendum.

D. Tetrafluoroborate (Boron)

Another element of interest to the agricultural chemist and to materials scientists working with alloys, refractory compounds, semiconductors, paints, and heat-resistant glasses is boron. This element can be easily converted to the fluoroborate (tetrafluoroborate) ion by reaction with hydrofluoric acid and then measured potentiometrically. A simple ion exchange procedure to perform this conversion has been described by Carlson and Paul [35]. In addition, they describe a potentiometric measurement procedure for fluoroborate concentrations down to $10^{-5}M$. Interferences from several anions and the rate of formation of fluoroborate in solution were also studied. It was found that anion interference problems and the slow rate of fluoroborate formation in solution can be overcome by the column technique described in their paper. Boron can be readily concentrated from dilute solutions using this procedure.

A subsequent paper by Carlson and Paul describes the potentiometric determination of boron in agricultural samples [36]. The boron conversion and electrode determination procedures are the same, but more details are given on materials and methods. To increase the sensitivity of the method, the final solution volume is decreased (from 25 ml [35] to 10 ml, *i.e.*, a 2.5-fold increase in sensitivity) by using 50 ml polycarbonate centrifuge tubes as the sample vessels. Results from electrode determinations on water, soil, and plant samples are compared with those determined by a modified curcumin method. The electrode technique is very accurate and in excellent agreement with the curcumin method. For water samples containing about 1 ppm boron, the average relative standard deviation ($\bar{S}_r$) was about 2%; for soil extracts containing 0.1 to 1.6 ppm boron, $\bar{S}_r$ was 7.1 to 1.4%, respectively; and for plant tissue containing 5.9 to 1508 ppm boron, the $\bar{S}_r$ was 7.2 to 0.9%, respectively.

E. PERCHLORATE

The third in this series of liquid anion-exchange membrane electrodes has not received the attention afforded the others. At present, published applications of the perchlorate electrode seem to have been limited to a single paper [37] in which the electrode is used as an end-point detector for the potentiometric titration of perchlorate with tetraphenylarsonium chloride. Although the titration of perchlorate with organometallic salts, including this one, is not original, the method is demonstrated to be simple and rapid, and the accuracy and precision are at least as good as other presently available methods for determining perchlorate. Based on replicate determinations on three perchlorate samples, the overall 95% confidence limits were 0.16%. Applications of this technique include perchlorate assay by chemical manufacturers and in determining perchlorate in explosives and solid propellants.

This study reports that the perchlorate electrode also responds to permanganate, periodate, and dichromate ions. The response curves for these ions are linear over approximately the same concentration range as perchlorate, but the selectivity ratios for these ions were not evaluated. It was suggested that this electrode might be useful as an indicator for titrations involving these ions.

F. HALIDES

The halides, with the exception of fluoride, have for many years been determined potentiometrically using silver-silver halide electrodes. With the development of halide electrodes of the membrane type, which are more resistant to surface poisoning, need no preconditioning or anodizing treatments, and, most importantly, can be used in the presence of oxidizing agents, new areas of application have opened up as a result of these improved characteristics. Furthermore, the convenience of these electrodes has resulted in their use for the more conventional measurements in place of the traditional halide-film electrodes.

At present there exist heterogeneous and solid-state membrane electrodes for chloride, bromide, and iodide, and an additional liquid ion-exchange electrode for chloride. Techniques employing these electrodes are the same as have been used with the traditional halide electrodes, *i.e.,* various direct potentiometric measurements and titrations, and these require little additional comment.

The applications, however, have increased to include measurements in both aqueous and non-aqueous systems, even in the presence of oxidants. In addition, the chloride liquid ion-exchange electrode can also be used in solutions containing sulfide and reducing agents, and is less subject to interference from bromide and iodide than is the solid-state electrode.

The chloride electrode has been applied to chloride-level monitoring in many materials such as foods, beverages, pharmaceuticals, plastics, and pesticides. In addition, a combination chloride electrode has been developed for direct chloride measurements on samples as small as 10 μl. This electrode is especially useful for rapid screening for cystic fibrosis by measuring sweat chloride levels directly on the patient's skin and can also be used for body fluids such as saliva, urine, and cerebrospinal fluid. For serum chloride measurements, the liquid ion-exchange electrode is more suitable and is also available in a flow-through configuration for anaerobic measurements.

An interesting method has been developed for the continuous monitoring of hydrogen chloride levels in gas and aerosol samples [38]. This technique resulted from a study of the generation of volatile pyrolytic decomposition products from a number of chlorocarbon polymers under simulated fire conditions. The device consists of a gas scrubber to absorb the HCl and a liquid ion-exchange chloride electrode with a flow-through compartment to measure the chloride concentration. A syringe pump delivers water to the top of the scrubber and withdraws sample solution from its base at equal rates, so that the volume of water retained in the scrubber for absorption remains constant. Over the range of 20 to 6000 ppm HCl, the reproducibility was within $\pm$ 5% for a gas sampling rate of 100 cm³/min. The response time for the system was about 1.5 min (to reach 99% of equilibrium).

The bromide-selective electrode is of use in photographic processing, the manufacture of pharmaceuticals, and in biomedical research. A titration technique adapted from the ASTM method D1562 for the determination of epoxy equivalents by titration with HBr has been suggested in which a potentiometric end point is used in place of the crystal violet visual end point [39]. The potentiometric titration of epoxy groups is easier to automate and can be used in the presence of colored epoxies.

The iodide electrode has been used for the determination of chloride, bromide, and iodide by a successive potentiometric titration with silver

[40]. The error caused by the adsorption of titrant on the silver halide precipitate was eliminated by taking the Fajans adsorption rule into account and adding barium nitrate to the sample solution. The silver halides are precipitated in the order: iodide, bromide, chloride; the end point of each titration being indicated by a distinct potential "break" (see Fig. 8). Thus, using the procedure described, the three halides can be successively determined by a single titration carried out in a couple of minutes.

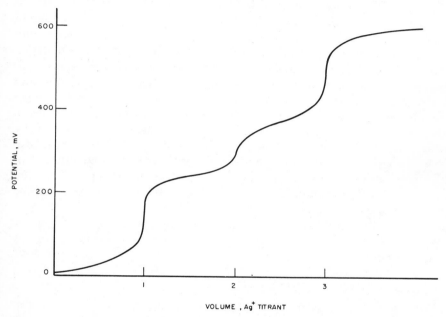

Figure 8. Titration curve for the successive titration of chloride, bromide, and iodide with silver. a) End point 1: $I^- + Ag^+ = AgI(s)$; b) End point 2: $Br^- + Ag^+ = AgBr(s)$; c) End point 3: $Cl^- + Ag^+ = AgCl(s)$. From B. Csakvari and K. Meszaros [40].

A study reported by Arino and Kramer [41] may be of some interest to nuclear and radiochemists. The specific activity of ^{131}I was calculated from the measured ^{131}I activity and the total iodide content, the latter being determined with a heterogeneous membrane iodide electrode. It was found that radiation levels as high as twenty curies of ^{131}I did not affect the electrode measurements. The direct potentiometric measurement of total iodide concentration could be made in less than five minutes with a precision of 1% (relative standard deviation).

Some additional halide references are given in the addendum.

G. CYANIDE

The cyanide electrode, which presumably is a silver iodide membrane electrode, is recommended for use in the concentration range from 10^{-3}

to $10^{-5}M$ cyanide, although it gives a useable response from 10^{-1} to $10^{-6}M$ cyanide. At concentrations above $10^{-3}M$, the electrode life is shortened due to the formation of soluble silver cyanide complexes resulting in a slow dissolution of the electrode membrane. The only serious anion interferences are sulfide and iodide, and for maximum sensitivity the pH should be kept above 10 to prevent the lowering of the free cyanide level by the formation of HCN.

A general paper by Pungor and Toth [42] describes a systematic study of various metal ion complexes with cyanide using their silver iodide heterogeneous membrane electrode. In addition to this type of study, the cyanide electrode should be useful for industrial pollution monitoring, measurements of free cyanide in plating bath solutions, and the determination of cyanide in foods and beverages.

The above example points up an important consideration in using ion-selective electrodes. That is, many of these electrodes can be used for the measurement of ions for which they are not nominally selective. In other words, when the "selective ion" is absent or present in sufficiently low concentration, it may be possible to use these electrodes for species normally considered interferences. Such applications are another reason for accurately evaluating and reporting the selectivity ratios for ions interfering with the various ion-selective electrodes. Of course, the main reason is still that these ratios allow one to anticipate difficulties due to solution interferences which can cause erroneous results and to compensate for or eliminate these problems.

H. SILVER SULFIDE

The silver sulfide solid-state membrane electrode responds to both free silver and free sulfide ions in solution. As in the case of the silver halide electrodes, the membrane is an ionic conductor for silver ions, and the emf developed corresponds to the ionic distribution of silver ions between the sample and inner reference solution. This distribution in turn depends on the activity of the silver ions in the sample solution, since the inner reference solution is of constant silver activity. The electrode also responds to sulfide ion since the silver activity is dependent upon the sulfide activity as related through the silver sulfide solubility product.

The electrode will respond to concentrations between 1 and $10^{-7}M$ in total silver or sulfide, or to free sulfide ion activities down to $10^{-17}M$ or below in the presence of sulfide complexes, and to free silver activities to $10^{-25}M$ in the presence of complexed silver ion. In fact, studies in this laboratory [43] indicate that the response to free silver ion is Nernstian from $10^{-1}M$ down to $10^{-25}M$ on sample volumes of 5 μl. This is equivalent to a probability of much less than one ion of free silver in this volume of test solution and indicates that the electrode at some point

begins to respond to the complexed silver. The results of this study
are shown in Figure 9 where the solid line is the theoretical Nernst
slope, and the dashed line indicates the electrode response to total
silver ion activity in silver nitrate solutions.

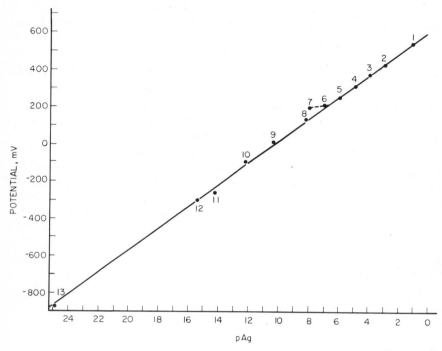

Figure 9.   Silver sulfide electrode response to silver activity (test solution vol. = 5μl)

(Solid line: 59.2 mV/pAg)

Point	Solution Composition	~ pAg (calc)	E(mV)
1	$10^{-1}M$ AgNO$_3$	1.1	+550
2	$10^{-3}M$ AgNO$_3$	3	+438
3	$10^{-4}M$ AgNO$_3$	4	+385
4	$10^{-5}M$ AgNO$_3$	5	+323
5	$10^{-6}M$ AgNO$_3$	6	+260
6	$10^{-7}M$ AgNO$_3$	7	+225
7	$10^{-8}M$ AgNO$_3$	8	+213
8	sat'd AgI	8.2	+150
9	sat'd AgI + $10^{-6}M$ KI	10.3	+21
10	sat'd AgI + $10^{-4}M$ KI	12.3	−91
11	sat'd AgCl + 1M Na$_2$S$_2$O$_3$	14.2	−256
12	sat'd AgCl + 0.1M KI	15.5	−298
13	0.1M Na$_2$S + 1M NaOH	24.9	−872

The use of this electrode for the direct potentiometric determination of silver at the parts per billion level is presented in a paper by Muller, *et al.* [44] in which the response of the electrode is found to be linear and Nernstian down to 13.5 ppb ($1.2 \times 10^{-7} M$ Ag^+).

In addition to trace and microchemical determinations, the silver sulfide electrode can be widely applied. As a sulfide electrode, it serves as a pollution monitor for industrial waste both in water supplies directly and in the air by aqueous absorption of the gaseous sulfides. Sulfide levels in drilling muds are of interest to petroleum chemists and, in the paper industry, the sulfide concentration in pulping liquors can be measured.

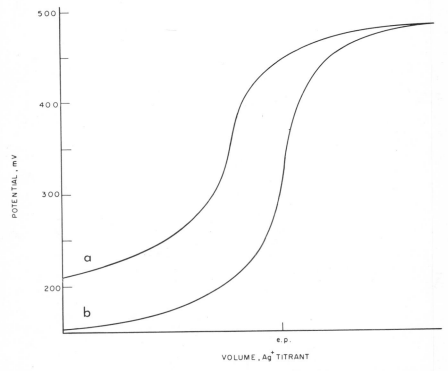

Figure 10.   Titration of chloride with silver in the presence of HNO_3 and Fe^{+3}. a) Titration curve obtained with Ag-Ag_2S electrode; b) Titration curve obtained with silver sulfide membrane electrode. From T. S. Light and J. L. Swartz [45].

For silver determinations, the only interference is mercuric ion, which forms the highly insoluble mercuric sulfide (approximately the same order of solubility as Ag_2S). In basic solutions, silver ion will precipitate as Ag_2O unless prevented by the presence of high enough levels of silver complexing agents, in which case only the free silver ion is detected unless a standard addition technique is used. As a sulfide detector, the electrode is interference-free, but again pH will affect the amount of free sulfide ion in solution. In all but the most basic solutions, sulfide will complex with hydrogen ion to form HS^- or H_2S. In such cases, total sulfide can be found by calculation using hydrogen sulfide equilibrium data, by titration with silver, or by a standard addition procedure.

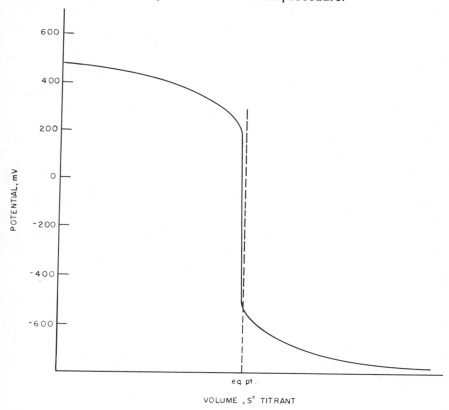

Figure 11. Titration of silver with sulfide. End point occurs at 98% of theoretical equivalence point. From T.-M. Hseu and G. A. Rechnitz [46].

As in the case of the silver halide electrodes, the absence of the metallic silver phase in the electrode membrane permits the use of this electrode in solutions containing oxidizing agents. An example of this type of interference is shown in Figure 10 where the silver sulfide membrane and silver-silver sulfide electrodes are used in $AgNO_3$ titrations of chloride solutions containing a large quantity of ferric ion and $1M$ in nitric acid [45]. In this titration, the silver sulfide membrane electrode is unaffected by the strong oxidants and indicates a typical titration curve and the correct end point. However, the silver-silver sulfide electrode shows a smaller end-point break which occurs well in advance of the true equivalence point.

In another analytical study of the silver sulfide electrode [46], the sensitivity, selectivity, and response characteristics are evaluated. In the titration of silver nitrate with standard sodium sulfide, it is shown (see Figure 11) that the inflection point of the titration occurs at 98% of the theoretical equivalence point due to the hydroxide ion (formed by hydrolysis of the sulfide) present in the titrant. That is, the hydroxide ion consumes silver by the formation and precipitation of silver hydroxide, *i.e.*, hydrated silver oxide. However, by standardizing the sodium sulfide titrant by potentiometrically titrating a standard silver nitrate solution, the effect of sulfide hydrolysis can be compensated by inclusion in the titre of the sulfide titrant. In this way, the inflection point of the titration curve will correspond to the equivalence point.

Additional references to applications of the silver sulfide electrode are given in the addendum.

I. DIVALENT CATIONS (MAGNESIUM)

The divalent cation electrode, developed primarily for water hardness measurements, exhibits an approximately equal selectivity for all divalent cations and only a limited response to sodium, potassium, and hydrogen ions. Although only one paper has been published in this area [47], the determination of water hardness is important in studies of scale formation, efficiency of water softeners, and as monitors of hardness in untreated waters. It is assumed, therefore, that this type of electrode has been used much more than is indicated by published studies.

Another application of this electrode is in the determination of specific divalent cations when others do not present a serious interference. An example of this is given by the direct potentiometric measurement of magnesium in sea water [48]. In this case, the electrode is calibrated with solutions already containing the various competing ions and varying only in the concentration of the magnesium ion. An ionized magnesium concentration of $0.048M$ was found for I.A.P.O. (International Association of Physical Oceanography) sea water (chlorinity 19.373 ppt) of $0.0534M$ total magnesium content. From this, it is concluded that about 90% of the sea water magnesium is ionized. Using an activity coefficient of 0.36, the activity of magnesium in sea water is calculated to be $0.0173M$.

This application represents another case where one of the ion-selective electrodes is used to determine an ion for which it is not specifically named (the manufacturer does suggest its use in determining calcium and magnesium), although it is not as extreme a situation as using an iodide electrode for the determination of cyanide, which under normal circumstances is an interference in the measurement of iodide. It is significant, however, that the divalent cation electrode is responsive to any and all of the divalent ions, in the order: $Pb^{++} > Zn^{++} = Fe^{++} > Cu^{++} > Ni^{++} > Ca^{++} = Mg^{++} > Ba^{++} > Sr^{++}$. In addition to the direct potentiometric measurement of these ions, the electrode can be used as the end-point detector in the titration of these ions with EDTA or other chelators.

J. Copper (Cupric Ion)

Although the original cupric ion-selective electrode was a liquid ion-exchange type, a solid-state membrane electrode has been recently developed which exhibits greatly improved characteristics. The liquid ion-exchange electrode was useful, as evidenced by its application to the study of the formation of copper complexes [49], but was limited to copper concentrations above about $10^{-5}M$ and was plagued by a large number of interferences, both cationic and anionic. On the other hand, the solid-state electrode is useable down to total cupric ion concentrations of $10^{-8}M$ (1 ppb) and is virtually interference-free with respect to the usual divalent cations. Electrode malfunction occurs with silver and mercuric ions, and ferric ion must be held below one tenth of the cupric ion concentration. The latter is easily accomplished by adjusting the sample pH to above 4.

The potential applications of a cupric ion electrode are many-fold and range from the measurement and control of copper levels in plating baths and etching baths for printed circuits to determining copper in various materials such as pharmaceuticals, foods, algaecides, and pesticides. With the importance of copper in today's commerce, it is likely that this electrode will prove to be a valuable analytical tool.

K. Lead and Cadmium

As in the case of the cupric ion electrode, the original liquid ion-exchange electrode for lead ion has been supplanted by a solid-state membrane electrode. This has again resulted in an extension of the useable range from $10^{-5}M$ lead for the liquid ion-exchange electrode to $10^{-7}M$ for the new electrode. The number of interferences has similarly been reduced to silver, mercury, and copper which must be absent from the test solution and cadmium and ferric ion, which should not exceed the lead ion concentration.

Lead ion can be determined by direct potentiometry and by titrations with EDTA or oxalate. The applications of this electrode include water and air pollution studies and the measurements of lead levels in food products, biological fluids, and various manufactured materials such as paints, glass, and pesticides.

The cadmium solid-state electrode has similar response characteristics, *i.e.*, total cadmium measurements down to $10^{-7}M$ and interference by silver, mercury, copper, ferric ion, and lead.

L. SULFATE AND PHOSPHATE

Analytical studies with prototype heterogeneous membrane electrodes sensitive to SO_4^{2-} and PO_4^{3-} were found useful for direct potentiometry and potentiometric titrations under very limited circumstances [50]. The sulfate electrode gave a useful response to concentrations as low as $10^{-5}M$ SO_4^{2-} and was approximately Nernstian above $10^{-4}M$. The potential of the phosphate electrode was less stable, drifting as much as 1 mV over a 10-min period. A crude calibration curve for phosphate was constructed over two decades of concentration, 10^{-2} to $10^{-4}M$, with a slope of only 7 mV/pPO$_4$ (theoretical: $\sim$ 20 mV/pPO$_4$).

Since neither electrode was particularly selective for its primary ion, they are probably best used as end-point detectors in potentiometric titrations where selectivity is not of utmost concern. Due to their unsatisfactory behavior for general solution measurements, these electrodes are not now commercially available, but it is hoped that improved versions will become available for the determination of these very important ions.

For the present, one possible procedure for the potentiometric determination of sulfate involves the titration of sulfate with standard lead perchlorate using a lead electrode as the end-point detector [51]. The lead sulfate precipitation is complete enough to provide a very good potential break at the end point of the titration (total emf change approximately 200 mV for the titration of millimolar sulfate in 50% dioxane solution). Although direct and continuous monitoring of sulfate is still not feasible, except perhaps by a continuous process titrator (Chapt. 10), the lead electrode titration procedure can be used to detect harmful sulfate levels in water supplies and to check the effectiveness of sulfate removal processes.

M. THIOCYANATE

The solid-state thiocyanate electrode responds to thiocyanate concentrations as low as $10^{-5}M$ but cannot be used in reducing solutions or solutions containing species that form silver complexes or insoluble silver salts.

N. MISCELLANEOUS

A recent paper by Coetzee and Freiser [52] describes the development of liquid-liquid membrane electrodes which respond to various organic and inorganic anions. Based on one of many possible solvent extraction systems, these electrodes use the salts of the methyl tricaprylyl ammonium cation dissolved in 1-decanol as the organic phase components. The electrodes exhibit a useful concentration range of 10^{-1} to 10^{-4} or $10^{-5}M$ for perchlorate, chloride, bromide, iodide, nitrate, sulfate, thiocyanate,

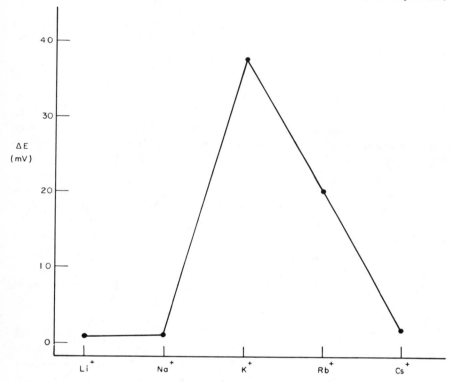

Figure 12.   Response of nonaction homolog membranes to monovalent cations. (ΔE/decade change in cation concentration.) From Z. Stefanac and W. Simon [53].

p-toluenesulfonate, acetate, formate, propionate, oxalate, and benzoate, and 10^{-1} to $10^{-3}M$ for salicylate. Most of the electrodes give an essentially Nernstian response which is linear over about two decades of concentration from approximately 10^{-1} to $10^{-3}M$.

Ion-association extraction systems, such as described above, and chelating extraction systems may be the forerunners of new types of ion-selective electrodes tailored to various organic ions. Developments along these lines could open up whole new areas for the application of these electrodes.

Even more exotic systems in which electrochemical cells using macrotetrolides (nonactin homologs) on various inert supports as membranes have been described [53] (see Chapt. 1 for details). These electrodes have a far superior selectivity for potassium over sodium than do the presently available ion-selective glass electrodes. In Figure 12, the response of nonactin homolog membranes is given in terms of the emf change produced when the cation concentration is increased by one order of magnitude. Over the concentration range of 10^{-3} to $10^{-1}M$ potassium chloride the response slope was approximately 32 mV/pK. By modifying the inert supports, the authors believe the speed of response ($\sim$ 2 hours for equilibrium) may be increased by orders of magnitude, and the response slope may become Nernstian.

O. Conclusion

In the discussions above, a brief survey of a very extensive topic was attempted. Many of the common applications and procedures were omitted in favor of presenting some of the more recent studies using ion-selective electrodes as they have appeared in publications over the past several years. Unfortunately, the newness of many of these electrodes has necessitated the very cursory treatment, especially concerning applications, given to several of the electrodes. Although some of the material dealing with electrode characteristics had been presented in earlier chapters, it was felt that some repetition was necessary to discuss the analytical uses and limitations of these electrodes properly.

The prospects for the future of ion-selective electrodes for analytical applications would seem to be bright indeed. This outlook not only includes the development of new electrodes, selective for many different ions and perhaps based on new systems for achieving better specificity, but also continuous and even automated analyses in which computers digest the data received directly from banks of miniaturized ion-selective electrodes and, using information on selectivities, simultaneously evaluate and print out the concentrations of dozens of ions in solution. Indeed, in such rapidly growing areas as oceanography, pollution, and biomedicine where rapid, or on-site, and often continuous monitoring and analysis are needed, the convenience of ion-selective electrode systems offers many advantages over more conventional techniques. In other areas of analysis, ion-selective electrodes will doubtless supplant many of the more "sophisticated" methods simply on the basis of their many superior characteristics. At present, research scientists working with these sensors are at the forefront of a new and rapidly developing technology — a renaissance of analytical potentiometry.

V. Addendum

Supplementary References

A. General Applications

"Membrane Electrodes in Chemical Analysis", Pungor, E., Toth, K., and Havas, J., Hung. Sci. Instr. **3**, 2 (1965).

"Membrane Electrodes Respond to Anions", (anonymous), Chem. Eng. News, Jan. 31, 1966, p. 24.

"Ion-Selective Electrodes", Rechnitz, G. A., Chem. Eng. News, June 12, 1967, p. 146.

"Selective Ion Electrodes", Light, T. S., Analysis Instrumentation 1967, L. Fowler, *et al.,* Eds., Plenum Press, New York, 1967.

"Study on Ion Selective Electrodes", Pungor, E., Hung. Sci. Instr. **10,** 1 (1967).

"Theory and Application of Anion Selective Membrane Electrodes", Pungor, E., Anal. Chem. **39,** 28A (1967).

B. FLUORIDE

"Electrode for Sensing Fluoride Ion Activity in Solution", Frant, M. S., and Ross, J. W., Jr., Science **154,** 1553 (1966).

"Fluoride in Chromium Plating Baths: Determination of Activity and Concentration", Frant, M. S., Plating **54,** 702 (1967).

"Direct Determination of Fluoride in Tungsten Using the Fluoride Ion Activity Electrode", Raby, B. A., and Sunderland, W. E., Anal. Chem. **39,** 1304 (1967).

"Modification of the Fluoride Activity Electrode for Microchemical Analysis", Durst, R. A., and Taylor, J. K., Anal. Chem. **39,** 1483 (1967).

"Potentiometric Titration of Fluoride with Tetraphenylantimony Sulfate", Orenberg, J. B., and Morris, M. D., Anal. Chem. **39,** 1776 (1967).

"The Rapid Determination of Fluoride in Mineral Fluorides Using a Specific Ion Electrode", VanLoon, J. C., Anal. Lett. **1,** 393 (1968).

"Lanthanum Fluoride Electrode Response in Aqueous Chloride Media", Mesmer, R. E., Anal. Chem. **40,** 443 (1968).

"Activity Measurements with a Fluoride-Selective Membrane Electrode", Srinivasan, K., and Rechnitz, G. A., Anal. Chem. **40,** 509 (1968).

"Evidence that there are Two Forms of Fluoride in Human Serum", Taves, D. R., Nature **217,** 1050 (1968).

"Determination of Fluoride in Mineralized Tissues Using the Fluoride Ion Electrode", McCann, H. G., Archs. Oral Biol. **13,** 475 (1968).

"Clearance of Fluoride from the Mouth after Topical Treatment or the Use of a Fluoride Mouthrinse", Aasenden, R., Brudewold, F., and Richardson, B., Archs. Oral Biol. **13,** 625 (1968).

"Determination of Fluorine in Feeds by the Fluoride Ion Activity Electrode", Torma, L., and Ginther, B. E., J. Assoc. Offic. Anal. Chem. **51,** 1177 (1968).

"An Evaluation of Some Methods for the Determination of Fluoride in Potable Waters and Other Aqueous Solutions", Crosby, N. T., Dennis, A. L., and Stevens, J. G., Analyst **93,** 643 (1968).

"Determination of Submicromolar Concentrations of Fluoride in Biological Samples", Taves, D. R., Talanta **15,** 1015 (1968).

"Evaluation of the Lanthanum Fluoride Membrane Electrode Response In Acidic Solutions: The Determination of the pK_a of Hydrofluoric Acid", Vanderborgh, N. E., Talanta **15,** 1009 (1968).

"Lanthanum Fluoride Electrode Response in Water and in Sodium Chloride", Warner, T. B., Anal. Chem. **41,** 527 (1969).

C. CALCIUM

"Calcium-Selective Electrode with Liquid Ion Exchanger", Ross, J. W., Science **156,** 1378 (1967).

"Calcium Electrode Method for Measuring Dissociation and Solubility of Calcium Sulfate Dihydrate", Nakayama, F. S., and Rasnick, B. A., Anal. Chem. **39**, 1022 (1967).
"Ion Specific Membranes as Electrodes in Determination of Activity of Calcium", Shatkay, A., Anal. Chem. **39**, 1056 (1967).
"Calcium and the Control of Mitosis in the Mammal", Perris, A. D., and Whitfield, J. F., Nature **216**, 1350 (1967).
"Cation Measurements in Biological Materials", Moore, E. W., Ann. N. Y. Acad. Sci. **148**, 93 (1968).
"Determination of Calcium and Oxalate with an Ion-Exchange Electrode", Mukherji, A. K., Anal. Chim. Acta **40**, 354 (1968).
"Electrode Determination of Salivary Calcium Ion Activity", Gron, P., Spinelli, M. A., and Hay, D. I., IADR Abstracts, p. 58 (1968).
"Measurement of Serum Ionic Calcium Using a Specific Ion Electrode", Arnold, D. E., Stansell, M. J., and Malvin, H. H., Amer. J. Clin. Path. **49**, 627 (1968).
"Use of Calcium-Selective Electrode to Measure Ionized Calcium Levels in Normal and Pathological Plasma", Oreskes, I., and Douglas, K. S., Clin. Chim. Acta **21**, 303 (1968).
"Studies with Ion-Exchange Calcium Electrodes: The Distribution of Ionized Calcium between Blood and Cerebrospinal Fluid in Man and Dog", Moore, E. W., and Blum, A. L., J. Clin. Invest. **47**, 70a (1968).
"Potentiometric Measurements with Calcium-Selective Liquid-Liquid Membrane Electrodes", Rechnitz, G. A., and Lin, Z. F., Anal. Chem. **40**, 696 (1968).
"Comparison of a Liquid Ion Exchange Electrode and the AOAC Method for Determining Calcium in Animal Feeding Stuffs", Allen, R. D., Hobley, J., and Carriere, R., J. Assoc. Offic. Anal. Chem. **51**, 1181 (1968).

D. Nitrate

"An Evaluation of the Performance of the Nitrate-Selective Electrode", Potterton, S. S., and Shults, W. D., Anal. Lett. **1**, 11 (1967).
"Use of a Selective Ion Electrode for Determination of Nitrates in Soils", Bremner, J. M., Buddy, L. G., and Agarwal, A. S., Anal. Lett. (in press).

E. Halides

"Analytical Study of an Iodide-Sensitive Membrane Electrode", Rechnitz, G. A., Kresz, M. R., and Zamochnick, S. B., Anal. Chem. **38**, 973 (1966).
"Study of Iodine Complexes by Means of the Membrane Electrode, System Pungor", Burger, K., and Pinter, B., Hung. Sci. Instr. **8**, 11 (1966).
"Potentiometric Measurements with Chloride-Sensitive and Bromide-Sensitive Membrane Electrodes", Rechnitz, G. A., and Kresz, M. R., Anal. Chem. **38**, 1786 (1966).
"Analytical Applications of Bromide and Chloride Ion-Selective Membrane Electrodes", Havas, J., Papp, E., and Pungor, E., Magy. Kem. Foly. **73**, 292 (1967).
"Analytical Application of Iodide-Selective Rubber Membrane Electrode, I.", Havas, J., Huber, M., Szabo, I., and Pungor, E., Hung. Sci. Instr. **9**, 19 (1967).
"Sweat Chloride Analysis by Chloride Ion-Specific Electrode Method Using Heat Stimulation", Hansen, L., Buechele, M., Koroschec, J., and Warwick, W. J., Amer. J. Clin. Path. **49**, 834 (1968).
"Dead Sea Brines: Degree of Halite Saturation by Electrode Measurement", Lerman, A., and Shatkay, A., Earth Plan. Sci. Lett. **63**, 5 (1968).

F. Silver Sulfide

"Specific Ion Determination of Hydrogen Sulfide in Beer", Owades, J. L., Blick, R., and Owades, S. H., A.S.B.C. Proc., 1967.
"Bestimmung von Sulfid mit einer Sulfidionen-empfindlichen Elektrode", Bock, R., and Puff, H. J., Z. Anal. Chem. **240**, 381 (1968).

VI. References

[1] deBrouckere, L., Bull. Soc. Chim. Belg. **37**, 103 (1928).
[2] Malmstadt, H. V., and Winefordner, J. D., Anal. Chim. Acta **20**, 283 (1959).
[3] Malmstadt, H. V., and Pardue, H. L., Anal. Chem. **32**, 1034 (1960).
[4] Malmstadt, H. V., Hadjiioannou, T. P., and Pardue, H. L., Anal. Chem. **32**, 1039 (1960).
[5] Malmstadt, H. V., and Winefordner, J. D., Anal. Chim. Acta **24**, 91 (1961).
[6] Durst, R. A., Anal. Chem. **40**, 931 (1968).
[7] Durst, R. A., and Taylor, J. K., Anal. Chem. **39**, 1374 (1967).
[8] Durst, R. A., May, E. L., and Taylor, J. K., Anal. Chem. **40**, 977 (1968).
[9] Frant, M. S., and Ross, J. W., Anal. Chem. **40**, 1169 (1968).
[10] Baumann, E. W., Anal. Chim. Acta **42**, 127 (1968).
[11] Ross, J. W., Jr., paper presented at the Amer. Microchem. Soc. Workshop, Penn. State Univ., Aug. 1968.
[12] Durst, R. A., Mikrochim. Acta **3**, 611 (1969).
[13] Durst, R. A., and Ross, J. W., Jr., Anal. Chem. **40**, 1343 (1968).
[14] Gran, G., Acta Chem. Scand. **4**, 559 (1950); see also Anfalt, T., Dyrssen, D., and Jagner, D., Anal. Chim. Acta **43**, 487 (1968).
[15] Baumann, E. W., Anal. Chem. **40**, 1731 (1968).
[16] Bock, R., and Strecker, S., Z. Anal. Chem. **235**, 322 (1968).
[17] Lingane, J. J., Anal. Chem. **39**, 881 (1967).
[18] Lingane, J. J., ibid. **40**, 935 (1968).
[19] Shane, N., and Miele, D., J. Pharm. Sci. **57**, 1260 (1968).
[20] Singer, L., and Armstrong, W. D., Anal. Chem. **40**, 613 (1968).
[21] Elfers, L. A., and Decker, C. E., Anal. Chem. **40**, 1658 (1968).
[22] Spencer, D. W., Woods Hole Oceanographic Inst., private communication, Sept. 1967.
[23] Brewer, P. G., Woods Hole Oceanographic Inst., private communication, Dec. 1968.
[24] Light, T. S., and Mannion, R. F., Anal. Chem. **41**, 107 (1969).
[25] Schultz, F. A., Petersen, A. J., Mask, C. A., and Buck, R. P., Science **162**, 267 (1968).
[26] Rechnitz, G. A., and Hseu, T. M., Anal. Chem. **41**, 111 (1969).
[27] King, J. A., and Mukherji, A. K., Naturwissenschaften **24**, 702 (1966).
[28] Orion Applications Bulletin No. 8, "Determination of Total Calcium Levels in Beer Using the Calcium Ion Activity Electrode", Orion Research, Inc. (1968).
[29] Liska, B. J., Purdue Univ., private communication, 1968.
[30] Muldoon, P. J., and Liska, B. J., J. Dairy Sci. **52**, 460 (1969).
[31] Thompson, M. E., and Ross, J. W., Jr., Science **154**, 1643 (1966).
[32] Dyrssen, D., Univ. of Gothenburg (Sweden), private communication, 1968.
[33] Orion Applications Bulletin No. 6, "Determination of Nitrate in Soils with the Nitrate Ion Activity Electrode", Orion Research, Inc. (1968).
[34] Paul, J. L., and Carlson, R. M., J. Agr. Food Chem. **16**, 766 (1968).
[35] Carlson, R. M., and Paul, J. L., Anal. Chem. **40**, 1292 (1968).

[36] Carlson, R. M., and Paul, J. L., Soil Sci. (in press).

[37] Baczuk, R. J., and DuBois, R. J., Anal. Chem. **40**, 685 (1968).

[38] Lee, T. G., Anal. Chem. **41**, 391 (1969).

[39] Orion Research, Inc., General Catalog, p. 5 (1968).

[40] Csakvari, B., and Meszaros, K., Hung. Sci. Instr. **11**, 9 (1968).

[41] Arino, H., and Kramer, H. H., Nucl. Applic. **4**, 356 (1968).

[42] Pungor, E., and Toth, K., Hung. Sci. Instr. **14**, 15 (1968).

[43] Durst, R. A., NBS, unpublished results.

[44] Muller, D. C., West, P. W., and Muller, R. H., Anal. Chem. (in press).

[45] Light, T. S., and Swartz, J. L., paper presented at the Pitts. Conf. on Anal. Chem. and Appl. Spect., Cleveland, Ohio, March 1968.

[46] Hseu, T.-M., and Rechnitz, G. A., Anal. Chem. **40**, 1054 (1968).

[47] Cummins, R. W., Deterg. Age, March 1968, p. 22.

[48] Thompson, M. E., Science **153**, 867 (1966).

[49] Rechnitz, G. A., and Lin, Z. F., Anal. Lett. **1**, 23 (1967).

[50] Rechnitz, G. A., Lin, Z. F., and Zamochnick, S. B., Anal. Lett. **1**, 29 (1967).

[51] Ross, J. W., Jr., and Frant, M. S., Anal. Chem. **41**, 967 (1969).

[52] Coetzee, C. J., and Freiser, H., Anal. Chem. **40**, 2071 (1968).

[53] Stefanac, Z., and Simon, W., Microchem. J. **12**, 125 (1967).

CHAPTER 12

SYMPOSIUM DISCUSSION

The transcription of selected segments of the discussion sessions is included in this volume because it supplements much of the material in the preceding chapters. In this chapter will be found comments on practical problems such as noise, interferences, and methodology and additional information on the principles of operation, construction, and applications of ion-selective electrodes.

The Symposium was arranged so as to provide time for questions at the completion of each lecture and, in addition, a panel discussion period was scheduled at the conclusion of each day's session at which all of the speakers were available to answer questions and comments from the audience.

The following discussions were transcribed with a minimum of editing and represent the spontaneous exchange of remarks of the various participants as they were recorded at the Symposium. Wherever possible, the participants have been identified and have had an opportunity to correct this transcription for technical accuracy.

THURSDAY MORNING SESSION

L. M. Chambers *(Procter and Gamble Company)*:   It seems to me that one of the limitations of the liquid ion exchange membrane electrodes is going to be their use in high ionic strength media looking for low-level materials; for example, measuring water hardness at the ppm calcium-magnesium level where the ionic strength of your samples may vary depending upon their source, anywhere from tenth molar on down. We know from calibration curves that the ionic strength does have an effect in a non-specific manner and, depending on the ion controlling the ionic strength, it could also interfere such as in the case of sodium ion. I am interested in knowing if anyone has had experience in either removing the interfering ions or using some better measurement technique.

J. W. Ross *(Orion Research)*:   It is certainly true, as has been just mentioned, that liquid electrodes are not highly selective systems as compared with the solid membrane electrodes, and that one does have a problem in measuring very dilute solutions of an ion in the presence of a high ionic strength background. In the case of solid electrodes, it is possible to get around this difficulty by intentionally adding a component to bring the ionic strength up to a very high level and swamp out ionic strength effects. If one tries this with liquid electrodes, in most situations one finds that he is inevitably adding an interfering ion by this ionic strength buffer-

415

ing procedure. There are still ways of compensating for this, however. One way of doing this is to measure the conductivity of the sample. You will find that you can get a very close approximation of the ionic strength of the sample. I would suggest that in water quality control applications this method makes a lot of sense, since conductivity is normally one of the parameters being measured as well as water hardness and a suitable nomograph can be derived for computing correction factors. Slightly related to this, Dr. Durst reported that EDTA-calcium titrations, using a calcium electrode, cannot be done in the presence of high sodium backgrounds such as found in sea water; the end-point break being too small, and this is certainly true. I would suggest here that either the copper electrode or the cadmium electrode, as I mentioned earlier, can be used for calcium end-point determinations by the indicator method of Reilley. Under these circumstances, one can titrate at the ppm level of calcium in the presence of a million-fold excess of sodium or chloride ions.

Anonymous: There seems to be some question whether chloride ion interferes with the fluoride electrode. Would you care to comment on that?

J. W. Ross *(Orion)*:   We have observed no case of interference. The interference could not be serious, and you would have to work at very high levels of chloride to be significant. One must be very careful in making up the chloride solutions to avoid contamination by trace fluoride. Some recent work at Oak Ridge National Laboratory has shown that apparent chloride interferences have been due to traces of fluoride in the chloride reagents used to make up the solutions. Again, we have not observed any chloride interference with the fluoride electrode.

R. G. Bates *(NBS)*:   I wonder if it isn't an over-simplification to attribute all of the departure from the Nernst equation to the activity corrections. We have found that variation in the liquid junction potential accounts for about one-third of the deviation. Would you agree?

J. W. Ross *(Orion)*:   I certainly would. In my discussion, I have conveniently ignored the existence of the liquid junction potential, and I am sure that anyone familiar with pH measurements knows the problems associated with this.

J. N. Butler *(Tyco Laboratories)*:   I would like to point out that the inflection point of a titration does not necessarily coincide exactly with the equivalence point. This must be determined either experimentally by titration of a solution of known concentration or else by a theoretical calculation of all the equilibria and kinetics of the reaction. A plot of $\Delta V/\Delta E$ is not easy to interpolate in the region of the end point. One of the better methods of determining the end point, where you do not have a dead stop potential to work from is to calculate the concentration of the titrant ion in the solution past the end point and extrapolate back on a linear graph of concentration *vs.* volume added. This is the original Gran method and has been used successfully in a number of laboratories where people have had to determine concentrations very accurately in solutions where there may be impurities. Impurities show up on this plot quite clearly as deviations from linearity. If you have very pure solutions and a very clean reaction, you get a precisely linear plot down to something on the order of 10^{-5} or 10^{-6} molar. It is not as good as a dead stop potential technique to a few millivolts, but this latter method cannot always be used.

THURSDAY AFTERNOON SESSION

J. W. Ross *(Orion)*: There was an obvious discrepancy between the solubility product for lanthanum fluoride determined by the electrode solubility measurement as compared with the solubility product determined from freshly precipitated lanthanum fluoride. This really shouldn't be too much of a surprise. A single crystal will always have a solubility product considerably smaller than the finely divided material, and this is particularly true for substances which form hard crystals, that is, where the surface free energy of the crystal is quite large. Lanthanum fluoride is perhaps an exceptional case, but there are other examples. We have looked at calcium fluoride which is much more soluble and easier to handle experimentally. We have measured the solubility of cleavage pieces of single-crystal calcium fluoride against freshly precipitated calcium fluoride and find differences of factors of a hundred between the two methods of preparation. I found this difficult to believe when it was first pointed out to me, but it generally seems to be true. Now, as you go to softer materials such as silver chloride, where the surface free energy is much smaller, this effect is not nearly as evident. This should have been obvious to me, being trained as an analytical chemist. That is, going back to the idea that if I precipitate barium sulfate I can digest this precipitate and, over a period of time, the little crystals grow bigger. This means, of course, that the smaller crystals are more soluble than the big ones.

J. N. Butler *(Tyco)*: I am amazed that this effect can be as large as a factor of 10^5.

J. W. Ross *(Orion)*: It really is, and I think if you go look at some of the geological data on silicates and other very hard materials, you will find a very large variety of solubility products over the range listed, depending on whether it is freshly precipitated, aged precipitate or single-crystal material. My second comment concerns the effect of hydroxide interference on the lanthanum fluoride electrode and the fact that it showed a time dependence. I expected a time dependence, of course, since the hydroxide ion is entering the crystal lattice at a very slow rate, but I don't know if I could estimate off-hand which direction that drift should be. It is more complicated than just assuming that the hydroxide ion participates in the charge-transfer process. The nature of the surface is continually changing, and it can go through all shades of gray from pure lanthanum fluoride to lanthanum monohydroxy difluoride, dihydroxy, and so on to pure lanthanum hydroxide on the surface. Since the nature of the surface is changing, the nature of the ion exchange equilibrium constant must also be changing, and the drift could go either direction. My final comment concerns the discouraging results you (Dr. Butler) had at high ionic strengths. This is a fact of life, I think, with the liquid ion exchange electrodes. To be on the safe side, tenth molar is probably as high as you should go, although your use of the different internal filling solutions is an elegant way to go still higher in some cases. However, you do get charge transfer of anions and such things at these ionic strengths.

Anonymous: On the lanthanum fluoride solubility product discrepancy, I was wondering if the crystal structures were determined? Were they the same?

J. W. Ross *(Orion)*:   Yes, the powder has exactly the same structure as the single crystal.

Anonymous: What methods were used to determine the solubility products in the case of the lanthanum fluoride crystals?

J. W. Ross *(Orion)*:   In the case of the solubility product of the single crystal, this was accomplished by equilibrating a lanthanum fluoride electrode with distilled water for several days and measuring the ambient level of fluoride produced due to the solubility of the crystal, using the electrode itself as the sensing device. In the case of the much higher value of the solubility product that Lingane gives, this is determined by the titration of fluoride by lanthanum nitrate and evaluated from the potential at the end point of the titration. Of course, the solubility product can be calculated from any point on the titration curve, but it is most convenient to do this at the equivalence point of the titration. This value obtained by Lingane refers to the freshly precipitated lanthanum fluoride. In addition to this, there had been some thermal measurements by Powell and Connick, I believe, at Berkeley several years ago. This again refers to the finely divided precipitated material, and their values agree quite closely with Lingane's. But again, it depends on the size of the crystal what the solubility product will be, and an interesting problem would be to look at the single-crystal material, and I would expect that you would have different solubility products for different faces of the crystal. A 111 cleavage plane would probably be more or less soluble than a cleavage plane parallel to the hexagonal axis. This may very well account for the tenfold discrepancy between our value and Rechnitz' value both of which were obtained on single-crystal electrodes. But, in manufacturing the electrodes, we make no attempt to reproduce the crystal orientation of the crystal section, and this may be a reflection of that.

R. de Levie *(Georgetown University)*: I might add that we have had a similar experience. We tried to measure the activity of lanthanum perchlorate with the fluoride electrode and didn't get a constant potential. The drift was not caused by the other (perchlorate) electrode. We did not form a precipitate, and apparently we cannot use the fluoride electrode as an electrode of the second kind.

J. N. Butler *(Tyco)*: That's very interesting because Lingane's solubility product measurements were made in a region where lanthanum ion was present in excess, and there was equilibrium between the lanthanum ion in excess and the precipitated lanthanum fluoride.

E. J. King *(Barnard College)*: While it is undoubtedly true that particle size will have an effect on solubility and solubility product determinations, the freshly precipitated character also has a very striking effect, and this is because of the non-equilibrium solid phase present. This is well known in the familiar sulfides of qualitative analysis which have solubility products that may be 10^5 larger for the freshly precipitated particles as against the stable crystalline material, a factor of the same order of magnitude as you reported for lanthanum fluoride.

J. N. Butler *(Tyco)*: This certainly is a possibility, but you would think that, if the same crystalline forms existed for both the freshly precipitated and the solid crystals, they would have much the same thermodynamic properties.

E. J. King *(Barnard)*: I don't believe that they are the same crystalline form.

J. N. Butler *(Tyco)*: I have no evidence, and I am just going on what Dr. Ross has already stated.

E. J. King *(Barnard)*: If they do have the same crystalline form, the difference may be in hydration. Gelatinous precipitates, such as the sulfides or aluminum hydroxide, do become much less soluble as they age without necessarily undergoing any profound change in crystalline structure. Lanthanum fluoride may be exhibiting this behavior.

PANEL DISCUSSION (THURSDAY)

Anonymous: I understand that silicone rubber is a very generic term. Now, from the point of view of constructing electrodes, could we have some specific comments on what is meant by the term silicone rubber, because I gathered that this makes a very great deal of difference.

J. W. Ross *(Orion)*: I have had some experience with the silicone rubber electrodes, but I am sure that Dr. Pungor would disagree with me, and I may be biased, but I happen to opt for the solid-state variety. I honestly can't see any difference in mechanism between a heterogeneous-impregnated membrane and a solid-state membrane when you are talking about such things as silver sulfide and the silver halides that are all good ionic conductors. The silicone rubber membranes are made in such a way that particle loading is high enough that you have particle-to-particle contact. The conduction process is the same, and the behavior of the electrodes should be virtually identical regardless of whether one is talking about a single crystal or polycrystalline membrane or an impregnated membrane. In my experience, though, the principle source of failure in electrodes in the case of the Orion electrodes, for example, is a failure of the seal between the insulating barrel material and the actual membrane material itself. In the case of the particle-impregnated membranes, I worry about the fact that there is a great surface interface present here and a correspondingly greater chance for failure of seals. As far as the matrix material goes, I don't think it makes any difference what kind of silicone rubber you use or whether it's silicone rubber or not as long as it makes a good seal to the actual conducting material.

J. D. Johnson *(University of North Carolina)*:   Since we generally must use reference electrodes with liquid junction, we need to choose between a porous-plug, fiber or sleeve type junction. Do we use a silver chloride or a calomel electrode? Do we use saturated KCl, tenth normal KCl or normal KCl in these electrodes? I realize that this question perhaps does not have an answer. But is there a best choice for a reference electrode when we standardize at one ionic strength and go out and measure at other ionic strengths?

J. W. Ross *(Orion)*:   To go right down the line, and this is largely personal taste on my part, I think silver chloride electrodes are better than calomel electrodes because the temperature hysteresis problem is considerably less. I have had no experience with the Thalamid electrodes which were discussed by Dr. Covington in his paper. With respect to the junctions, I think that a sleeve-type junction is better than a ceramic-plug junction which is better than a fiber-type junction. This is based mainly on the fact that clogging problems are less serious when you have the larger flow. Now, what goes inside of that junction is again, I think, a matter of taste within reason, and I think we have been wedded to saturated potassium chloride too long. For example, if one is making measurements in highly alkaline solutions, one might be better advised to use a potassium hydroxide or sodium hydroxide solution in the junction to try to eliminate the contribution of hydroxide ion to the junction potential. Similarly, in acid solution, HCl might be a better choice than saturated KCl. If one is making measurements in very dilute solutions, one ought to be able to use a somewhat more dilute filling solution, perhaps an equi-transferent mixture of potassium chloride-potassium nitrate. It is very hard to generalize, and there probably isn't any one best solution. One has to be reasonably intelligent in choosing, depending on the particular problem one has in mind, and make a decision on that basis.

J. N. Butler *(Tyco):* The thing that surprises me is that the Beckman fiber-junction calomel electrode, that everybody carries around with his pH meter, has such really high reproducibility.

R. G. Bates *(NBS):* I would like to add to Dr. Ross' comments that I feel that we have been wedded too long to the saturated calomel electrode and would like to put in a plug for using 3.5 molar KCl. I think that a lot of the problems associated with saturated calomel electrodes arise when you change the temperature and get the electrode plugged with KCl crystals. As far as we can tell, the liquid junction potential is very much the same at 3.5 molar as it is with saturated KCl. As for the choice between calomel, silver chloride, and Thalamid, I think it depends a great deal on the temperature range in which you are going to make measurements. The calomel electrode is very unstable above 80 °C, but I think at room temperature the calomel is not too bad. The silver chloride is inclined to dissolve in strong KCl solutions.

J. W. Ross *(Orion):* In getting away from saturated KCl with both the calomel electrode and the silver-silver chloride electrode, the solubility of the silver and the mercury in these solutions is quite large, approaching 10^{-3} or 10^{-4} molar. If one is making sulfide measurements, for example, what one has is either silver or mercury sulfide precipitating in the junction, if one is using a single junction reference electrode. By going to more dilute chloride filling solutions, the solubility of the silver or mercury goes down dramatically, and one can get away from this problem.

J. N. Butler *(Tyco):* This is an especially important point in some non-aqueous systems such as aprotic solvents like dimethyl sulfoxide and dimethyl formamide. Here the solubility of silver chloride is approximately equal to the concentration of excess chloride so that it is quite essential to develop liquid junction potentials of the correct character or else to use materials such as thallous chloride where the solubility is relatively low.

T. S. Light *(Foxboro Company):* I'd like to add some comments concerning reference electrodes. As already indicated, there is no one best reference electrode. We have been working with electrode systems for a number of years, and receive many questions concerning trouble shooting problems. We have come to the conclusion that between 50 and 90% of the troubles are directly traceable to problems with the reference electrode. The process chemical industry has, by and large, standardized on silver chloride reference electrodes. There are a number of reasons for this. One is that when dealing with the food processing industry, the possibility of breakage might introduce contamination by toxic mercury or calomel. In other industries, such as the photographic industry, mercury vapors are objectionable, and calomel electrodes are not permitted in the plant. Again, concerning reference electrode problems, difficulties may be created for various other reasons. For example, sulfide, as cited by Dr. Ross, precipitates either silver sulfide or mercuric sulfide in the liquid junction of a reference electrode, and these are two of the most insoluble substances known. In effect the reference electrode has been made a measuring electrode for mercuric or silver ion. My advice if this happens is to throw the reference electrode away. It cannot be repaired, since the silver or mercuric sulfide cannot readily be dissolved and causes errors in the liquid junction potential which are much greater than any of the standard calculable liquid junction potentials that are known to exist with good reference electrodes. The temperature coefficient also must be considered, and I am a strong advocate of the lower potassium chloride concentrations away from the saturation point, to avoid the problem of crystallization in the liquid junction. As far as stirring is concerned, one should find no effect on most cell emf's whether the solution is stirred or not. If a stirring effect is obtained, there is a possibility that something is happening in the reference electrode junction. With a clean fresh junction, stirring effects are seldom observed except for the liquid ion exchange electrodes which have a different mechanism for cell potential. In this case, a steady stirring or flow rate is desirable.

G. D. Christian *(University of Kentucky)*:   Dr. Bates has pointed out the advantage of using standards very close to the concentration of the unknown system to reduce the residual junction potential and for other reasons. Do you visualize a system whereby you can prepare a series of standards over a range of concentrations using metal complexes of a pK fairly close to the pM that you need? I can see many difficulties, but this would enable you to at least prepare some standards over a wide range of concentrations especially for dilute solutions.

R. G. Bates *(NBS)*:   To rephrase your question, you are asking whether it is possible to visualize a series of metal buffers which would vary greatly in metal ion activity and perhaps not vary greatly in ionic strength. I think there is some hope for that, but I don't think we have the possibilities that we have with pH standards where there are weak acids of widely varying pK. In some respects this would not solve the problem because the liquid junction potential you wish to cancel out varies with the ionic strength of your unknowns so widely that if you had a series of buffers of 0.1 ionic strength it might not be very effective in nullifying the liquid junction potential of your series of unknowns. I think this is an interesting proposal, and it is one to which we have given some idle thought but haven't been able to come up with any great series of possibilities which would give us any useful plurality of metal buffers.

W. C. Shaner *(Sun Oil Company)*:   Is it possible to use the electrodes, such as the sulfide electrode, for measurements in non-aqueous systems such as crude oil?

J. W. Ross *(Orion)*:   Yes and no. All of the solid-state electrodes function quite well in non-aqueous solvents provided the solvent does not attack the electrode barrel. The electrode barrel is epoxy so that things like pyridine or nitrobenzene are not allowed, but methanol, acetone, acetonitrile, and crude oil would be alright. However, in order to make the measurement, you have to have some conductivity in the sample solution. Otherwise, the resistance between the sensing electrode and the reference electrode would be far too high. You would have many megohms floating in the air and a good deal of noise generated. It would be possible to use the electrode in crude oil if it were first diluted with something with a fairly high dielectric constant such as methanol in fifty-fifty dilution. Then, provided one calibrates in that solvent background, one can get honest ionic activity values. In fact, one of the recommended titrations of fluoride is done in non-aqueous solvents.

S. H. Katz *(Eastern Pennsylvania Psychiatric Institute)*: Dr. Butler, you pointed out that sodium is a major interfering ion in the use of the calcium ion-selective electrode. I am very interested in the physiological effect of this. Did you bother to calculate what the effect of the sodium ion concentration is on the ambient calcium ion concentrations in the physiological range? If you need those numbers, I'd say roughly $0.15M$ sodium *vs.* 100-times less than that for calcium.

J. N. Butler *(Tyco)*: I don't think you would get any interference in that range. Its only in very concentrated solutions that the selectivity begins to fall off. I believe that Dr. Moore knows much more about those ranges than I do.

E. W. Moore *(Tufts University Medical School)*: Thank you Dr. Butler. The selectivity of the calcium electrodes in the physiologic concentration ranges for Na^+, K^+, Mg^{++} and H^+ has been carefully evaluated by Dr. Ross at Orion and also in our laboratory and our results agree rather closely. This will be discussed in some detail in tomorrow's session. On a mole basis, the selectivity for Ca^{++} over Na^+ is about 10,000 to 1, *i.e.*, it requires about 10,000 times as much Na^+ to generate a given electrode potential. The selectivity for Ca^{++} over Mg^{++} is about 100 to 1. In serum and other extracellular fluids containing $150\,mM$ Na^+ and 0.5-$1.0\,mM$ Mg^{++}, overall sodium and magnesium error is therefore believed to be about $+2\%$ in apparent calcium ion concentration.

S. H. Katz *(E. Pa. Psych. Inst.)*: May I ask a second question that is directed towards the standards concept? Has anyone decided upon or have suggestions for the use of standards for mixed ionic solutions such as would be present in serum?

R. G. Bates *(NBS)*: All I can say in reply is that this is in the second phase of the program, so to speak, and the simple phase has to be decided first. I think the activity of sodium and calcium in pure aqueous solutions must be established by a convention before we can go to what will probably have to be secondary standards. When we get a series of primary standards that are satisfactory, then I think inevitably one will have to consider these standards for very important media such as isotonic saline, sea water and so on.

Anonymous: I think I know the answer, and the answer should be no, but I want to make sure. Do you know of some specific electrode for chloride ions but for which bromide and iodide do not interfere at all, no matter what the concentration?

J. W. Ross *(Orion):*   No!

End of First Discussion Session

FRIDAY   MORNING   SESSION

C. Pittinger *(Vanderbilt University Hospital):*   Dr. Moore, you mentioned your apparatus and that of Orion using two different temperatures, body temperature on yours and 25 °C on the Örion. What effect does the 12 °C or so difference have on the measurements?

E. W. Moore *(Tufts):*   Binding of calcium to the serum proteins is temperature — dependent as well as pH-dependent. Loken and associates have found by ultracentrifugation that free calcium (largely Ca^{++}) is 10-12% higher at 12 °C than at 37 °C, suggesting that it would be 5-6% higher with the Orion flow-through electrode at 25 °C than with our static electrode at 37 °C. Comparison of serum Ca^{++} values with the two types of electrodes must also include pH effects. Our static electrode values were those at the original whole blood pH; flow-through Ca^{++} concentration values were those at the pH of serum after separation under oil, about 0.08 pH units higher than blood pH. Both our data and those of Loken indicate that this 0.08 pH increase would decrease the Ca^{++} concentration about 3-4%. The temperature and pH effects are therefore opposite in direction; Ca^{++} values with the flow-through electrode would be expected to be about 2-3% higher than those with the static electrode. This is almost exactly the difference observed, with respective mean Ca^{++} values of 1.16 mM and 1.12 mM.

FRIDAY   AFTERNOON   SESSION

A. Weisstuch *(Betz Laboratories):*   I would like to know, in a continuous system such as cooling water or boiling water applications, what would be the operational lifetime of an electrode, and what are the problems with fouling?

T. S. Light *(Foxboro):*   I would first like to mention that one should not generalize about ion-selective electrodes; each has its own limitations and problems. For example, a calcium ion-selective electrode is an organic liquid ion exchanger type and has an upper temperature limit of about 50 °C. As with pH measurements, familiarity with the system is desirable. There are pH systems requiring very little standardization for months on end. However good laboratory or plant operations suggest more frequent checking. Standardization once a week is a reasonable frequency for many applications. It is well known that pH electrodes may have coating problems. In public water supplies, reagents such as Calgon may be added; and calcium phosphate then coats the pipeline and helps preserve it; it also coats the electrode and interferes with the measurement. In this case, rinsing the electrodes with acid may be required once a week or even once a day. If a problem exists with coating on a pH monitoring system, the same problem may exist with an ion-selective electrode system. With the fluoride monitoring system, measuring at the one ppm fluoride level, we have arbitrarily set up suggested standardization checks for once a week. This is being safe and conservative. The electrode systems seem to be stable because the temperature compensation is taken care of, and these are reproducible reference electrode junctions because we can afford to keep the KCl flowing out fairly rapidly from the reference electrode. In summary, I would say that experience dictates the frequency of standardization.

A. J. Panson *(Westinghouse Research)*: I would like to point out another application, and this is the direct analysis of oxygen in the gas stream. Apparatus is now commercially available which features solid electrolyte galvanic cells operated at high temperature, about 800 °C. Here the oxygen is measured in the gas phase with no need for scrubbing or equilibration with a liquid phase. The oxygen reacts directly at a platinum electrode which is interfaced with a zirconia electrolyte. The counter electrode is another platinum electrode on the other side of your zirconia electrolyte referenced generally with air. Quite accurate analysis of oxygen in the gas stream can be made in this way.

T. S. Light *(Foxboro)*: This is a potentiometric measurement, not an amperometric measurement, is that correct?

A. J. Panson *(Westinghouse)*: Yes, that is correct; it is a potentiometric measurement. Quite accurate Nernstian response for a four electron reaction is observed. This system can be used for trace amounts of oxygen, for example, in inert gas atmospheres to be use in a processing furnace. Solid electrolyte cells of this type have been used to measure oxygen activity in liquid sodium in heat transfer systems for fast breeder nuclear reactors.

T. L. Bohl *(Hays Corporation)*: I have a question concerning the aluminum-iron complexation on the fluoride analysis of drinking water. To what extent does this complex? For example, will 1 ppm aluminum complex 1 ppm fluoride, and what do you do practically when you're monitoring public water systems?

T. S. Light *(Foxboro)*:   As you mentioned, in public water supplies, the two ions that pose a problem, for complexation of fluoride, are aluminum and iron. Fortunately, however, the pH of public water supplies is in the range of 5 to 8. In this range, both aluminum and iron form insoluble hydroxides, and the free iron and aluminum content is very low, a few tenths of a ppm. But I also have a question. Suppose one does lose 2 or 3 percent of the fluoride present by complexation, what is desired in the public health situation? Is it the free or the total fluoride? In the past, analytical procedures have given total fluoride, but I have wondered if it isn't the free fluoride that is wanted. However, if the answer desired is total fluoride and the iron and aluminum present are not tied up by complexation with citrate or hydroxide, then some of the fluoride may be lost to the measurement.

T. L. Bohl *(Hays)*:   Although I am not completely conversant with this area, I believe that it is the total fluoride that is of interest, and it is my interpretation that this is because the public health people do not know what use the water is going to be put to when it leaves the treatment plant. Changes may occur that would release additional fluoride from the complexed state.

PANEL   DISCUSSION   (FRIDAY)

J. E. Garvin *(Northwestern University Medical School)*:   First, I would like to express my astonishment and joy at Dr. Moore's exposition, but I wonder if it would be possible, having had some small experience with these, to inquire into a few of the details of the sample preparation and conduct of the actual measurement. Our experience suggests that there are a number of little tricks that make this marvelous output possible.

E. W. Moore *(Tufts)*:   I would not say that there are any particular little tricks involved; it is more a matter of being extraordinarily careful all along the line — from sample collection to electrode fabrication. One should be particularly careful to avoid pH changes in the sample, either from loss of CO_2 in preparation of serum or gain in CO_2 from prolonged venous stasis.

J. E. Garvin *(Northwestern Univ.)*:   Do you take the tourniquet off then and collect it from freely flowing blood?

E. W. Moore *(Tufts)*:   No, we usually leave the tourniquet on throughout the collection, but it is only for a minute or so. Judging from the pH values obtained in normals (venous pH 7.30-7.40) there does not appear to be any significant venous stasis under these conditions. It should be emphasized that the blood sample, once collected, is handled anaerobically, *i.e.,* the blood is spun under oil, the serum is separated under oil and again placed under oil. Some investigators have used Vacutainers for collecting blood, but we have not studied this specifically.

J. N. Butler *(Tyco)*: Could I make a comment in this connection? In private discussions, it has come up several times that the geometric configuration of the interface between the liquid ion exchanger and the aqueous solution makes a difference in the potential because of the electrostatic charge that this interface carries. Unless the calibration solution and the test solution are measured under identical conditions of hydrostatic pressure and geometric structure of the interface, one may have systematic errors of several millivolts resulting from this source, and I think this should be pointed out.

E. W. Moore *(Tufts)*: Yes, this was a problem with the first generation electrode, *i.e.*, those prepared with a Viscose cellulose membrane, and we were careful to avoid differences in hydrostatic gradients between standards and unknowns, *i.e.*, the electrode was immersed to about the same depth in all measurements. This does not appear to be a problem with the flow-through system.

J. W. Ross *(Orion)*: No, with the flow-through electrode, the geometry is fixed so you are always guaranteed that you have identical conditions.

E. W. Moore *(Tufts)*: There is a slight streaming potential with the flow-through system, and it is advisable to obtain measurements in standards and unknowns at identical flow rates.

J. W. Ross *(Orion)*: There are flow rate problems with serum. At low flow rates, one observes apparently less calcium in the sample than you do at higher flow rates, although there is a plateau beyond which increasing the flow rate produces no further change. We have tentatively identified this as loss of CO_2 through the membrane itself and, with a fixed sample of very small volume, this loss can become appreciable, but in a flowing system above a minimum flow rate, there doesn't seem to be any problem.

E. W. Moore *(Tufts)*: Yes, I would add to that that approximately 75% of the inquiries we get about these electrodes are situations in which people will put a series of standards in and get their curves, then put their serum in and notice that the whole standard curve has shifted. Whereas, if you keep going back and forth between sample and standards, you will find that it is fairly stable for the rest of the day. It is just that first shock that is troublesome. I don't think we really understand it yet, unless it is the CO_2 as was mentioned by Dr. Ross.

Anonymous: Do I understand you to mean that you put your standard solution through, then you put the serum through, then you put another standard through, and you maintain a continuous or repeated pattern so that the electrode is, in a sense, repeatedly conditioned?

E. W. Moore *(Tufts)*: Yes, exactly. The shift in the standard curve sometimes noted upon the first introduction of serum into the electrode appears to us to be more or less random in its direction. Several investigators have told us that their electrodes tend to shift toward a more negative millivolt reading upon the first introduction of serum. Because of this, we have recently looked carefully at our last 6 months' data but could not determine anything systematic about it. There is no doubt, however, that something often happens when you first put serum into the electrode.

J. W. Ross *(Orion)*:   Another possibility is that it might have something to do with the liquid junction as well. A liquid junction that has been exposed to serum may be somewhat different than one that has only seen pure aqueous solutions.

J. N. Butler *(Tyco)*:   It may also change the interfacial tension of the organic-aqueous interface.

J. W. Ross *(Orion)*:   I would be surprised. The exchanger itself is quite hydrophilic at the surface, that is, the surface is a surface-active agent. I would think its effect would swamp out any effect from the serum itself.

F. Rothstein *(Tufts University Medical School)*:   I'd like to address myself to the question of protein adsorption on surfaces. Those of us who have been in protein chemistry for many years are fully aware that proteins are extremely surface active and studies have indicated that if you take serum you will find, using the method of Langmuir and Blodgett plus ellipsometry as the testing technique, that on hydrophilic surfaces you will have protein multilayers being deposited from serum. Then, if you go to a hydrophobic surface, you will find other proteins also forming multilayers. I would address myself to the problem of the nature of the membrane in the case of the calcium electrode. I know for a fact that on cellophane, for instance, you will have adsorbed protein on it unless you really keep the solution moving over the surface. Some of the preliminary work we've done in Dr. Moore's lab indicates to us at least that the so-called conditioning might be a reflection of a weakly adsorbed monolayer or multilayer on the membrane. I am very uncomfortable with the ease with which this problem is being set aside. I think it is a very important problem not only of proteins but any surface active agent, and this problem should be under consideration. The second point, Dr. Ross, is it possible to use an Amicon membrane in this electrode because of the rapidity of transport? My last point is the possibility of having in the calcium flow-through system a pH electrode so that you simultaneously measure the pH and pCa.

J. W. Ross *(Orion)*:   Let me start with the last question and work forward. Yes, there is no reason why you cannot put a flow-through capillary pH electrode in series with the calcium flow-through system using the same reference electrode and two meters and determining both species simultaneously. We have worked with the Amicon membrane. I assume you're thinking of a device to keep the protein off the surface of the selective membrane or do you mean using it as a selective membrane itself? We have looked at a early type of Amicon membrane, but nothing recently. I understand they have a number of different types of membrane available now. With the early material we looked at, which we hoped would act much as a piece of cellulose dialysis membrane, we found that there was residual selectivity in the Amicon membrane because of the presence of unsatisfied charge sites which complicated matters for us. We have not investigated beyond that point. Getting back to protein adsorption, maybe it does take place; we can't say that it doesn't. If there is a protein layer on the surface, it really should make no difference in the calcium reading of the electrode, if we assume that the inside of that protein layer and the outside are in equilibrium with the sample calcium activity. One could conceive that it might slow down the time response of the electrode, however, we have not observed changes in time response on exposure to serum. If anything, the electrode responds faster to serum samples than it does to aqueous solutions, probably because the serum sample is buffered with respect to calcium, whereas the aqueous calcium solution is not. As far as the so-called protein effects we were discussing, most of these can be reproduced by using a bicarbonate-buffered calcium chloride solution with no protein present. So, I am inclined to favor the theory that this is a CO_2 effect and not a protein effect, simply because it's a simpler theory.

E. W. Moore (*Tufts*): I think you should emphasize that you are allowing for the presence of the calcium bicarbonate complex in your standard calculations.

J. W. Ross (*Orion*): Yes, that is correct. Bicarbonate does form a modestly stable calcium complex.

E. W. Moore (*Tufts*): I might add, Dr. Ross, that the problems just alluded to by Dr. Rothstein may apply to the second-generation calcium electrode, *i.e.,* the Model 92-20 static electrode marketed by Orion. Although at least two papers have been published on the use of this electrode in serum, in our hands it was quite unsatisfactory. It generally gave unstable potentials with more-or-less continuous drift in serum, although it worked quite well in protein-free solutions. We assumed therefore that proteins were responsible for the drift, possibly through a coating of the membrane, despite vigorous stirring. The behavior of this electrode therefore appears to be quite different from that of the flow-through electrode.

R. G. Bates (*NBS*): It occurs to me there might be quite a difference between the protein error on a glass electrode and that on other types of membrane materials such as lanthanum fluoride. Is this the case, Dr. Ross?

J. W. Ross (*Orion*): I don't know if anyone has looked at the lanthanum fluoride electrode in protein solutions specifically for this effect, but my guess is that the effect is probably very similar. Lanthanum fluoride is a very polar surface. Fluoride ions on the surface are not entirely unlike the oxide ions on the surface of a glass. I would think that anything bad that happens on glass might very well happen on the lanthanum fluoride material as well.

R. De Pablo *(Diamond Shamrock Corporation)*:   I would like to know if you have studied the influence of thiosulfates and polysulfides on the sulfide electrode.

J. W. Ross *(Orion)*:   Yes, we have looked at polysulfide formation, and this occurs in samples from paper pulp plants which contain sulfide and a good deal of free sulfur from air oxidation. The sulfur stays in solution as polysulfide ions. The electrode only senses the free sulfide ion in equilibrium with these, and one could distinguished between them by a direct measurement for free sulfide followed by a silver titration which gives, in addition, the sulfide bound to the sulfur and you get polysulfides in this way. You can also determine mercaptans by this technique as well. As far as thiosulfate that you mentioned, this ion has no effect on the sulfide electrode. The silver-thiosulfate complex is not stable enough to cause any interference.

F. J. Tavora *(Colorado School of Mines)*:   I have a question for Dr. Light. Concerning your differential cell, I wonder whether you could give examples of other ions that could be determined with this arrangement or detected indirectly with the already existent ion-selective electrodes?

T. S. Light *(Foxboro)*:   Another example in addition to the determination of aluminum by measuring the loss of fluoride, would be the determination of cyanide using as reagent an aluminum fluoride complex in which the fluoride is displaced by cyanide. The amount of fluoride displaced would be proportional to the cyanide activity. This might appear to be an impractical example since a cyanide electrode also exists, but the cyanide electrode is limited to dilute solutions. I think one can begin to have a lot of fun being chemically ingenious in this manner. For another example, at the present time we do not have a good sulfate electrode, but there is a good lead solid-state electrode. Using this lead membrane electrode and lead reagent solutions, the change in lead activity on one side of the membrane would be a measure of the sulfate concentration. I think you can begin to see how all of the analytical chemistry that we have learned through the years can begin to be applied indirectly to using the ion-selective electrodes and getting a lot of answers out of them.

T. R. S. Wilson *(Woods Hole Oceanographic Institution)*:   I wonder if anyone would care to speculate on the source of noise in electrode measurements? The reason I ask this is that I have been working with a differential type cell, such as the one that Dr. Light mentioned, which has no liquid junctions, matched electrodes in good thermal contact, well thermally isolated and electrically shielded, and we can get noise levels down to below a microvolt. I wonder if anyone would care to apportion the blame for the noise one sees with normal electrode systems between the various possible sources.

T. S. Light *(Foxboro)*: Am I to understand you correctly that you're complaining about noises at the microvolt level?

T. R. S. Wilson *(Woods Hole)*: I'm not complaining. It's taken a long time to get to this level, and it is an illustration of the powerful nature of the technique you mentioned, if you match your electrodes well and keep them in good thermal contact.

J. N. Butler *(Tyco)*: I would say that the most prevalent source of noise is insufficient electrostatic shielding, particularly if you are in an area where there are a lot of RF machines melting things in other rooms, and this RF noise makes it difficult to bring the dc noise level down because you get rectification in all kinds of contacts. You have to use special solders to bring these noise levels down. If you are working in a very high impedance circuit, you can pick up enormous amounts of noise from apparently no source at all, simply the ac lines in the building even if you build Faraday cages around your equipment.

T. R. S. Wilson *(Woods Hole)*: May I just mention, in case someone is interested, that we are using a Keithley millimicrovolt meter to measure these voltages, and we have to use electrodes of quite a large surface area because the input impedance is a little low on that meter.

G. Eisenman *(University of Chicago)*: What is the frequency spectrum of this one microvolt noise?

T. R. S. Wilson *(Woods Hole)*: We are using a chart display, and the chatter on the record is on the order of one-tenth of a microvolt or less. There is a drift, which is not troublesome to us in our present application, on the order of microvolts per hour due to temperature changes in the room.

G. Eisenman *(Univ. of Chicago)*: Well, I think that one general comment that may be made is that since the noise is not coherent then statistical methods can reduce it as low as you want, if you have an infinite amount of time by which to reduce it. So in principle, it's not a problem.

T. S. Light *(Foxboro)*: As you may have gathered from my talk, I am investigating the region below a tenth of a millivolt and, everytime we do fight it down there, we find "noise," as you do, we go after it and try to clean it up. And lo and behold, we do clean it up after finding something to blame it on. We don't use statistical devices to get rid of it either. For example, I complained yesterday about reference electrodes and noisy liquid junctions. You have raised the question of shielding. I know there is an excellent article by Moore on shielding problems with pH measuring assemblies. In the microvolt region, spurious signals may be electrical measuring noise and have nothing to do with the electrode systems. I honestly don't know how good electrodes are, but I suspect they are inherently good in the microvolt region. One example concerns shielding. Laboratory pH meters do have good shielding but not completely adequate. On our instruments, we go to a concept called a driven shield where the potential of the shield is maintained at the potential of the inner wire. This cleans the signal considerably. Someone already mentioned Faraday cages, these are all devices which frequently solve measurement problems extraneous to the electrodes. I am willing to go on record as saying that electrodes are able to go down to the microvolt region. I believe they will obey the Nernst and other equations better than generally believed now, and we're just arriving at the stage of being able to prove it.

J. R. Cels *(Babcock and Wilcox Company)*:   I would like to ask Dr. Light about the working curves which were designed to go through zero at the desired operating level of concentration, so that the shifts with temperature were minimized around that point. Would you elaborate on how this was done?

T. S. Light *(Foxboro)*:   Yes, this is no great problem to elaborate on, and I would first refer you to Dr. Bates' book on pH where the same concept is treated. Most modern pH meters zero around a pH of 7, and this is accomplished by having the internal filling solution of the measuring electrode, whether it is a pH electrode or a fluoride electrode, set to match the solution concentration that is most common. For example, for the pH electrode, the internal solution is buffered around a pH of 7. Two potentials dictate the internal of the measuring electrode, the solution inside and the internal reference electrode which is usually either a silver-silver chloride electrode or a saturated calomel electrode. The internal potential is set by the pH and the chloride concentration, and this chloride content is matched to that of the external reference electrode. In the case of the fluoride electrode, it becomes apparent then, when using a 1 molar potassium chloride reference electrode, one should have a 1 molar potassium chloride internal filling solution in the fluoride electrode. The fluoride electrode internal solution should also have a fluoride activity of 1 milligram of fluoride per liter of solution. Now, this electrode system immersed in a 1 milligram per liter fluoride solution will read zero emf. If the temperature changes, the two silver-silver chloride reference electrodes change in the same fashion so there is no net change in the emf. This is called the symmetrical cell concept and has been described in the pH literature.

R. G. Bates *(NBS)*:   I should like to add just a word to that, if I might. I think that it is not quite sufficient to have a symmetrical cell because the RT/F factor is going to change with temperature, and you want the pH to nullify that change in order to maintain a zero standard potential. We've recently done some work in this area with regard to pH electrodes, but unfortunately it is still not published. It is possible to choose the composition of the inner buffer solution so that its temperature coefficient is such that it does nullify the E°. We found, for example, that a THAM buffer in a sodium chloride solution is a very good choice to nullify the E° of the saturated calomel electrode.

T. S. Light *(Foxboro)*:   I guess I should have emphasized that the electrode has to be tailored to the particular measurement problem involved.

J. B. Dawson *(S.U.N.Y.-Stony Brook)*:   Could I add some medical nitty-gritties to Dr. Moore's beautiful paper? Do you think the hyponatremia, which was not mentioned as one of the problems in cirrhosis, makes any difference to your calcium readings? I presume the effect is probably pretty small and doesn't make any difference, but the sodium/potassium ratio is way out of whack in a cirrhotic and may be relevant.

E. W. Moore *(Tufts)*:   There are several possible effects to be considered in Ca^{++} analysis in cirrhotics and also in other pathologic sera. The hyponatremia which you mentioned is associated with some reduction in serum osmolality, *i.e.,* there is a reduction in total ionic strength. This effect on calcium activity can probably be neglected, however, except in the most severe cases. Several years ago, Dr. Ross and I found that the activity coefficient of $CaCl_2$ in the presence of 150 mM NaCl was about 0.54, as calculated from the observed mean NaCl activity (using a sodium-selective glass electrode and Ag-AgCl electrode); at 100 mM NaCl, the activity coefficient was about 0.58. Your second point concerning a change in the Na^+/K^+ ratio refers, I assume, to possible differences in electrode selectivity for Na^+ and K^+. This can be entirely neglected I think, since the selectivity for these two ions is very similar, *i.e.,* about 10,000/1 on a mole basis. A point perhaps more important is the level of Mg^{++} in the sample, since the selectivity for Ca^{++} over Mg^{++} is only 50-100/1. We are hopeful that a suitable Mg^{++} electrode can be developed; it would surely be a great boon to biology and medicine. The questions which you have raised emphasize the difficulties encountered by all clinical investigators — how does one apply a given finding or regression equation obtained from data in a heterogeneous population to a given individual?

J. B. Dawson *(Stony Brook)*:   May I just add one plea to this beautiful technique of yours? Are you planning to do patients with long-term renal failure? I am thinking in terms of Relman's buffer pool, buffering the hyperacidity with the patient's body calcium. Are you doing any long-term runs to see whether they're running a high ionized calcium level? This would be a lovely group to look at.

E. W. Moore *(Tufts)*:   Yes, we have just begun studies of renal dialysis

patients, to include the immunoassay of parathormone. I believe the
electrode will find particular usefulness in these patients.

A. W. Meiselbach *(DuPont)*:   I noticed that a number of the electrodes
discussed today have a fair sensitivity to interference by ferric ion. Is it
possible that we can get ferric measurements with some of the available
electrodes?

J. W. Ross *(Orion)*:   I think ferric ion is interfering with many of the
solid-state electrodes because it is a fairly good oxidizing agent. I don't
think there's much chance of using these electrodes for determining the
ferric ion. This is quite an irreproducible effect.

J. N. Butler *(Tyco)*:   I can also add that, at the Gordon Conference in
Santa Barbara last week, Isaac Tractenberg of Texas Instruments
described some electrodes he had made using some complex selenium
glasses of undefined composition which he said were specific to iron in
aqueous solution, but I'll have to refer you to him for details.

R. P. Buck *(University of North Carolina)*:   In the determination of lead
or copper, I was wondering if I could use the silver sulfide electrode but,
prior to that use, I could take powdered copper sulfide or powdered lead
sulfide and stir it up in my solution? My second question has to do with the
use of the silver sulfide electrode in extreme conditions. A good deal was
said about the use of the silver sulfide electrode when the sulfide activity
was as low as 10^{-18} molar. That doesn't bother me so much because, in
those circumstances, if equilibrium prevails, a large number of silver ions
are present. It's the silver ions that make the difference. What's incredible
about the silver sulfide electrode is that it operates in one molar sulfide —
one molar hydroxide solution where there is a very low silver ion activity.
Would you comment on that, and do you have any feeling for what
goes on at the surface of these solids in conditions of low electrolyte concentrations in general?

J. W. Ross *(Orion)*:   Yes, one could use a silver sulfide electrode for
doing a copper analysis by throwing in some powdered copper sulfide
which, by a direct reaction, gives an equivalent release of silver. This
idea works very well on paper and, in fact, this is what lead us to the use
of the mixed-precipitate membranes to make use of this same effect. In
practice, it doesn't work too well, particularly at low concentrations,
because you're putting in a huge surface-area precipitate. The ions that
are released are, for the most part, adsorbed on the surface of this
precipitate and are not available in solution for the electrode to measure.
At high concentrations, it would work quite well, again, if one were
willing to wait for the reaction to complete itself which may take some
time since it involves a solid phase. We've done a little work on the use of
the silver sulfide electrode at low concentrations recently. In principle,
with these very insoluble sulfide membranes, one should be able to go

down to something like 10^{-20} molar. What really does determined the lower level of measurement is inevitably something on the order of 10^{-8} molar, very rarely lower than that. My current view, which is based on a very limited number of measurements, indicates we are limited by ion adsorption on the surface of the electrode itself. It is a well known fact that any crystal surface will selectively adsorb common ions from solution onto the surface. So if one starts out with the best distilled water one can get, puts a silver sulfide electrode in it, and then starts adding small increments of silver ion, one finds that the first increments that you add all wind up adsorbed on the surface of the electrode and are not available in solution for the electrode to sense as the free ion activity. In general, the larger the electrode surface area, the worse this problem becomes, which again leads me to the assumption that it is adsorption on the crystal surface itself. This is much the same for all the silver salt electrodes.

J. N. Butler (*Tyco*): I might also add that even thermodynamically speaking, although you may be sensing 10^{-35} moles per liter sulfide ion, the mechanism may proceed through a complex and still give the same thermodynamic potential as it would have had the mechanism proceeded through the sulfide ion itself.

J. W. Ross (*Orion*): Right, you are not asking to have a large number of the ions you're trying to measure at the surface. What you're asking is that you have mobile equilibria that can produce this very low fixed level at a rapid enough rate to stay ahead of any interfering reactions, and this does seem to be the case for the silver sulfide equilibrium which is quite rapid and mobile.

Anonymous: I would like Drs. Light and Ross to thrash something out. Dr. Light, when talking about the practical applications of these electrodes, talked about using n electrodes, all of which experience interferences, then correlating the results to get the n correct answers. On the other hand, Dr. Ross seems to almost dismiss the idea of using selectivity factors in this way. I was wondering, where is the truth? Somewhere in the middle?

T. S. Light (*Foxboro*): In order to make this correction with some kind of a signal processor or computer, you have to have equations and be able to solve them. This is my starting premise. Now, some selectivity coefficients have been indicated to be quite valid and reproducible. I believe Dr. Ross cited an example of a selectivity coefficient that changed as the composition changed and, if this is so, then the equation wouldn't be satisfactory.

J. W. Ross (*Orion*): I am very disenchanted with the idea of correcting an electrode which is experiencing an interference to remove the effect of that interference. Yes, one can always develop a more complicated equation with more parameters to fit the data and perhaps to get a better correction, except for the fact that it has been my experience that electrodes that are undergoing interference have other problems. They have slow, drifting responses, and time dependent phenomena of this sort would be awfully hard to handle. Other types of computation, however, are valid, and I think doing computations makes a great deal of sense in this situation. Suppose you have a sample where you trying to measure fluoride or sulfide or some other ion whose free ion activity is pH dependent, and you want to know both the free ion concentration and the total concentration. In this case, it is quite possible to independently measure pH, the pH electrode being another electrode in this string of n electrodes, and go through magnificient calculations to get all of the separate species out of this. These are perfectly valid equations because you are doing computations relating to species in chemical equilibria in the solution, and it has nothing to do with the electrode interference. Here, I think this ability of being able to do extensive computations makes a great deal of sense. But, with the liquid electrodes when they are experiencing interference of something entering the membrane, those potential values, in my view, just aren't to be trusted. With the solid electrodes, as I pointed out in my talk, the interference effect is different. In the usual situation, there is either no interference or the electrode isn't working. You are over that abrupt fall off onto some other function and here a calculation makes no sense whatsoever.

A. K. Covington *(University of Newcastle upon Tyne)*:   I think the answer is to get the solution to the right state before the electrode sees it, by addition of another reagent, maybe just changing the pH or something much more complicated. But we should utilize these ion-selective electrodes knowing their limitations to get the process stream right before the electrode sees it.

J. N. Butler *(Tyco)*:   I might underscore something that I said in my talk yesterday which was that, although the selectivity ratio is a useful qualitative concept for solid-state and liquid ion exchange electrodes, it does not have the quantitative significance that it does with the glass electrodes. Especially in concentrated solutions, it may change by several orders of magnitude as you change the solution composition. This is something to keep in mind.

End of Symposium

INDEX

U.S. GOVERNMENT PRINTING OFFICE : 1969 OL—348—381